# READER'S DIGEST
## Condensed
# BOOKS

# READER'S DIGEST

*Condensed*

# BOOKS

*Winter 1951 Selections*

THE READER'S DIGEST ASSOCIATION

Pleasantville, N. Y.

# Contents

*Decorations by Constantin Alajálov*

# ANYBODY
# CAN DO ANYTHING

*A condensation of the book by*

BETTY MacDonald

*P*UBLISHERS agree that humor is the rarest commodity in the literary market place today. Betty MacDonald, author of *The Egg and I, The Plague and I* and this latest best-selling volume of personal history, has almost a corner on the kind that springs from gaiety and courage, and leaves a warm glow around the reader's heart.

In *Anybody Can Do Anything* Betty tells the hilarious story of her job-hunting (and job-losing) experiences with sister Mary, a highly executive young woman whose creed was that anyone could fill any position without any training — especially Betty. Together, the sisters cut a swathe through dozens of Seattle offices, leaving behind a trail of bewildered employers and furnishing readers with some of the strangest scenes of office life ever put into print.

"The merriest, maddest book of the year."
—Chicago *Tribune*

"Sister Mary was rocket-propelled dynamite, with Sister Betty serving as incandescent tail. ... A very, very funny book."
— New York *Herald Tribune*

# CHAPTER 1

## "ANYBODY CAN DO ANYTHING, ESPECIALLY BETTY"

THE BEST thing about the depression was the way it reunited our family and gave my sister Mary a real opportunity to prove that anybody can do anything, especially Betty.

Mary's belief that accomplishment is merely a matter of application was inherited from both Mother and Daddy. Mother, who has acquired a bewildering array of skills of her own, was working for a dress designer in Boston when she met my father, an ambitious young mining engineer who, though rowing on the crew, working all night in the Observatory and tutoring rich boys during the day, graduated from Harvard with honors in three years. The union of these two spirited people produced five children — four girls and one boy — all born in different parts of the United States, all tall and redheaded except my sister Dede, who is small and hardheaded.

Mary, the oldest of the children, was born in Butte, Mont., and indicated at an early age that she had lots of ideas and tremendous enthusiasm, especially for her own ideas. I, Betty, the next child, emerged in Boulder, Colo., and from the very first leaned toward Mary's ideas like a divining rod toward water.

The rest of the family proved to be firmer textured, not so eager to be Mary's guinea pigs, so she has always generously allowed them to choose between their own little old wizened-up ideas and the great big juicy ripe tempting ones she offered.

Among my first memories of being the Trilby for Mary's Svengali was the time Mary tried to invent perpetual motion and knocked out all my front teeth.

Mother had bought me a new Lightning Glider sled and we were out in the back yard, a steep slope about a hundred feet long, reaching down to a small level place behind the house. Suddenly, at the bottom of the hill, Mary jumped off the sled, dashed into the cellar and came out brandishing the clothes pole.

"Betsy," she said. "I have a wonderful idea. We'll both get on the sled at the top of the hill, I'll hold this pole out in front of us [the pole was about eight feet long] and, when we slide down, the pole will hit the house and push us back up the hill again. Then down we'll go, then up, then down, then up and we'll never have to climb the hill."

It sounded like a terribly good idea to me, so when we had pulled the sled back up the hill I climbed on the front and put my feet up on the steering bar and Mary got on the back and we both held the pole out in front of us in a direct line with my mouth. Mary gave us a big shove to send us off and whee! how we flew down the little hill. Then everything went black and I began spitting blood and teeth onto the white hard-packed snow, for the pole, when it hit the house, had been forced well back into my mouth. "Oh, Betsy," Mary said, her face so pale her freckles looked like brown moles, "I didn't mean to hurt you. I'm so sorry," and I knew she was because she gave me her most treasured toy. Anyway, they were only first teeth.

As I look back on it, I couldn't have been too bright because only one year later, when I was seven, Mary and a redheaded friend named Marjorie got me to jump from the loft of a neighbor's stable onto a very small armful of straw, which they had carelessly thrown on top of an upturned rake.

We were playing vaudeville this time because Mary and Marjorie had recently been taken to a show whose wonders had included a human bird and a man who balanced steel balls on his ears. I couldn't balance steel balls but I could be Betty, the Human Bird, the Greatest Jumper of All Times, which was why on that bright summer morning I was standing shivering in the little doorway of the unused loft. It was only about a ten- or twelve-foot jump but I'll never forget how high up I felt.

Big Butte, an extinct volcano which had always seemed to us to be the highest mountain in the world, was right in front of me. The big M-1915, painted in white on its black rock side by the daring School of Mines boys, was now at eye level. I could see the School of Mines where Daddy taught. I could see Mary the Cook hanging out washing in our back yard. I could see hundreds of great big blue mountains. I could see Mary marching around the yard with a stick pointing at me and shouting "Ladees and Gentlemen! Look up at her, Betty, the Human Bird, the bravest child in the whole world. Just a little girl of seven who will jump from that terribly high building down onto this little pile of straw!"

I looked down at the pile of straw and it certainly was little. My stomach felt ice-cold and my heart seemed to have moved up into my head, but Mary had promised me that if I jumped I would be able to fly like the man in the vaudeville show.

"Come on, Betsy, dear," she was calling. "I'll count and when I get to ten you jump." I looked down at the admiring faces of the neighborhood children as Mary began counting in ominous tones. "Oneh, two-ah, three-ah." I took a deep breath, closed my eyes and jumped when she got to ten-ah. I did not fly. I landed hard on the pile of straw and two tines of the hidden rake went through my foot. Mary and Marjorie, truly appalled by their carelessness, carried me all the way home. At least, Mary carried me and Marjorie held up the handle of the rake.

When we got home Mother called the doctor and while we waited for him I soaked my foot in a basin of hot Epsom salts and water and Gammy, my father's mother who lived with us, comforted me by saying, "Cheeldrun are nothing but savages. It won't surprise me at all if they have to cut off Betsy's legs."

"Not both legs," Mary said. "Only one." I had been very brave up to this point, but now I began to bawl. "I don't want to have my leg cut off and only wear one roller skate," I sobbed.

Mary said, "Never mind, Betsy, dear, we'll make a little tiny roller skate for your crutch and in winter I'll pull you to school on the sled." Which, to her dismay, only made me bawl louder.

Then the doctor arrived, examined my foot and gave me a tetanus shot; Daddy came home, examined my foot and gave Mary a spanking with the bristle side of the brush; Mother said of course my legs weren't going to be cut off and called Gammy an old pessimist, which immediately cheered Mary and me because we thought pessimist was a bad word.

As we grew older Daddy's cultural program, which included lessons in piano playing, singing, folk dancing, French and ballet, added further proof to Mary's theory that anybody can do anything and, in her case, without practicing.

Our favorite piano teacher among many, and the one we clung to longest, was a Miss Welcome, a very temperamental European who calcimined her arms dead-white up to within an inch of her short sleeves, dressed entirely in fuchsia color, wore turbans with flowing veils when she taught and always had fish breath. She counted on our backs with her strong fingers digging into the flesh, "Bun and boo and bree and bour," screamed, "Feel, f-e-e-l, FEEL IT!" as she paced around the room with her veils flying, her calcimined arms beating out the rhythm like big plaster casts, and often produced real tears (to our delight) when we made mistakes. "Oh, dear God, no, not B-flat!" she'd moan, covering her face with her hands and sobbing.

Miss Welcome never bored us with scales or exercises or any of those stupid little Pixie-in-the-Glen or Lullaby-for-Tiny-Hands type of thing. Everybody studying with her started off the very first day on some great big hard well-known composer. If, by our third lesson, we couldn't manage the full chords or the fast parts in, say, Rachmaninoff's "Prelude in C-Sharp Minor," Miss Welcome cut them out. She cut the bottoms off octaves and the tops off grace notes without turning a hair. "Now try it," she'd say and if we still couldn't play it she'd take out her ever-ready pencil and x out the whole hard part. "Now," she'd say, "let's hear some feeeeeeeeeling!" and with the fervor of relief we'd bear down and pound feeling into what was left.

Because I had long, thin hands and was so scared of Miss Welcome that I bawled at every lesson, she told me I was very very sensitive and gave me long sad selections with enormous chords and huge reaches. "Bun and boo and bree and bour, now come on, Betsy, play, play, PLAY!" she'd yell at me and I'd begin to cry. "I can't reach the notes," I'd sob, my long, unyielding hands trying to reach the two keys over an octave so unreasonably demanded by Schumann. "You must reach it. You CAN AND YOU MUST!" Miss Welcome would hiss into my tear-stained face. I tried and tried. I practiced one and two hours every day on my sad, great pieces but my heart wasn't in it. I didn't want to play slow, sad things with huge chords that gave me bearing-down pains. I wanted to be like Mary, who talked back to Miss Welcome, hardly ever practiced, played entirely by ear (she didn't learn to read music until after she was married), chose her own loud, showy pieces, and whose small freckled supple hands flew over the keys like lightning.

When Daddy and Mother had company we children usually performed. First Dede, who had perfect pitch even at two, sang "My Country 'Tis of Thee"; then our brother, Cleve, until his clarinet playing had progressed to solos, recited, then Mary and I played the piano.

I would give a sweaty-fingered, uninspired performance of my latest piece exactly as it was written and exactly as Miss Welcome had taught me even to the lowered wrists, high knuckles and leaning forward and pressing heavily on the keys for depth of tone. I knew my pieces and never made a mistake but nobody cared — I could tell from the bored rattle of newspapers, nervous scraping of chairs, even snores, so audible during the long, long waits between notes required by the dramatic Miss Welcome. "That's very nice, Betsy," Mother would say when I finished.

Then it was Mary's turn. Up she would flounce to the piano and effortlessly dash off Grieg's "Carnival," "Anitra's Dance," "Le Papillon" or "Rustle of Spring," and everyone would say, "Isn't she talented?" and only I, in my envy, noticed that each was seasoned with the other and they all reflected strongly the influence of composer Mary Bard.

We both took singing from our Sunday School teacher's sister, or rather Mary took singing and I played her accompaniment, but we always referred to it as our singing because it took both of us for a performance.

Mrs. Potter, our teacher, had an enormous, thick contralto voice. She was supposed to be a very good teacher and to know Madame Schumann-Heink, which fact she just happened to mention at least ten times during every lesson. "Watch my diaphragm," Mrs. Potter would demand as she sang, "Caddy me bok to old Vugiddy. Deeahs wheah de cottod ad de sweed bodadoes grrrrow. . . ."

At first Mrs. Potter wanted me to study singing, too, but Mother thought that, as I had once had very bad tonsils, I'd better be Mary's accompanist, which was fine for a while.

"Pale hahnds I loved beside the Shalimah . . . ah, wheah ahhh you now, oh wheah ahhh you now?" Mary wailed. "When the dawn flames in the sky, I love yewwwww. When the birdlings wake and cry, I love yewwwww. . . ." Mary's rendition of "At Dawning" was to me the most beautiful thing in the world and always brought tears to my eyes. Her soprano voice was clear and true but not that good, so probably adolescence had something to do with it.

Then Mary entered and won an elocution contest.

"Fat black bucks in a wine-barrel room,
Barrel-house kings, with feet unstable,
Sagged and reeled and pounded on the table... !"

she shouted as she sagged and reeled around the kitchen, pounding on the table so hard her fist stuck to the oilcloth.

"Beat an empty barrel with the handle of a broom,
Hard as they were able,
Boom, Boom, BOOM,
With a silk umbrella and the handle of a broom,
Boomlay, boomlay, boomlay, BOOM."

she roared. Then suddenly half-crouching, with eyes like slits, she reached behind her and got her right arm and thrust it directly at us, the stiff index finger appearing suddenly at the end like a knife blade on a cane. Still crouching, her squinty eyes on the pointing finger, she slowly moved the arm in a half circle and hissed through clenched teeth:

"Then I saw the Congo, creeping through the black,
Cutting through the jungle with a golden track."

"That girl ought to be on the stage," Mrs. Watson, our cleaning woman, said. I thought so, too, and was delirious with happiness when Mary offered to coach me.

After studying me from every angle, she decided that I was the "cute" type, though why I'll never know, because at the time I was painfully thin, pale green, wore a round comb and had a mouth filled with gold braces. My first cute recitation was "Little Orphant Annie." Mary taught me to stick out my lips like a Ubangi, wrinkle my high forehead, roll my eyes, waggle my forefinger and say in baby talk, "An' the gobble-uns 'll git you, ef you don't watch out!" Then came, "The carpenter man said a bad word, he said, 'Darn,'" only Mary had me say "corpenter" and "dorn" as being cuter.

The family were openly nauseated by my performances, but when I recited at school the girls thought I was cute and begged for more so I learned, "Elthie Minguth lithsps the doeth, the liveth wite croth the threet from me...." Mary, terribly proud of her handiwork, took me down to her elocution teacher, who

*I wiggled noticeably*

said that I should study, which we took as a compliment.

As elocution was very popular and most of our friends studied, some reciting at the drop of a hat whole chapters from *Daddy-Long-Legs, Tom Sawyer* and *Rebecca of Sunnybrook Farm,* I probably would have studied except that Daddy died that year and we stopped all of our lessons but piano and ballet. Mother could have stopped these, too, as far as I was concerned.

"One, two, three, LEAP!" shouted our ballet teacher, as she pounded her stick on the floor. Mary leaped so high they had to pull her down off the ceiling but I, who had also seen Pavlova and the Duncan Dancers, rubbed my ballet slippers in the rosin and dreaded my turn. The other girls did arabesques that made them look like birds poised in flight. I wiggled noticeably and the leg that was supposed to point up toward the ceiling hung down like a broken wing. When we stood at the bar I pulled and strained and kicked but my bones were as stiff and unpliable as pipes and I seemed to have fewer joints than the rest of the class. In spite of it all, I finally got up on my toes and appeared in many recitals.

In one recital our class, clad in short silk accordion-pleated skirts with pieces of the same material tied low around our foreheads and cleverly arranged to go over only one shoulder yet cover our budding bosoms, were supposed to be Greek boys, leaping around, pretending to be gladiators and drive chariots. Unfortunately, just after we had come leaping in, driving our chariots, the top of Mary's costume slipped and it immediately became apparent to the audience that at least some of these dancers were not Greek boys. "Hey, Mary," I hissed at her, "your costume's broken." Mary ignored me. She leaped and whirled and stamped through the entire dance and not until we were taking our final bows did she deign to fix the shoulder strap. "My dear girl," she said to me, "did you think that Pavlova would have stopped to fix a shoulder strap? No matter what breaks, the show must go on." Our teacher held Mary up before the entire dancing school as an example of a true artiste.

As time went on I became convinced that Mary was right and that anybody could do anything, but I had sense enough to realize that it was a lot harder for some people than for others.

## CHAPTER 2

### *WHAT'S A WHITE RUSSIAN GOT?*

WHEN WE were 18 and 20 I married and went to live in the mountains on a chicken ranch, and Mary plunged headfirst into a business career, which eventually resulted in her being fired from every firm of any size in the city of Seattle.

Mary's being fired was never a reflection on her efficiency, which was overwhelming, but was always a matter of principle, usually involving the morale of the entire firm. The head of a large law firm for which she worked arbitrarily ruled that all his stenographers had to go to the restroom at 10:30 a.m. and 3:15 p.m. "I don't care if you're the biggest lawyer in the city of Seattle, you can't control my bladder," Mary shouted at him.

"Go pinch somebody who can't type," she told a surprised and amorous lumber exporter.

"Henry Ford has proved that a rest period and something to eat in the morning and afternoon raises efficiency 200 percent and, as Henry Ford's got a lot better job than you have, I'm going out for coffee," she told one personnel manager.

"If you want to say 'he don't' and 'we was,' that's your affair," Mary told a pompous manufacturer, "but I won't put it in your letters because it reflects on me."

Even though Mary's jobs didn't last long, she never had any trouble getting new ones. "There are only two ways to apply for

a job," she said. "Either you are a Kick-Me-Charlie and go crawling in, anxious for long hours and low pay, or you march into
your prospective employer with a Look-Who's-Hit-the-Jackpot
attitude and, for a while at least, you have both the job and your
self-respect." Anyone could see that all Kick-Me-Charlie's kept
their jobs the longest but they didn't have as much self-respect
or meet as many people as Mary.

While Mary changed jobs and met people, I raised chickens,
had two children and didn't meet anybody. Finally in March
1931, after four years of this, I wrote to my family and told them
that I hated chickens, I was lonely and I seemed to have married
the wrong man. Mary, who was supporting the entire family, replied in typically dependable and dramatic fashion by special
delivery registered letter that she had a wonderful job for me and
that I was to come home at once.

I wrote back that I didn't know how to do office work and it
was five miles to the bus line. Mary wired back, "Anybody can
do office work and remember the White Russians walked across
Siberia. Your job starts Monday."

It was late on a rainy Friday afternoon when a neighbor
brought the telegram, but I checked the bus schedule, dressed
the children and myself in our "town clothes," stuffed my silver
fish fork, my graduation ring and a few other things into a
suitcase, wrote a note to my husband and, leading three-year-old
Anne by the hand and carrying year-and-a-half-old Joan and
the suitcase, set off toward the six o'clock bus to Seattle.

According to real estate standards Mother's eight-room
brown-shingled house in the University district was just a modest dwelling in a respectable neighborhood, near good schools
and adequate for an ordinary family. To me that night and
always, that shabby house with its welcoming porch, dark woodwork, cluttered dining-room plate rail, large fragrant kitchen,
easy book-filled firelit living room, four elastic bedrooms—one

of them always ice-cold—and huge cluttered basement, repre-
sents the ultimate in charm, warmth and luxury. It's something
about Mother, who with one folding chair and a plumber's
candle, could make the North Pole homey, and it's something
about the warmth and loyalty and laughter of a big family.

It's a wonderful thing to know that you can come home any-
time from anywhere and just open the door and belong. That
everybody will shift until you fit and that from that day on it's a
matter of sharing everything. When you share your money,
clothes and food with a mother, a brother and three sisters, your
portion may be meager but by the same token when you share
unhappiness, loneliness and anxiety about the future with a
mother, a brother and three sisters, there isn't much left for you.

On returning home I noticed two things immediately. Mother
still smelled like violets and Mary still believed that accomplishment was merely a matter of will power.

"I hear that we are sliding into a depression and that jobs are
very hard to find," I told Mary one morning.

Mary said, "There are plenty of jobs but the trouble with most
people is that they stay home with the covers pulled up over their
heads waiting for some employer to come creeping in looking
for them. Anyway, what are you worrying about? You've got a
job as private secretary to a mining engineer."

I said, "But, Mary, I don't know shorthand and I can only
type about 20 words a minute." Mary looked directly at me with
flashing amber eyes, "Leave the 90 words on the typewriter and
the 150 words a minute in shorthand to the grubs who like that
kind of work," she said. "You're lucky. You have a brain. Use
it! Act like an executive and you get treated like an executive!"
(And usually fired, she neglected to add.)

It was very reassuring, in spite of a sneaking suspicion I had
that if put to a test I would always prove out the grub type, not
the executive, and that only by becoming so proficient in short-

hand that I could take down thoughts would I be able to hold
down even a very ordinary job.

"I have been planning to go to night school," I told Mary.

"Not necessary at all," she said. "Experience and self-confidence are what you need and you'll never find them at night
school. Have you ever taken a look at what goes to night school?
No? Well, they aren't executives, I'll tell you that. Now just
forget about shorthand. I'll always be able to find us jobs doing
something and whatever it is I'll show you how to do it." That
was Mary's slogan at home. Downtown it was, "Just show me
the job and I'll produce a sister to do it." And for some years,
until Dede and Alison were old enough to work and she had
figured how to fit Mother into her program, I was it. That night
I dreamed I was going to play in one of Miss Welcome's recitals
and I hadn't practiced and didn't know my piece.

Sunday afternoon, Mary's new boss, a Mr. Chalmers, who was
coming to Seattle to instill some new methods into the lumber
industry, called from New Orleans and talked to Mary for an
hour. The conversation left her full of enthusiasm.

"At last, I've found the perfect job," she said. "Mr. Chalmers
is much more of an executive-thinker than I am. 'Don't bother
me with details and hire all the help you need,' he said. He also
asked me to find him a bootlegger, one who handles Canadian
liquor, put his daughters in school, send for his wife, introduce
him to the right people, have his name put up at the best clubs,
get him an appointment with a dentist to make him a new
bridge, open charge accounts with the Yellow Cab Company,
a florist, office furniture company and a caterer, and I'm to rent
him a suite of offices in a building in the financial district."

We all listened to Mary with admiration and I asked her if,
in this new wonderful well-paid secretarial job, typing and
shorthand had been requirements.

Before answering, Mary lit a cigarette, pulling her mouth

down at one corner in true executive fashion, a new gesture, then said, "Betty, for heaven's sake stop brooding about shorthand. There were hundreds of applicants for this job, among them many little white-faced creeps who could take shorthand 200 words a minute and could type so fast the carriage smoked, but who cares? Do they know a good bootlegger?" "Do you?" someone asked, and Mary said, "No, but I will by the time Chalmers gets here. To get back to shorthand, the world is crawling with people who can take down and transcribe somebody else's good ideas. We're lucky, we've got ideas of our own." It certainly was nice of her to say we.

## CHAPTER 3

### *"MINING IS EASY"*

Monday morning my hands trembled like Jello as I adjusted the neat white collar on the sage-green woolen office dress Mary had lent me. I was very thin, pale with fright, and with my long red hair parted in the middle and pulled tightly back into a knot on the nape of my neck, I thought I looked just like one of the white-faced creeps Mary had derisively described. Mary said I looked very efficient and very sophisticated. Mother, as always, said that we both looked beautiful and not to worry about a thing. I kissed the children, who didn't cling to me as I had expected, and had just started out the front door to catch a streetcar when Mary called out, "Where are you going?" "To catch a streetcar," I said. "Come back," she said. "From now on we ride to work in taxis. Mr. Chalmers wants us to." "Not me," I said. "Only you." Mary said, "Betty, Mr. Chalmers couldn't have me for his private secretary if it weren't for you. Don't you forget that and I'll see that he doesn't. Now sit down and relax,

I've called the cab." And that is the way we set off to inject our personalities and a few of our good ideas into the business world.

The mining engineer's office, where I was to work, was on the top floor of a building in the financial district. The other occupants of the building were successful lawyers, real estate men, brokers and lumbermen, most of whom Mary seemed to know quite well. To everybody we met in the lobby she explained that she had just brought me down out of the mountains to take her place as private secretary to Mr. Webster, in her enthusiasm making it sound a little as though she had had to wing me to get me down out of the trees.

"Listen, Mary," I said when we got out of the elevator, "I have little enough self-confidence without your introducing me to those people as the little Mowgli of the Pacific Coast."

Mary said, "You're just lucky I didn't ask you to show them some of your old arrow wounds. Anyway, what difference does it make? Most of those people have such dull lives I feel it my duty to cheer them up every morning."

Mr. Webster's offices were luxuriously furnished in mahogany and Oriental rugs and had a magnificent view of Puget Sound and the Olympic Mountains. My little office was also the reception room and after Mary had showed me where to put my hat and coat and how to get the typewriter to spring up out of the desk I wanted to sit right down and begin to practice.

Mary would have none of it. Sitting herself down at Mr. Webster's desk and lighting a cigarette, she said, "Stop being so nervous and watch me. Learn how to act in an office." I said, "I wouldn't be so nervous if I knew what time Mr. Webster gets here." Mary said, "Oh, he's out of town and won't be back for two weeks." My sigh of relief almost blew some rocks off his desk. "Does he know about me?" I asked. "Nope," said Mary. "You're going to be a surprise."

The phone rang. Mary answered it in a low well-modulated

voice and Standard English. "Mr. Websteh's office, Miss Bahd speaking," she said. Somebody on the other end of the wire said something and Mary said, "Well, you big stinker, what do you expect when you don't call until 8: 30 Saturday night?"

While she was still talking to the big stinker, who she later said could take her to lunch, someone came into the reception room. Mary, still on the phone, waved to me imperiously to see who it was. It was a large fat man who held up a little canvas bag and shouted, "Where's Webster?" I said, "Mr. Webster is out of town, may I help you?" The fat man said, "Sister, I got the richest placer property the world has ever seen!" He handed me the little bag and a business card and said, "Give this sample of ore to Webster and tell him to call me the minute he gets in town," and left. I rushed back to Mary.

"The man said that this is the greatest placer property the world has ever seen," I said excitedly, giving her the business card and the ore sample. "Do you suppose we should telegraph Mr. Webster?" Mary glanced at the card and with a bored look dropped both it and the sample into the wastebasket.

"Mary Bard," I said, "what are you doing?" She said, "I'm doing just what Mr. Webster would have done. In other words I'm saving him trouble, which is the first duty of a good private secretary. Now I'm going to pound a few facts into that humble little head of yours. In the first place, you have two of the greatest assets a mining engineer's secretary could possibly have. *A,* your father was a mining engineer; *B,* you have seen a mine and when Webster talks about an assay you don't think he's referring to a literary composition. The rest is all a matter of common sense and practice. Here's the telephone number of the smelter, here's Webster's address. Open and read all the mail and keep a record of all telephone calls."

"What about visitors like the fat man?" I asked. Mary said, "For a while you can keep all that trash and show it to Webster.

After you get more used to things you'll be able to tell the crack-pots from the real mining men. Or, at least, you can pretend you can," she added honestly.

"What about the home office?" I said. "They're one of the richest corporations in the world. How will they feel about me?" "They'll never know about you," said Mary. "We're both Miss Bard, and to the richest corporation in the world, a Miss Bard more or less at $100 a month in the Seattle office isn't that much." She snapped her fingers and we went out for coffee.

In spite of Mary's vehement assurance that I possessed two of the greatest assets a mining engineer's secretary could possibly have, I had such an uneasy feeling about Webster's probable reaction to a secretary who could neither type nor take shorthand that as his return became imminent I grew more and more terrified. Every morning when I took out my key and inserted it in the lock of the door marked menacingly, *CHARLES WEB-STER, MINING ENGINEER,* I drew a deep quivering breath and prayed that Mr. Webster's office would be empty.

Then one morning when I opened the office door there in Mr. Webster's office was Mr. Webster. I almost fainted. Mr. Webster had very brown skin and nice blue eyes and he called out, "Who are you?" So scared I had tears in my eyes, I said, "Well, ah, I'm Mary's sister Betty and I'm your new secretary." He said, "Where's Mary?" "Oh, she's in an office right across the street," I said, adding hurriedly, "She said that if you wanted to dictate to call her and she'd come right over." He said, "This all sounds very much like Mary. Well, as long as she's deserted me she doesn't deserve the present I've brought her. Here," and he handed me a huge green barley-sugar Scottie dog.

I took the dog and, because I was nervous and felt guilty, I was too effusive in my thanks and kept saying over and over and over, "Oh, Mr. Webster, you shouldn't have done it!" as though he were trying to force a diamond anklet on me. Then,

God knows why, but in an effort to offer further proof of my gratitude, I bit into the candy dog and one whole enormous green leg came off in my mouth just as Mr. Webster, who by this time was sick to death of me, looked up to ask if there had been any mail or calls. I couldn't answer. I just stood there in my hat and coat, trying desperately to maneuver the huge leg around in my mouth, my eyes full of tears and green sugar running down my chin. It was not a sight to inspire confidence in my efficiency, but Mr. Webster was very kind and had been a good friend of Daddy's, so he went over and looked out the windows at the mountains while I pulled myself together.

It would have been cheaper and less of a strain for Mr. Webster to have dispensed with me and hired a cleaning woman because, eager though I was to help, all I could do well was to dust the furniture and his ore samples and clean out cupboards. I typed a few letters but I was so nervous that I made terrible mistakes, and the finished product usually had little holes in it where my eraser had bitten too deeply.

The first day Mr. Webster was back he took Mary and me to lunch at a small French restaurant in an alley. While we ate goslings *en casserole* and drank Chablis, Mary told him that he had nothing to worry about because she had figured out everything. Whenever he wanted to dictate he was to tell me and I would call her on the phone and while she took his dictation I would go over and answer her phone. To my intense relief Mr. Webster laughed and said that he thought it was a wonderful scheme, and it did work well until Mary's very demanding boss arrived in town and it became harder for her to get away.

Then Mr. Webster suggested that I take his easier dictation and I did and one morning when I had written "dead sir" and "kinkly yours" on a letter, he offered to send me to night school. So, for three months I went to night school, which Mr. Webster paid for at the rate of $15 a month, and studied shorthand and typing. But it was no use. I couldn't learn shorthand. I got *p*'s and *b*'s mixed up, I couldn't tell *m* from *n* and even when I could write it I couldn't read it back. In fact, I was such a miserable failure at night school that the only thing that kept me from shooting myself was the amazing fact that, although by then everyone else in the class — and there were 42 of them — was an expert typist and shorthand dynamo, I was the only one with a job. When I told Mary, she said, "Naturally. I told you you wouldn't find any executives at night school."

I never did get to feel like an executive and I never did conquer my obsession that there was a mysterious key to office work which, like holding a letter written in lemon juice over a candle, would one day be revealed to me all at once; but by the end of June I had stopped getting tears in my eyes when Mr. Webster called me for dictation, and the letters I typed had fewer, smaller holes in them. Files were one of the worst things I did to dear, kind Mr. Webster, but I never was able to figure out the filing system, such as why letters were sometimes filed under the name of the man who wrote them and sometimes under the name of a mine. If I'd stopped batting around the office like a moth around a night light, had read the correspondence and asked a few intelligent questions, I might have learned the secret of the filing system. But I operated on the theory that always hurrying wildly, never asking questions and shutting up Mr. Webster with "I know, I know," any time he tried to volunteer information, were proof of great efficiency. Because of this unfortunate state of affairs, Mr. Webster is still looking for things.

But the worst thing I did to dear, kind Mr. Webster was the maps. A mining engineer's maps, like an architect's drawings, are the visual proof that he knows what he is doing, and one rainy, dull morning, when Mr. Webster was away on a short trip and I was flitting around the office, I happened to bump into the map case. Now there was a messy thing. Thousands of maps, all rolled sloppily and stuffed in the case every which way.

"How does poor dear Mr. Webster ever find anything?" I said, settling myself for a good thorough cleaning job.

By the time I was finished, I had unrolled all the maps, and sorted them out according to size, putting the littlest ones on the top shelf and the biggest ones on the bottom. I was very tired and dirty when I finished but I glowed with accomplishment.

"I told you mining was easy," Mary said that night at dinner when I told her about my wonderful progress at Mr. Webster's.

Then Mr. Webster returned from his trip, accompanied by an important man from Johannesburg, South Africa, and for the first time since I had been working there, he asked me to find him some maps. "Get me those maps on the Conner mine," he said and I jogged happily over to the map case. But when I got there I realized that with my new filing system, it wasn't the name of the map that counted but the size.

I called to Mr. Webster, "What size is the Conner map?"

He answered rather testily, "What do you mean, 'what size'? It's that big bundle near the front on the bottom shelf."

My spirits fell with a thud that rattled the glass doors of the map case as I suddenly realized that the big bundle near the front on the bottom shelf was now about 25 bundles on all the shelves. So Mr. Webster, the man from Johannesburg and I spent the rest of the day on the floor unrolling maps. We had found most of the Conner mine by 8:30 and I was released.

The next morning there was a note on my desk. "Betty: Have gone to Denver, will be back Monday — please return maps to their original confusion — Webster." Before I finished, however, the home office closed the Seattle office and mining was over.

# CHAPTER 4

## *"SO IS LUMBER"*

"YOU THOUGHT you couldn't learn mining," Mary told me after she had installed me as her assistant in the office across the street. "There's nothing to lumber, it's just a matter of being able to divide everything by 12."

"Does Mr. Chalmers know you've hired me?" I asked.

"He knows that I've hired an extremely intelligent young lady who has spent the last four years practically living in logging camps in the greatest stand of timber in the United States and anyway what's it to him? You're my assistant."

I was quite sure that as soon as Mr. Chalmers found out about me he would fire me, but what worried me more was a fear that he would also fire Mary. I was reckoning without Mary or Mr. Chalmers.

About 10:30 Mr. Chalmers made his entrance into, or rather descent upon, the office. The door to the outer office crashed open and banged shut; the door to his private office crashed open and banged shut; then the buzzer on Mary's desk began to buzz with short angry bursts like a bee in a tin can.

Mary, who was checking some lumber reports, didn't even look up. The angry buzzing continued. Finally, anxiously I asked, "Do you want me to see what he wants?" Mary said, "I already know what the old stinker wants. He wants somebody to yell at because he is nasty in the morning. Come on, let's get a cup of coffee. He'll be pleasanter when we get back."

She picked up the phone, pressed a bell at the side of the desk and said, "Mr. Chalmers, I'm going out for coffee; will you please take any calls?" There was a roar from the inner office

29

and the phone sputtered like water on a hot stove, but Mary put it back on the hook, and we skittered out of the office and down the stairs to the next floor to wait for the elevator. While waiting, we could hear Mr. Chalmers charging around on the floor above, slamming doors and bellowing, "Miss Bard! Miss BARD!"

I certainly did not look forward to meeting him and couldn't understand how Mary could laugh and talk and eat a butterhorn in the coffee shop while that monster waited for her upstairs. She said not to worry, he would be cooled off by the time we got back, and he was.

Mary dragged me in, quivering, to introduce me, and Mr. Chalmers, looking like a seal with a cigar in its mouth, smiled at me kindly and said, "Humph!" For the next two or three days he buzzed for me (my signal was two short) to get him drinks of water, to open and close the windows, to pick up scraps of paper off the floor, to lower the Venetian blinds four inches and to unlock the safe and get him his whisky. Once he asked me some questions about logging on the Olympic Peninsula and when I was able to answer he seemed terribly pleased and retaliated with stories of logging in the cypress swamps.

When I wasn't answering the buzzer and ministering to the little personal needs of Mr. Chalmers, I was typing reports for Mary, learning to cut stencils, running the mimeograph or working on a story we were writing called "Sandra Surrenders."

Then Mr. Chalmers announced one morning that from then on I was to read *The Wall Street Journal, The Banker's Digest* and a couple of other financial papers, pick out all items of importance and interest and relay them weekly, by means of an *interesting* (he stressed this word vehemently) bulletin to all the lumbermen in the State of Washington.

I actually read all the boring financial magazines, but as Mr. Chalmers never took the trouble to check my sources, I shook everything I had read up in a big bag and issued in my own

words and well-seasoned with my own personal prejudices a
bulletin as to the state of the world's finances. I remember one
bulletin that I headed, "War with Japan Inevitable!" I don't
know where this dope got that dope.

In the meantime, Mary took Mr. Chalmers' dictation, arranged bouquets of lovely out-of-season flowers for his desk
and hers, ordered his whisky from Joe the bootlegger and left
me alone with him in the office more and more.

He would buzz for her and I would go in and he would roar,
"Where's Mary?" and I would tell him that she was out paving
the way for him to meet the right people and he would say,
"Humph, well as long as you're here, lower that Venetian blind
three and five-eighths inches, empty this ash tray and fill my
pen." When I had finished, he would say, "Betty, did I ever tell
you about the time I organized the lumber industry in Louisi-
ana?" and I would say no and he would say, "Sit down," and
hours later when Mary returned he would be pouring little
drinks of bourbon and tap water and I would be listening to
Volume XVII, Chapter 32 of *Mr. Chalmers Is Smarter Than
Anyone in the World, Living or Dead*. Lumber was a lot of fun.

Occasionally Mr. Chalmers became irritated at Mary and me
and flew off the handle. One day he left for Chicago by plane
without his teeth, which he had left at his club. "Go to Athletic
Club and airmail me bridge," he wired Mary. "You can starve to
death, you disagreeable old—," said Mary, throwing the telegram in the wastebasket. "Mary, send bridge or you are fired!"
was the next wire. Mary threw it out the window. "Am calling
tonight," was the next wire so Mary air-mailed his teeth that
afternoon and when he called she was like honey and told him
that she had mailed his teeth the minute she had gotten his first
wire and she did hope he was chewing and having a good time.

The very closest we came to being fired was on the occasion
of Mr. Chalmers' visit to New Orleans and arrival back at the

office a week ahead of schedule. It was a very hot summer afternoon and Mary and I, who had received a rather unexpected
invitation to dine on board a battleship, were in Mr. Chalmers'
private office freshening up. We had washed out our underwear
and stockings and pinned them up to dry. We had steamed out
the wrinkles in our silk-print office dresses by holding them over
Mr. Chalmers' basin while we ran the hot water full force, and
had hung them on hangers on the Venetian blinds.

We had washed and pinned up our hair and finally in bare
feet and slips were taking refreshing sponge baths in Mr.
Chalmers' basin, when there were knocks on the outer door,
which we had locked. Mary called through the transom, "Mr.
Chalmers is in conference — who is it?" It was a telegram so
she told the boy to put it through the mail slot.

"Everything is just working out perfectly," we exulted as
we felt our underwear and stockings, which were almost dry,
and I ran the water for my bath. Suddenly there was a loud
pounding at the outer door. "Shall I call through the transom?"
I asked, taking my right foot out of the basin full of warm suds.
"No," Mary said, "it's almost five. We'll pretend we've gone
home." Finally the knocking stopped.

Mary was patting eau de Cologne on her shoulders and I was
drying my left thigh on the last of Mr. Chalmers' hand towels,
when I thought I heard the outer-office door open, and voices.

"Stop being so nervous!" said Mary, spreading her make-up
out on Mr. Chalmers' desk. "You know we're going to a lot of
trouble considering the fact that all the Navy men I've ever
met were liars, short and married." We both laughed.

Just then the door of Mr. Chalmers' office opened and in
charged Mr. Chalmers like a bull out of a rodeo chute. His
face was pomegranate-colored, his cigar hung from his lips
like brown fringe, and his voice was a hoarse croak as he roared,
"Who locked the door? What in hell's going on here?"

Behind him stood the building office manager, swinging some keys and looking embarrassed. Mary, sitting at Mr. Chalmers' desk in slip and pin curls with all her make-up spread out on his blotter and her pocket mirror propped against his inkstand, said quite calmly, "You're not supposed to be here."

*"You're not supposed to be here," said Mary, quite calmly*

Mr. Chalmers dropped his brief case and suitcase and yelled, "I'm not supposed to be here? What in hell's going on?"

Mary said, "You said you weren't coming back until next week."

Chalmers said, "I wired you this morning."

Mary said, "I didn't get it."

He said, "Of course you didn't. I found it unopened under the door. Here," and he threw the telegram at her. "Now clean up this Chinese laundry and get out! You're fired!" He tripped over his brief case, kicked it and slammed through the door.

Mary and I finished dressing, wiped up the spilled bath water and eau de Cologne, lowered the Venetian blinds, put Mr. Chalmers' mail on his desk and prepared to leave. Perhaps because Mr. Chalmers was hot and tired and we looked so clean and fresh, he rescinded the order about firing and in gratitude we took him to dinner with us on board the battleship, where he had some excellent Scotch and sat next to the Executive Officer, who turned out to be a bigger "and then I said to Andrew Mellon" and "Otto Kahn said to me" than Mr. Chalmers.

By the end of six months, Mr. Chalmers' office force had been increased to include, besides Mary and me, a certified public accountant and a liaison man between Mr. Chalmers and the lumbermen. They were very nice but they kept Mary and me so busy we never did get to finish "Sandra Surrenders" and they insisted on taking sides in our fights so that they were seldom on speaking terms with each other, and one or the other was always not on speaking terms with one or the other of us.

Mary and I had many violent fights, but we made up instantly and it was most disconcerting to come back from lunch and find the fight of the morning still hovering around the office like stale smoke and the accountant and the liaison man wanting to take sides and talk about us, one to the other.

They thought I really meant it when I screamed at Mary,

"It's no wonder you're an old maid, for 25 years you've always gotten your own way and you think you can boss everybody!" and Mary screamed back, "It's better to be 25 years old and un-married than to shuffle through your old marriage licenses like a deck of cards," and "You haven't done a stroke of work in this office since I came — all you do is smoke and order me around like a slave," and, "I will continue to order you around like a slave as long as you act like a slave, think like a slave and smell like a slave."

By the fall of 1932, the depression was very bad and we were sure that the lumbermen weren't going to put up with Mr. Chalmers much longer. Everyday I got up timidly and with dread, expecting to find the dark despairing mask of unemploy-ment staring at me. Mary, on the other hand, was so unworried about it all that she took two hours for lunch, another hour or two for coffee, and when Mr. Chalmers finally took her to task, she told him that the interesting part of his job was over and she guessed she'd leave and sell advertising.

For a few terrible weeks I had to stop dusting and filling pens and take Mr. Chalmers' dictation. In between times I had to listen to him develop the theory that the depression was the direct result of inferior people like me wearing silk stockings and thinking they were as good as people like him.

One day my brother, Cleve, came in to take me to lunch and caught the tail end of one of these little talks. "The only way to get rid of troublemakers is to line them up against a wall," said kind old Mr. Chalmers, chewing his cigar. "I feel the same way about low-down heels like you," said my tall, hand-some, red-haired brother smiling in the doorway. Chalmers went into his office and slammed the door shut. Cleve and I went to lunch.

Two days later the office closed. Its closing, like the death of an invalid who has hovered for long wearisome months at the brink of death, brought relief rather than sorrow. I cleaned out my desk and wondered how I would say good-bye to Mr. Chalmers. For in spite of his bluster I was fond of him, knew that his job had been in the nature of his last stand and worried about what was to become of him.

At 10:30 he came slamming and banging into the office, rang the buzzer furiously and demanded that I call Joe the bootlegger and order him a case of Canadian Club. Old Custer was all alone but he was still commanding, still shooting.

I dialed Joe's number and wondered if being out business would affect our credit. Joe's wife answered. I asked for Joe. She said, "He can't come to the phone. He's dead." I said that I was very sorry and she said, "That's okay, honey, we all gotta go sometime. What did you wish?" I said, "I want to order a case of Canadian Club." She said, "All we got now, honey, is the alcohol and the labels." I wondered if she also had the sand and seaweed with which Joe used to adorn his bottles and offer as final proof that it was the real stuff brought from Canada by water. I told her that I'd talk to Chalmers and call her back and she said, "O. K., honey, I'll be here all day."

I told Chalmers about Joe and he said, "Humph!" put on his hat and left and, though I waited and waited, he never came back. At a little after one I took my package of personal belongings and went home. I never saw Mr. Chalmers again. I called his club and left word for him to call me but he didn't and when I called again I learned he had checked out and left no forwarding address.

Lumber was over.

# CHAPTER 5

## *"NOBODY'S TOO DULL OR TOO SHORT FOR MY SISTER"*

MOST FEMALES between the ages of 13 and 45 feel that being caught at home dateless, especially on a Friday or Saturday night, is a shameful thing, like having athlete's foot. I used to harbor the same silly notion and many's the lie I've told to anyone tactless enough to call up at 9:30 and ask me what I was doing. "What am I doing?" I'd say, brushing the fudge crumbs off the front of my pajamas and marking the place in my book. "Oh, just sitting here sipping champagne and smoking opium. My date had trouble with his car."

Which is why, now that I've had time to heal, I'm really grateful to Mary for deciding that along with making me self-supporting, she would use me as a proving ground for dates.

Mary has a great love for people, any people, and is not at all critical, which qualities though laudable in a friend are perfectly awful in a matchmaker. The first time I heard her say, "I can't go but Betty will," I protested.

Mother said, "Remember, Betsy, a rolling stone . . ." Mary, always quick to seize an opportunity, repeated, "Yes, remember a rolling stone." Only I could tell, after a few dates, that her interpretation of the old saying was, "Come out from under that stone and, no matter how mossy, you're a date for Betty."

As "I can't go but Betty will" became Mary's stock answer to any phone call, so "Oh, please God, not *him!*" was my usual reaction.

Mary launched my business and social career the same day. The business career with mining, the social career with Worthington Reed, who when he called and asked Mary to lunch was told, "I've already got a date but you can take my sister Betty." I was surprised and terribly thrilled when, just before 12, Worthington appeared in a big wrinkled tweed suit, pipe and raised eyebrow, and said, "Come on, you." He was very handsome and because of his dress, which was so casual it included a few spots and a hole in the heel of one sock, I decided immediately that he was also very intellectual. "Ah, this is the life," I thought ecstatically as I locked the office door. "A job, the city and a brilliant man to take me to lunch."

The restaurant, too, was romantic. Dark woodwork, brick floors, real leather on the seats, and dim lights that hid the darns in the tablecloths and the shaking of my hands as I lit cigarette after cigarette and tried desperately to cast the first stone into the deep pool of silence between Worthington and me.

Frantically, I searched around in my mind for something to say. Something sophisticated enough to go with wrinkled tweeds and a pipe. Worthington, who was slouched comfortably back in the booth, seemed very relaxed. He pulled on his pipe and looked over my head at the people entering and leaving the restaurant. Finally, desperately, I said, "My, this looks like real leather." "Uppa, uppa, uppa," said Worthington's pipe. "It feels like real leather, too," I said, running my hand over the seat. Worthington said nothing. "It smells like real leather, too," I said, sniffing. Worthington raised his eyebrow but said nothing.

What could I talk about? What beside real leather? I tried to recall some of the brilliant witty things Mary's intellectual friends had said over the week-end but all I could remember was one remark made by an odd boy, who lay around on the floor under the furniture with his eyes closed, hating everything. He had said, "Oh God, not Bizet! He's so nauseatingly rococo."

"Do you care for Bizet?" I asked Worthington hopefully. "Biz-who?" he said through his pipe, as the waitress brought

rolls and butter. "Bizet," I mumbled, afraid that I had pro-
nounced it wrong, that it should have been Busy, Bizette or
Byzay. Worthington didn't answer so I took a roll and had just
started to butter it when suddenly he reached across the table,
took a firm grip on my hand, looked into my eyes and said,
"Do you have any sexual desires?" Needless to say, for the rest
of that lunch hour I never did go back to rococo old Bizet.

"What you need is fun!" Mary said, as she hung up the phone
after telling somebody named Clara that of course I'd love to go
dancing with her Cousin Bill.

"Not when your idea of fun is defending yourself in a pitch-
black taxicab while trying to figure out the German for CUT
THAT OUT!"

"Oh, you mean Hans!" Mary said. "Europeans don't have the
same attitude toward sex that we do. Anyway, he's gone back
to Germany."

I said, "I'm not going tonight. You've never seen Clara's
Cousin Bill."

Mary said, "Betty, you know Clara, and she and her husband
are going. Please, Betsy, just this once and I promise I'll never
get you another blind date. Anyway, I only got you a date with
Hans because Helen said he was going to offer you a job."

"He did," I said. "Shooting wild goats in Austria. I was to
tally the kill and carry the one sleeping bag."

Mary said, "Anyway, Bill is an American."

I said, "How tall is he?"

Mary said, "He's 27 and sells advertising."

I said, "How tall is he?"

Mary said, "I forgot to ask Clara about that, but she says he
has a sense of humor."

"I don't care how funny he is," I said. "I'm sick of looking
down at midgets."

Mary said, "Betty, you know that some of the dates I've

gotten you have turned out all right. You've even had a wonderful time occasionally. I've already told Clara you would go and you'll never heal those wounds sitting around home brooding."

"I wasn't brooding," I said. "I was studying shorthand and I'm not worried about those old wounds. My idea is to keep from getting any new ones."

They came for me on the dot of seven. Cousin Bill was exactly my height, five feet seven inches, but we weren't twins because I had on high heels and five feet of him was torso, and his legs looked as if they'd been meant for somebody else. He wore a turquoise-blue suit and a big pompadour smoothed greasily over a heavy tangle of hair, like a tarpaulin thrown over a brush pile. I thought he was the funniest-looking thing I'd ever seen but I didn't feel like laughing.

Clara and her husband, Carmen—a large gray real estate man—thought he was funny and doubled up convulsively when he pulled the tablecloth over our laps and shouted at me, "Hey, baby, no fair, you've got most of the sheet," or pretended one short leg was shorter than the other short leg when we danced, or clapped his hands with the dirty fingernails together and yelled, "Hey, Garsong," to the waiter. After we had danced, we had Chinese food and Cousin Bill further convulsed Clara and Carmen by yelling, "Pass the bug juice, Baby!" or, "Who'll have another piece of sea gull," or calling the waiters "Chow Mein" or "Foo Young."

Occasionally Mary would get caught in one of her own traps and for a short time thereafter would be slightly cagey about lonely friends of second cousins of switchboard operators in the offices of former customers.

One such happy occasion was the arrival in town of two young mining engineers, friends of Mr. Webster's, who had been in South America too long. Mr. Webster called Mary at Mr. Chalmers' office, where we were both working, and asked her if we would have dinner and go dancing with his friends. Mary said yes and they could pick us up at 7:30 at home.

At six or thereabouts, we were sitting in our bathrobes in the breakfast nook drinking coffee and complaining to Mother about how unfairly we were treated everywhere, when the doorbell rang and Alison came out to the kitchen and said that there were two funny-looking men at the door asking for Mary and me.

We went to the door and there were our dates — one with a tiny head like a shriveled brown coconut, one with a huge white melon-shaped dome; both in Norfolk jackets belted in the back, and both with pipes. It hadn't taken as long on the trolley as they thought it would, haha, and they guessed they were a little early. Mary and I asked them in, left Mother to entertain them and went upstairs to get dressed.

While we dressed, we sent spies downstairs to pick up tidbits of information. "They're going to take you on the streetcar!" Alison reported in a loud voice. "Oh, no!" Mary groaned as she fastened the brilliant buckle on the belt of her long green dinner dress. "Was it the Incas who shriveled heads?" Dede asked as she came upstairs to report that little head's name was Chester and big head's Colvin. "Mother likes them, I can tell," Alison reported. "They're talking about Mexico and she's asked them for dinner on Sunday."

"If she likes them so well, she can go out with them," Mary said. "I'm not going *anywhere* on the *streetcar!*"

I said, "Oh, yes, you are. You're going to get a taste of what you've been doing to me for months and months."

We went, but not on the streetcar because Mary called a cab. I drew Colvin with the big head and I guess he'd been in South America for a very long time because we'd been dancing for quite a while before he caught on that the man is supposed to put his arm around the girl — not vice versa. Mary said Chester held her the right way but kept springing up and down on her toes as if she were a diving board.

At 10:30 Mary looked at her watch, shrieked and said, "Mother will die if we aren't home in 15 minutes," called a taxi and we jumped in and charged it to Mr. Chalmers.

Sunday morning we were delighted to wake up and find four inches of snow on the ground. "No trolleys, no dull little miners!" we thought exultantly. By 4:30 the snow was almost six inches thick, the house was filled with our friends and Mary and I were giving a demonstration of Chester's and Colvin's dancing techniques, when there were thundering raps, the front door opened and there, snow-covered and eager, were Chester and Colvin. They had *hiked* out from town. "Nothing to it," they said, stamping the snow off their big laced hiking boots. "Often hiked 60 or 70 miles in South America."

"Any chance of your getting lost?" our gentle little sister Dede asked.

"Unh — unh," said Colvin and Chester simultaneously. "We can find our way anywhere."

When they left about 11:30, Cleve gave them explicit instructions to follow on the return trip, even kindly drawing them a map and explaining that he'd made a couple of minor changes in the regular route — changes involving a detour along the coast of the Pribilof Islands. The last we saw of them they were standing in the snow under a street light studying Cleve's map.

As time went on and I made friends of my own, Mary had to resort to ruses other than a promise of just plain fun to get me to go out on some date she had arranged. Sometimes it was the promise of a good job. "Now I'm taking you to this cocktail party so you can meet Pierre," she'd say. "He's very French, quite old, separated from his wife, but he needs a secretary. He's a very successful broker and his secretary left last week."

I was eager for a good job and so I went.

Pierre was small and nimble, smelled of bay rum, had his initials on his cigarettes and, after we were introduced, propelled me over to a corner to talk business. He began the interview by stroking the inside of my bare arm with one finger, as though he were honing a razor, and talking about "loff."

After an hour of this I worked my way over to my hostess. She said, "Have you and Pierre settled about the job?"

I said, "Unh — unh, he's been sharpening his finger on my arm and talking about 'loff.'"

She said, "Oh, he's so French. Did he tell you about women being like violins and cellos and plucking the strings?"

"Yep," I said. "For one long hour. Will I have to take that stuff in shorthand?"

She said, "Oh, Betty! Now let's just go talk to Pierre."

We did and Pierre said, "Talk business at a cocktail party?

*"American women are afraid of loff"*

Nevaire!" So I had lunch with him the next day. After we had settled ourselves in a booth in an obscure Italian restaurant and Pierre had pulled the dark red velvet curtains, I thought, "Now he'll talk about salaries and bonuses and things like that." I brightened my eyes, firmed my lips and tried to look efficient.

Pierre took a bite of bread stick and said, "American women are afraid of loff. They are afraid of loff because they don't know anything about it. They are like children afraid of the dark. You are afraid of loff. You have been married, yes, but to an American. In ways of loff you are a child." He took a large bite of anchovy and hot pepper and added, "But once awakened, Betty, my dear, you will be an exciting woman."

I took an hour and a half for lunch, almost got fired from the job I had, and I didn't learn a single thing about Pierre's job. After all, when someone is telling you that you are a potential night-blooming cereus, you can't interrupt and ask things like, "Are you closed on Saturdays?"

I told Mary that I thought I'd forget about Pierre and his mythical job. It wasn't that all his talk about "loff" had made me afraid to work for him, because I had a hunch that Pierre's virile luncheon talk was like the posing on top of a diving tower by a man who can't swim. It was just that I couldn't get him down to cases. One day Mary said, "Let's go up to his office and see if he has a secretary," so we did and he did. A dusty little woman in a gray cardigan and Ground Gripper shoes, who looked as if she had been there all her life, intended to stay and had never been interested in "loff."

"I'll bet he's got a wife, too," Mary said. And he did. A dusty little woman with gray hair and thin lips, who looked as if she had been there a long time, intended to stay and had never been interested in "loff."

But there was something worse than having Mary get me dates, I learned; it was having a man, any man, get me a date with a pal. The thing about men is that they establish friendships on such a flimsy basis and they're so unreasonably loyal. "You can't talk that way about Charlie," Johnny'd say. "Charlie's my friend. What if he did get sick on the love seat?"

A man not only doesn't see anything wrong with little peccadillos like that, he doesn't notice other details like black patent-leather Oxfords, maroon silk socks, turquoise-blue suits or a long bob tucked behind the ears. Nor does he notice faults such as dipsomania, kleptomania, remembering old bridge hands, or a vocabulary of seven words, six of them dirty.

To him Charlie is, was and always will be "Good old Charlie who got me out of that shell hole" or "Old Fraternity Brother Charlie" or "Old Golf Pal Charlie" or "My Best Friend in High School Charlie" or "Old Outfielder Charlie." Which all adds up to the fact that men are basically much nicer than women but haven't any more idea than a corn borer what constitutes eligibility.

"Hello, Betty, this is Jock [Jock was a current fiancé of Mary's]. A pal of mine from California is in town and I thought it would be nice if we all went out on the highway for dinner." This was my first experience and I said yes.

Old pal's name was Stan and his first glaring fault was no chin. None at all. I realize that this didn't keep him from being true-blue or from making home runs on the baseball diamond but I had my standards and one of them was that all my dates must have chins. I said as much to Jock and he exploded.

"Oh, you women make me sick. Stan's one of the whitest guys that ever lived."

I said, "I don't care if he's so white he shines in the dark he hasn't any chin and he can't dance."

Jock said, "God, women!"

Mary's friend Richard said, "Betty, Osbert, an old college friend of mine, is on his way to Honolulu and I thought we'd all go dancing. I know you'll like Osbert, he's a wonderful guy."

Osbert referred to my daughters, Anne and Joan, as "the tykes and little folks." He called dogs "poochies," he called Mother "Mom," he called me "Doll Face" and he called Mary "Ginger." He didn't drink, he didn't smoke and he didn't dance, but when the floor show came on and a girl wearing three strategically placed, very small patches came walking out on her hands under a blue spot, Osbert rammed and shoved his way into the very front row and became so absorbed that he didn't even notice when the man next to him pressed the burning end of his cigar against his sleeve and set him on fire.

After the number was over, Osbert invited the eccentric dancer over to our table for a drink. She came but she turned down the drink with, "No, thanks, I haven't never smoked or drank." So Osbert ordered for her, at her request, "a chicken sangwidge on whoite bread with all whoite meat."

The fact that she and Osbert were practically engaged before the second floor show was over didn't hurt my pride any. What bothered me was where he was going to pin his fraternity pin.

## CHAPTER 6

### *"I WON'T DANCE, DON'T ASK ME"*

FEBRUARY 1933 was a terrible time to be out of a job.
The HELP WANTED — FEMALE section of the papers offered "Egg Candler — Piecework Basis" and "Solicit Magazine Subscriptions at Home." Every day found a little better class of people selling apples on street corners. The employment agencies had very few jobs but were packed to overflowing with applicants — the overflow often sagging wearily against the walls clear around corners and down to the elevators.

I never did learn to enjoy applying for jobs as Mary did, and I hated the smell of employment offices — the hot, varnishy, old-lunchbaggy, desperate smell — "but at least," I told myself after Mr. Chalmers' office closed, "now I've got experience." I was a private secretary of almost two years' duration and could lower a blind or kill a fly with the best of them. Mary said, "Remember, tell them you can do anything and in any language and say you can use *all* the machines."

At the first employment agency I heard the woman at the desk turn down about 20 applicants because of lack of experience. "Sorry, kids," she said, "but you gotta have experience."

Instinctively I brightened. But when it came to my turn to be interviewed, the woman glanced at my card on which I had checked typewriting, shorthand, filing, stencil cutting, legal forms, dictaphone, calculator, switchboard, addressograph, adding machine, multigraph and bookkeeping, in spite of never having seen most of the machines, and said sadly, "Too old."

"Too old!" I said in amazement. "I'm only 24."

"Sorry," she said. "For general office work, most firms want girls around 18."

The next employment agency was across the street and was run by a woman Mary loved, who had gotten her dozens of jobs.

"Now, let's see," she said, "what's come in this morning. Nursemaid, practical nurse, experienced furrier, medical secretary, waitress and car hop. Things are tough, Betty, they really are. What's Mary doing?"

"Selling advertising," I told her. She said, "Well, tell her to scout around for you. You'll stand a lot better chance of getting a good salary."

Even Mary's unofficial employment agency went through a slump that year but just being around her was invigorating and gave us new slants on the employment situation.

"More girls have lost their jobs because of red fingernail

polish than for any other reason," Mary told Dede one day, pounding emphatically on the table in a tearoom.

"Absolutely the only way to get a job," she announced another time, "is to pick out the firm you want to work for, then march right in and announce that you are going to work there because they need you."

I said, "What if they say they do not?"

Dede said, "Show them your colorless nail polish. They'll hire you."

Another time when she wanted me to take a job as a practical nurse, Mary said that there was no point in even trying to get an office job any more — that girls in offices were past history — that from now on everything was to be machines.

Somewhere in between red fingernail polish and the machine age, Mary got me several different jobs. The first she heard about from a friend of an office boy who used to work for a shipping firm she sold advertising to. The job was described as being private secretary to a mining engineer, which at the time seemed too good to be true.

The mining engineer was staying at a small but elegant hotel and we were to meet him at two o'clock on the mezzanine. We arrived on the dot. The mining engineer, a Mr. Plumber, who was not only very prompt, but had aristocratic silvery hair and a firm handshake, got right down to business.

"Do you like to dance?" he asked me.

"Yes, I do," I said.

"Do you have some girl friends who also like to dance?" he asked.

I looked over at Mary and she was shaking her head and spelling something out with her lips. I said, "I thought this was a secretarial job."

Mr. Plumber reached over and patted my knee and said, "It is, haha, but you girls will work at the placer mine, haha, and the boys down there like to dance in the evenings and would a little girl like you be afraid to stay up at a beautiful mountain camp in California with a lot of young engineers sitting around the campfire evenings strumming guitars and singing?"

I was just going to say, "Haha, I should say a little girl like me wouldn't. When do we start and can I bring the children?" when Mary grabbed my arm, stood us both up and said, "Come on, Betty, we'll be late for that appointment. Mr. Plumber, the job sounds fascinating but we'll have to talk it over with the family."

He said, "Fine, fine, and what about your girl friends?"

Mary said, "We'll send them down to see you."

Mary kept a firm grip on my arm but didn't say anything until we got to the lobby. Then she rushed into a phone booth and began dialing furiously. "What are you doing?" I asked. She said, "Calling the Better Business Bureau. Secretaries, indeed! That man's a white slaver."

Instead of getting properly excited, the Better Business Bureau didn't get the point at all. They kept talking about interstate commerce and they wanted Mary to come down and get a lot of forms for Mr. Plumber to fill out. Finally in exasperation Mary said, "Oh, my God!" hung up and went up to see a friend of ours who was a lawyer.

He said, "Probably just a lonely old buzzard who wants to meet some girls."

Mary said, "Don't be ridiculous, Andy. This man's a white slaver. Why, he didn't even ask Betty if she could type. All he was interested in was whether or not she could dance."

Andy said, "Maybe he's a front man for Arthur Murray."

"No wonder this country's rotten to the core!" Mary said. "You business men are such ostriches you refuse to recognize the fact that 80 percent of our high school graduates are being shipped to the Orient as prostitutes."

"Do they require a diploma before shipment?" Andy asked, and Mary said, "You wouldn't do anything about a white-slave ring if it was operating in your desk drawer," and slammed out of the office. She was very pleased the next day to be able to call Andy and report that the Better Business Bureau had called her and told her that Mr. Plumber had checked out of the hotel, minus his brace of secretaries, and had left no forwarding address.

The next job Mary found for me was to be at the Western Insurance Company being private secretary to "a perfectly darling man named Welton Brown." "Welton puts out the monthly magazine for the company," she said, "and I went in this morning to see him about an ad and he told me his secretary is leaving and offered me the job. I told him I already had a job but you didn't. We both decided that you are perfect for it."

"Is it a regular secretarial job?" I asked.

"No," said Mary a trifle too enthusiastically, "and that's what makes it so interesting and why, because you're so talented, you are the only person who can do it."

Instantly alerted for trouble whenever Mary started telling me how talented I was, I tried to keep my voice normal as I asked, "Just what have you told this Welton Brown I could do?"

Mary said, "Stop interrupting and you'll find out. Because Welton gets out a magazine, his secretary has to be able to type and take shorthand, know all about insurance, be familiar with advertising and layouts, draw well enough to illustrate the magazine and be able to write and edit articles. He'd really prefer someone who has been published."

I started to protest that I could do none of these things but Mary interrupted: "Listen, Betty, I've known you for 24 years and you've never thought you could do ANYTHING! Now there's a depression and jobs are hard to find and you've got two children to support and it's about time you grew up and changed your thinking to things you can do instead of things you can't do. Mull over your talents and build up your ego."

It was raining when I left the house. A driving, drenching rain that soaked the backs of my stockings, yanked straggly pieces of hair out from under my hat and made it very difficult for me to fan the meager flame of my self-confidence. By the time I finally got the streetcar and arrived downtown, I was feeling as soggy and unappetizing as leftover salad.

Welton Brown confirmed all my worst fears about job-hunting by first giving me a talk on what a happy family they were at old Western; how they really didn't care half as much about their employes' work as they did about their fitting into the "family"; how you didn't just work at Western, you "lived Western." Then suddenly he thrust a shorthand notebook at me saying, "A little test on that shorthand, just routine but part of the requirements," and began dictating in a rapid monotone a long, very hard article on the stock market.

Pride made me pretend to take the shorthand and, like stenographers in the movies, I filled and flipped over the notebook pages with meaningless scratches and amazing rapidity, even cleverly seeming to hesitate over certain words. When I finished, Welton handed me a single sheet of yellow paper and told me to go to the typewriter in the corner and transcribe my notes.

To kill time and because I didn't have any notes, I took off my coat, carefully adjusted it on the back of the chair, smoothed out the fingers of my gloves and laid them just so beside my purse and, after monkeying a lot with the margin setter on the typewriter, was starting to feed the single sheet of paper into the machine when the door opened and the secretary came in and informed Welton, in a low spy voice, that "somebody upstairs" wanted to see him. Murmuring, they went out and closed the door behind them.

Quick as a flash, I leaped to my feet, grabbed the *Financial*

*World* from Welton's desk, rushed back to the typewriter and in my hurry copied the wrong article. It didn't make any difference because when Welton returned he didn't even look at the article but told me the job paid $75 a month.

I said, "Only $75 a month for someone who knows shorthand, typing, insurance and advertising and can draw and write, too?"

He said, "There is a depression. We are letting many of our people go."

"How? By unlocking their leg irons?" I said to myself as I left.

## CHAPTER 7

### *"YOU NAME IT, BETTY CAN DO IT"*

MARY was convinced that I could do much better than $75 a month and suggested that I go in with her.

"What do you do when you sell direct-mail advertising?" I asked Mary.

"It's the simplest thing in the world," she said. "You get an idea, then you convince somebody who has never had one that he thought of it and it is so outstandingly brilliant, so unusual, that it should be mimeographed and sent to some long list of people. Say the Boy Scouts of America or the Teamsters' Union, whichever list has the most names on it."

"Sounds simple," I said. "But how do you know what kind of an idea they want?"

"Well, in the first place, any idea is better than none, which is most people's problem," said Mary. "In the second place, the only thing people are interested in these days is sales promotion. Ideas that will sell more shoes, davenports, permanent waves, gasoline, or popcorn to the public. Now take Standard Oil. . . ."

Which was one of my few criticisms of Mary, she was always taking Standard Oil or Sears, Roebuck, or some other great big important firm whose name scared me to death, to use as testing grounds for either my ability or her ideas. I didn't want to sell advertising at all. I wanted some sort of very steady job with a salary, and duties mediocre enough to be congruent with my mediocre ability. I had in mind sort of a combination janitress, slow typist and file clerk. Not for a moment did Mary entertain any such humble idea. She had in mind for me any job up to and including the President of the United States.

The thing about selling is that you're either a salesman or you're not. If you are the type of person who remembers your second-grade teacher's pinching you on the neck because you exhibited a doll dress your mother had made as your own handiwork at the school carnival; who buys brown print dresses that are too short in the waist and are unbecoming anyway, because you are afraid of the saleswoman or who could never ask the butcher for half a turkey, then the chances are you would be the next to the worst salesman in the world. I was the worst.

I followed Mary up- and downtown and in and out of offices for three days and all I learned was a lot of basic differences between Mary and me and the location of 14 coffee shops where a butterhorn and coffee were only ten cents. Mary, who seemed to get an order with every call, used the same approach on steamship offices, bakeries, garages, oil companies, candy stores, department stores, shoe-repair shops or lending libraries.

The approach was that she was vitally interested in every single person in the organization, knew the location and condition of every tumor, sacroiliac, heart condition, bunion and crippled relative, knew who was mistreated and knew who had gone where on their vacations and who had been gypped out of theirs, who was in love and who was lonely.

On one of our first calls she learned from a long sallow stenographer that her mother, with whom she lived, had a tumor. Mary said, "Oh, think nothing of it. I had two huge tumors. Had them both removed at once and now I'm better than ever." I looked at Mary, who had never even been in a hospital, with some astonishment. Later I said to her, "Mary, you know that nobody in our entire family for generations and generations has ever had a tumor."

Mary said, "What difference does that make? Evelyn's mother's got one and nobody likes to have a tumor all alone."

It was fun making calls with Mary but I dreaded the day when I'd have to go alone. I didn't dread it half enough.

On Wednesday morning, Mary gave me a little stack of cards, some briefing and sent me off. My first call was on a Mr. Hemp in an automobile agency. Mary had said, "Sell him that list of Doctors and Dentists — they're about the only people who can afford cars now. Sell him on the idea of a clever but dignified letter stressing price and mileage per gallon of gas."

I left the office. It was a soft spring morning. The sky was a pale bluing blue and the breeze from the Sound smelled salty and fresh. The automobile company was about 15 blocks up-town but I decided to walk, both to save carfare and because I wanted to delay as long as possible the moment for seeing Mr. Hemp and selling him the clever idea I didn't have.

The automobile company's wide front door was propped open with a wooden wedge and four salesmen with their hats pushed to the back of their heads lounged in the sunshine on tilted-back chairs, smoking and looking sad. Timidly, I asked one of them for Mr. Hemp. The man gestured toward some offices at the back. All the salesmen watched my progress across the huge showroom, which made me so self-conscious I walked stiff-legged and cut a zigzag path across the shiny linoleum floor.

The offices were guarded by a long counter, behind which several girls were talking and laughing. I asked one of them for

Mr. Hemp and she said she wasn't sure he'd have time to see me but she'd ask him. She went into a glass-enclosed cell and spoke to a man who was lying back in his swivel chair, his feet on his desk, talking on the phone. He turned around and looked at me and shook his head. The girl came back and said, "Did you want to see him about a job?"

I said, "No, I don't want to see him about a job."

She waited for me to reveal why I wanted to see him but for some silly reason I was ashamed to tell her and acted sneaky and as though I were selling something either dirty or "hot."

The girl went in and whispered to Mr. Hemp and I watched him peer at me and then shake his head. When she came back she said, "Mr. Hemp's busy this morning and can't see anybody."

I said, "Oh, that's all right, I'm busy myself. I've got another appointment," and I hurried out leaving my purse on the counter. I missed it after walking a block or two, and when I came back to get it the girl looked at me with such a puzzled look I didn't leave my Advertising Bureau card, which by now was quite bent and sweaty anyway.

My next call was a collection agency. As I walked back downtown, I kept glancing at my watch, praying for it to be noon or too late to make any more calls. But it was only 10: 30 when I reached the large office building that housed the agency.

I got off at the third floor and walked uneagerly down to room 309. The door was frosted glass. Clutching my notebook of collection letters and taking a deep quivering breath, I turned the knob, pushed open the door and was immediately confronted by a pair of eyes so hard they sent out glances like glass splinters. The owner of the eyes, standing at a counter sorting some cards, said, "Wadda *you* want?" as she slapped the cards down into little piles.

I said, "I'm from the Advertising Bureau. . . ." She said, "We don't want any more of those bum collection letters." I said, "I have a new series. I wrote them myself and I think they're pretty good." She said, "Wadda you mean new series? We already sent out one through five." I said, "Now we have five through ten," and began looking for my notebook. The woman said, "Don't bother gettin' them out. I don' wanna see them. It's all a waste of money." I said, "All right, thank you very much." She said, "Wadda *you* thankin' *me* for?" and laughed. I left.

My next call, in the same building, was on a school for beauty operators. I entered the La Charma Beauty School with the same degree of enthusiasm Daniel must have evinced when entering the lions' den. A woman with magenta hair, little black globules on the end of each eyelash, eyebrows two hairs wide, big scarlet lips and a stiff white uniform, was sitting at a little appointment desk. The minute she saw me she shoved a paper at me and told me to sign it. So I did and she said, "Black or brown?" I picked up the paper and it seemed to be a waiver of some sort having to do with La Charma not being responsible if I went blind.

I said, "I don't understand; I'm from the Advertising Bureau." She laughed and said, "Gosh, I thought you was my ten o'clock appointment. An eyelash dye job. Say, hon, Mrs. Johnson wants to see you. She wants a letter to all the girls who will graduate from high school this June." I almost fainted. Somebody *wanted* to see me. I was going to sell something.

Mrs. Johnson, who looked exactly like the woman at the appointment desk except that she had gold hair, was very friendly, offered me a cigarette and thought my ideas for a letter were "swell and had a lotta bounce." I left with a big order and my whole body electrified with hope.

My next call was on a shoe-repair shop. I went in smiling but the little dark man said, "Business is rotten. No use throwin' good money after bad. I don't believe in advertisin'. Good work advertises itself. Go wan now, I'm busy." So I slunk out and went back to the bureau.

Mary was so very enthusiastic about the beauty shop and my first order that I didn't tell her about the other calls. We took our sandwiches, which we brought from home unless we were invited out for lunch, and walked to the public market where for five cents we could get an unlimited number of cups of wonderful fresh-roasted coffee and the use of a table in a large dining room owned by the coffee company.

I must admit that I had false pride about taking my lunch. Furthermore, I hated the days when it was Mary's turn to fix the sandwiches as she would slap them together and stuff them into any old thing that came to hand — a huge greasy brown paper bag, an old printed bread wrapping, or even newspaper tied with a string.

Mary, one of those few fortunate people who are born without any false pride, laughed when I went to a Chinese store and bought a straw envelope to carry my sandwiches in. The straw envelope made everything taste like mothballs and incense and squashed the sandwiches flat but it looked kind of like a purse. Mary said, "So we have to take our lunch, so what?" and went into I. Magnin's swinging her big brown greasy paper bag.

I forced myself to make calls the rest of that week but I diluted the agony with visits to secondhand book stores. I rationed myself: one call, one secondhand book store. Saturday morning I told Mary that we might as well face the fact that I couldn't sell anybody anything.

Mary argued with me a little but finally had to admit that she would never get me in a frame of mind where I thought my ideas were better than Standard Oil's.

"I guess you should take an office job," she said. "Only don't try to find one for yourself or you'll end up paying them and working 24 hours a day. Leave it to me."

The next job Mary got me she told me about by saying, "It's certainly fortunate you're so thin." I was so anxious to go to work I already had one arm in my coat but I stopped right there and came back to face her.

"Is this job stenography?" I asked.

"Well," she said, "it's a combination bookkeeper and fur-coat modeler. That's why it's so lucky you're tall and thin."

"It would also be lucky if I could keep books," I said. Mary ignored me.

"I told Mr. Handel you'd be down this afternoon," she said, writing the address on a scrap of paper. So I put my other arm in the other sleeve of my tweed coat and headed toward the manufacturing district.

The farther downtown I went the more congested the streets were with aimless, unemployed people. It had been raining all morning — it seemed to me it always rained when I was out of work — and the sky between the buildings was heavy and gray, the sidewalks were wet and everybody looked miserable.

The address Mary had given me was down past the Skid Road, Seattle's flophouse district and the hangout of the unemployed loggers and millworkers, as well as the gathering place for all radicals, bums and religious crackpots.

"This will be a good place to study the unemployed and test Mary's theory that only the inefficient are out of work," I thought, but as I worked my way farther and farther downtown, my progress along the streets was hailed with so many catcalls and whistles that I had to abandon testing and keep my eyes straight ahead. Finally I asked a policeman where the address was and he pointed out Handel's sign in the window of a very old red brick building.

Mr. Handel had apparently been crouched behind the door waiting for me, for when I timidly opened the door I almost fell over him. I apologized but he, not at all nonplused, grabbed me and shook my hand clear to my shoulder.

"Come in, come in," he said. "Glad to see you. Take off your

coat and let's see what kind of shape you got." I disentangled my
hand and arm and took off my coat and Mr. Handel looked me
over very, very carefully, then said, "Kid, you got elegant lines
and real class. Now let's see you walk." The office was only
about six feet square but I walked back and forth, weaving sinu-
ously to avoid Mr. Handel's groping, fat little hands.

He said, "That's fine but don't be in such a hurry, Baby. Now
I'll get a coat and we'll see how you look." He went out and
returned with a silver muskrat coat, a fur I had never cared for,
even before it came equipped with Mr. Handel's arms as an
extra dividend.

I shrugged away from him, dodged behind the desk and asked
about the bookkeeping. "Oh, that," he said. "We usually do that
at night." Just then a man with a tape measure around his neck
and a white fox fur in his hands came to the door and beckoned
to Handel, who said, "Wait for me, Baby, I'll be back in a minute." I didn't. I ripped off the muskrat, grabbed my tweed and
ran.

"Mary Bard," I yelled ten minutes later when I burst into her
office, "I'll go back to the farm before I work for that Mr.
Handel. He pinched and prodded me like a leg of lamb and he
said we'd do the bookkeeping at night."

Mary said, "He used to be such an old wolf I had to sell him
his advertising from across the street, but I thought he'd
changed."

"What made you think so?" I said.

"Oh, I saw him up at the Olympic Hotel at a fur show and he
seemed very quiet and dignified. Of course, we were in the main
dining room," she added reflectively.

The next job she got me was tinting photographs. She said,
"This darling little woman has a photographic studio just a few
doors from here and she needs somebody to tint photographs
and she's swamped with work."

"Does the fact that I've never tinted photographs interest you?" I asked.

"No, it doesn't," said Mary, "because I know somebody who knows how and she's going to teach you this afternoon. Her name's Charmion and she works across the street in that sporting-goods store. She's waiting for you now."

Charmion had green eyes and black hair and while she was teaching me to dip dabs of cotton in paint and rub it on photographs she also sold basketballs, golf clubs and duck decoys and told me all about her three husbands. The next morning, armed with my new accomplishment, and with the knowledge that we needed a ton of coal, I reported for work at Marilee's Photo Studio.

*Brides wearing glasses*

The studio, which was narrow and two-storied and gave the impression of a tall thin person squeezed into a dark doorway out of the rain, had a small show window with a skimpy, rather soiled tan half-curtain across the back and a bunched-up ratty piece of green velvet on the floor. Arranged on this were tinted photographs of bold, feverish-looking girls, brides wearing glasses, and sailors and girls leaning on each other. The subjects of all the photographs bore a remarkable resemblance to each other, due to the wholesale application of purple on cheeks and lips, red in the corners of the eyes, red to the lining of the nostrils and large white dots in the pupils of the eyes.

I tried the door but it was locked, so I flattened myself against the doorway, out of the rain, and waited. At length a pair of black licoricy galoshes turned into our entryway and I recognized Marilee instantly because she looked exactly like all her photographs, even to the rimless octagon brides' spectacles, except that she had ash-blond hair instead of the black or bright brassy yellow that adorned most of her clientele.

Marilee smiled at me, winked, said, "Wet enough for you?" and unlocked the door. Inside the studio, a square room with an appointment desk and a table with a screen around it, were hundreds more pictures of the bespectacled brides, bold girls and sailors. There was not one picture of a plain man, a child or somebody's mother.

Marilee removed her black-satin belted raincoat and black-felt policeman's cap, revealing a black pin-striped suit, a high-necked white blouse, black patent-leather pumps, big pearl earrings and orange silk stockings. She snapped on a light over her desk, checked her appointment book, winked at me and said, "Good weather for ducks. Let's see. Nothing doing till 9:30. That'll give us time to get you started."

She ushered me behind the screen, gave me a very dirty Kelly-green smock, handed me a huge stack of pictures and said, "Your sis says you was experienced, so I'm going to start you right in on some orders. Now, up here in the corner I've wrote the color of hair, eyes and so forth and so on. When you get done with a photo put it over here on this rack to dry. Here's the cotton, here's the paints, here's the reducer, but don't use much. I like the color strong. Now I gotta get set up for my first appointment. If you want to know anything, just holler."

I picked up the first pictures. A brunette with pale eyes, a heavy nose and a straight thin mouth stared boldly right at me. I looked at the slip of paper clipped to one corner. "Eyes — blue

. . . hair—black . . . light-complected," it read. I gave the girl turquoise-blue eyes, luminous white skin, a bright pink mouth, a shadow on her bulbous nose, and blue highlights on her black hair. It took me quite a while but the girl looked pretty and not nearly so hard when I had finished.

I was doing the mouth when I heard the studio door open and close and then voices. The appointment said, "I vant yust the head. Not the body. Yust the head." Marilee said, "Four dollars, payable in advance, entitles you to four poses and one five-by-seven without the folder. A tinted photo is $2 extra. Now do you want to fix up any before I take you?"

"No," said the appointment. "Yust the head. My modder vants to see how I look before she die."

"Okay," said Marilee. "Now sit right here. Look over here. Look over here. Look right at me. Now look up here at my hand. Now you're all done. You can get your proofs Wednesday."

Marilee's next customer was a fat girl with scarlet cheeks, who shyly asked if she could be posed to look thinner. "The camera don't lie," said Marilee heartlessly. "Four dollars in advance, do you wish it tinted and what type folder?"

I peeked around the screen. The fat girl was crouched on the piano bench on which Marilee posed her subjects, looking as if she were about to have a tonsillectomy without anesthetic. Marilee came out from under her black cloth and squinted at the girl. "Come on, honey," she said winking, "let's have a nice big smile, look at the birdie now. Tweet, tweet."

She adjusted her light so that its several hundred watts illuminated the fat girl's miserable face harshly without any shadows, reduced her eyes to squinting pin points and changed her from a nice shiny apple to a doughy pudding. Still not satisfied Marilee clicked over on her shiny black slippers, gripped the girl by the chin and the back of her head, and forced her head to the side and back into a most unnatural tortured position.

"That'll give you a neck," she said. "Now, let's have a great big smile."

The girl tried again. Marilee said, "Oh, golly, honey, that was a dream and would it look good tinted! Our tinting's only $2 for a great big five-by-seven. Now look right at me. Think of that boy friend. Now to the left. O.K. All done. You can git your proofs Wednesday. With your coloring you should really have one tinted." The girl mumbled something and Marilee said, "That'll be $2. All tinting's paid for in advance." I checked my colors to be sure I had a full tube of red for those enormous cheeks.

At noon Marilee came in to examine my work. I had all my finished pictures on the rack and was frankly proud of them. Marilee squinted her eyes, clicked her tongue with her teeth and said, "God, honey, you're not gettin' the idea at all. When people pay for tinting they want color. Now here, watch me."

She grabbed one of my best pictures, a girl with copper-colored hair, amber eyes and coral lips, and went to work. She changed the hair to bright unrelieved orange, the eyes to turquoise blue with large white dots in the pupils, scrubbed plenty of magenta on the cheeks and lips and then carefully, with a toothpick dipped in paint, put red jabs in the corners of the eyes and outlined the nostrils in bright red. The girl, except for the color of her hair, now looked exactly like Marilee and all the other pictures. Marilee said, "That's better, eh? Now fix up the rest."

After that I tinted the photographs the way she wanted them and the work went much faster.

By Saturday noon I had caught up with all the orders and Marilee and I were "real girl chums." I knew all about Mama, who was a Rosicrucian, sister Alma who was married to a sailor and Marilee's boy friend, Ernie, who was a chiropractor and would love to give me a treatment any night after work.

She said, "Honest, some nights Mama is all tied up in knots

and Ernie works her over and you can hear her bones crack a block away — it's just like pistol shots. Mama says she don't think she could carry on if it wasn't for Ernie."

I didn't want any bones cracking like pistol shots and I didn't relish being worked over by Ernie, but I didn't want to hurt Marilee's feelings, so I said I'd call her and set a date.

She said, "Gosh, honey, it's been like a shot in the arm havin' you here. I'm real sorry the work's all caught up but I'll call you the minute I pile up some more orders."

Marilee gave me $28.45 in crumpled bills and a little package. "Open it," she said, winking and smiling. "It's a surprise. Go wan." I did and there in a little leather frame was a tinted photograph of me. "Oh, it's beautiful! Thank you, Marilee," I squealed, looking with horror at the orange hair, turquoise-blue, hard, sexy eyes, flaring red-lined nostrils and purple lips.

Marilee said, "You remember that day I asked you to pose for me so I could adjust the camera?" I remembered. "I tinted it last night," she said.

I kissed her good-bye and promised to have her out to dinner but I never did, because when I went to look for her, I found her little shop closed, the bespectacled brides and sailors and girls gone from her show window.

I asked the shoe-repair man next door if he knew what had happened to Marilee but he said, "I don' know. People coma and goa inna depresh."

Then I went to work in a credit bureau typing very dull reports implying that everybody in Seattle but the President of the First National Bank had rotten credit. One day when my boss was out of his office I looked up our family's credit. We took up almost a whole drawer and from what I read it sounded as if the credit bureau not only wouldn't recommend us for credit, they wouldn't even let us pay cash. This, however, didn't make me feel too badly because I knew they didn't like anybody.

ANYBODY CAN DO ANYTHING        65

The next job Mary got for me was taking dictation on a dock
for a purse seiner, who was trying to settle an estate involving
hundreds of relatives all named Escvotrizwitz and Trckvotisztz
and Krje and living in places called Brk, Pec, Plav and Klujk.
My shorthand, feeble enough in English, collapsed completely
under Mr. Ljubovija's barrage of Serbo-Croat mixed with a few
By Gollies and Okays, which he fondly thought was English.
Finally, I told him that if he'd give me an idea of what he
wanted to say and spelled out the names, I would write the letters.

I could not understand why he wanted the letters in English
when there was a good chance that as none of the family, including him, spoke it, not one would be able to read it, but he
was insistent. To him, writing in English was synonymous with
success. He was a very nice man and I loved sitting in the sun
on the dock listening to the raspy-throated gulls, smelling the
nice boaty smells of creosote and tar and watching the purse
seiners work on their nets.

Then Mary got me the job with the gangster.

His name was Murray Adams, he had an office in a funny old
building that housed beaded-bag menders, dream interpreters,
corn removers and such, and I still don't know what he intended
to do. He was big and dark and handsome and wore an oyster-
white fedora and a tan camel's-hair overcoat even in the office,
which was hot.

Mary met him in some oil promoter's office and he asked her
if she knew of a girl to sit in his office and answer his phone.
Mary naturally said of course she did, her sister Betty, and so
there I was.

Murray — he told me to call him that — told me that he'd
been a member of a mob in Chicago and a rumrunner on the
Atlantic Coast and had "a bucket of ice in hock in Washington,
D. C." He was very sweet to me and used to take me out for
coffee and tell me about different "dirty deals" he had gotten

from different "babes," but he used to make me nervous when he sat by the office window, which was on the second floor, pretending that he was holding a Tommy gun and mowing down the people in the street.

"Look at that bunch of slobs," he'd say. "Not one of 'em got anything on the ball. Jeeze I'd like to have a machine gun and ah-ah-ah-ah-ah-ah [he'd make motions of moving a machine gun back and forth] I'd let them all have it. Especially the dames."

I don't know why Murray had me and I certainly don't know why he had a telephone because whenever he left the office he told me to tell whoever called that he wasn't in and whenever he was in the office he said to tell whoever called that he was out. I had a typewriter but nothing to type, so I wrote letters to everyone I had ever known. Murray paid me in crisp new bills, $20 a week for three weeks and then left town owing his rent, telephone bill, and for his furniture. I never heard of him again.

"This is the best job I've ever gotten you," Mary said. "You get $25 a week for being Mr. Wilson's private secretary and you have a chance to make thousands more on the dime cards."

So I went to work for Mr. Wilson and his dime-card scheme, which was the depression version of the present-day Pyramid Clubs. Mr. Wilson, an advertising man, thought up the dime-card scheme and if Seattle hadn't been such a stuffy city he might have made a million dollars and I about ten thousand.

The idea, as I remember it, was very complicated, involving the purchase of printed shares in Prosperity which the purchaser sold in turn to two other people, etc., and like all get-rich-quick chain-letter schemes, it held out the promise of an eventual killing for everybody. A principal feature of this particular scheme was the circulation of dime cards (cards with round slots for ten dimes each and ten places for signatures). Because I was the originator of several chains I got 90 cents from the first four cards, 80 cents from the next eight, 70 cents from the next 16 and so forth. As each share was turned in to the office I entered the name on a chart, so that I knew who had bought from whom and where the dimes were or weren't.

After the first week the office was a madhouse, and I had to hire four girls to help me and every night at home all the family sat around and picked dimes out of Mary's and my dime cards. One night we counted $72 worth of dimes. All day long people stormed into the office demanding a share in Prosperity and then rushed out again to sell their shares and start their chains. I knew that there had to be an end to this delightful game some time because Seattle only had about 300,000 citizens, but I didn't anticipate how or when it would come.

One day after the office had been running for about six weeks, a fat man came in and asked me to explain the dime-card game to him. I did, slowly and succinctly, and he said, "That's it, sister. I'm closing up this joint!" Whereupon he called in a huge task force of policemen, who came loping in swinging their billy clubs. The girls working for me began to bawl, and I tried vainly to locate Mr. Wilson, who had gone to the bank.

"I'm from the D.A.'s office and I'm going to take you all to the station house," the fat man said. I said, "You are not. We only work here and, anyway, what's the matter?"

"Plenty's the matter," said the fat man.

Then a photographer took a lot of pictures of the policemen seizing the files, which was pretty ridiculous as nobody was holding onto them. Finally, in an hour or so a small pleasant gray-haired officer appeared, dismissed the fat man, sent all of us home, and that was that.

"Crime is too nerve-racking," I told Mary. "Just get me a plain job." So she did. Typing estimates for an engineer. The work was dull and so was the engineer but it was a job.

# CHAPTER 8

## "ALL THE WORLD'S A STAGE AND EVERYBODY IN THIS FAMILY IS GOING TO THE FOREIGN MOVIES AND LIKE BACH"

IT SEEMS to me, as I look back, that when we were the poorest we had the most fun. Our ability to enjoy ourselves in the face of complete adversity was astounding to the people who believed that you had to have money to have fun; appalling to those others who believed that it is effrontery for the poor to laugh. I am not sure that individually we would have been so "happy in spite of it all," but together we felt we could survive anything and did.

Mary accepted the depression as a personal challenge. She always had a job, she tried to find jobs for her family and hundreds of friends and, while she was looking, propped up everyone's limp spirits by defying big corporations.

When the telephone company threatened to disconnect our telephone because the bill hadn't been paid, Mary marched right down to see the president and told him that if he cut off our phone and left us with no communication with the outside world, she was going to sue him personally. Her exact words, which she recounted to our amusement at the dinner table, were, "I told him a telephone and telegraph company is a public service operating under a special grant from the state. If you cut off my telephone you will not be performing a public service and I will sue you. In fact from this day on I'm going to be known as the biggest suer in the city of Seattle." It did keep the telephone from being disconnected and it certainly bolstered our morale. She tried the same thing with the power-and-light company, but they turned off the lights anyway and for a week or so left us to burn old Christmas candles and skip the ironing.

During this interlude, Mary, who was inclined to keep up with our friends of private school days, brought home to dinner a terribly snobbish young man who remarked, as we sat down to our candlelit vegetable soup, "You Bards absolutely delight me. You have a simple meal of vegetable soup and toast and then you make it elegant by serving it by candlelight." He was so elegant, of course, that he didn't go out into the kitchen to note that we were also washing the dishes by candlelight.

When we ran out of fireplace wood, Mary unearthed a bucksaw and marched us all down to a city park two blocks away, where we took turns sawing up fallen logs. We were just splitting up our first log when two park gardeners came up and asked us what the hell we thought we were doing. Mary told them exactly what we were doing and why and to our surprise and relief they helped us saw and carry the wood up to the house.

During the depression we all came home right after work and Mary brought home to dinner, to stay all night, or to live with us, everyone she met whom she felt sorry for. Some of these people were brilliant, talented and amusing. Some were just ordinary people. Some unconscionable bores. Mary didn't care.

Every night for dinner we had from two to ten extra people to tax Mother's ingenuity in stretching leftovers and improvising beds. After dinner we played bridge or charades or Chinese checkers or the piano, rolled old cigarette butts into new cigarettes on our little cigarette-rolling machine, and drank gallons of coffee which was 17 cents a pound.

Every Saturday in the fall, Mother made a huge kettle of chili and we all sat around and listened to the football games. Mother, an ardent fan, kept a chart, groaned in agony over the stupidity of the announcers who commented on the crowd and didn't tell where the ball was and invariably told us that there was no football spirit in the West, we should go to a Yale-Harvard game. When our side made a touchdown we all shouted at the top of our voices, which made the dogs bark, and the children wake up from their naps and bawl.

I always looked forward to Saturday. I loved Saturday's dusk with the street lights as soft as breath in the fog or rain, the voices of the children, filtering home from the matinee, clear and high with joy and silliness; the firm, thudding, comforting sound of front doors closing and shutting the families in, the world out; the thick exciting sound of a car door slamming in front of the house; the exuberance of the telephone bell. Everybody we knew came over Saturday night, brought friends and stayed until three or four Sunday morning.

Sundays we all pitched in and cleaned the house, Mother made an enormous meat loaf (hamburger was 12 cents a pound), then Mother and Dede left for church while Mary and I filled a washtub with cleaning fluid and sloshed our office dresses, our skirts, even our coats in it, then hung them slightly less spotty and dripping gasoline on a line under the porch. By dinnertime the whole house was pervaded by the strong smell of gasoline and meat loaf, mingled with that of shampoo and scorch from the iron.

Parties in those days were indistinguishable one from another, the food was always spaghetti, garlic bread and green salad; the drinks were either bathtub gin and lemon soda or cheap red wine; the entertainment sitting on the floor and listening to Bach. I didn't care for Bach, even when partially anesthetized by bathtub gin, but red-hot nails in my eyeballs wouldn't have made me admit it because Mary had made it clear to me that everybody who was not down on all fours liked Bach, Baudelaire, Dostoevski, Aldous Huxley, Spengler, almond paste on filet of sole, Melachrino cigarettes and the foreign movies.

I liked Baudelaire, Huxley and Dostoevski, I loathed Spengler, felt that almond paste on fillet of sole had a lot in common with chocolate-dipped oysters, Melachrino cigarettes tasted like camel's hair and the foreign movies would have been dandy if only they hadn't been foreign.

There is a state of ennui in which I become engulfed immediately when confronted by a flickering, speckled film and a lot of unfamiliar actors batting their eyes and saying, *"Ai bisogni si conoscon gli amici,"* or *"A pobreza no hay vergüenza,"* or *"Battre le fer pendant qu'il est chaud,"* or *"do svidanya."*

The foreign movies were on Wednesday nights at 11:30 at a University district theater. The reason I kept going, aside from a false pride that made me say I thought they were "magnificent," "delicately directed," etc., when I really thought most of them were boring and dull, was the fact that after each one the management served little cups of black coffee and free cigarettes.

"An amazing picture, grrrreat photography," I announced loudly in the foyer, as I stuffed my pockets with cigarettes.

Another simple pleasure we enjoyed in those poverty-ridden days was looking at real estate. My brother Cleve through a long involved series of trades, beginning, I believe, when he was ten years old with a saddle Mother had had made in Mexico, had acquired a long low cream-colored Cord convertible with dark blue fenders and top. On spring Saturday afternoons we would all climb in the Cord and go house-hunting.

I suppose in a way it was taking unfair advantage of the real estate dealers, who invariably, when they saw our gorgeous car drive up, came careening out of their offices brandishing keys and carrying fountain pens and a contract. But on the other hand they tried awfully hard to take advantage of us.

"This magnificent structure," they would say, as they tried to force open the sagging door of a termite-infested old mansion, "was the home of one of Seattle's finest old families and is being sold for taxes. Just given away." In we would all troop, the children racing up the stairs or down, the rest of us walking slowly, examining everything and noting with amusement the empty whisky bottles, lipstick-smeared walls, and other evidence that this fine old family must have been supplementing their income by making whisky or dabbling in white slavery.

Sometimes we found wonderful bargains. One was a huge brick inn, north of the city, about an $85,000 structure, on sale for $5500. There were 13 bedrooms, a living room 80 feet long, a dining room, breakfast room, library, music room and billiard room, every room with a fireplace, magnificent barns, a stream and ten acres of land, and we had many violent fights over who would have which room. The real estate dealer finally got so sick of taking us out there that he gave us the keys and we used to take picnics and make plans while we ate our peanut-butter and pickle sandwiches. The real estate dealer was more than anxious to make an even trade for our very salable house in the University district and we were all ready to move in when Mary, distressingly practical, pointed out that the nearest bus line was five miles away, the nearest school about 18 miles and the former owner had, upon questioning, admitted that it cost from $200 a month up even to take the chill off the lower floor.

## CHAPTER 9

### *"NIGHT SCHOOL"*

UNTIL I STARTED to night school, my life was one long sweep of mediocrity. While my family and friends were enjoying the distinction of being labeled the prettiest, most popular, best dancer, fastest runner, highest diver, longest breath-holder-under-water, best tennis player, most fearless, owner of the highest arches, tiniest, wittiest, most efficient, one with the most allergies or highest salaried, I had to learn to adjust to remarks such as, "My, Mary has the most beautiful red hair I've ever seen, it's just like burnished copper and so silky and curly — oh yes, Betty has hair too, hasn't she? I guess it's being so coarse is what makes it look thick."

Then I started to night school to learn shorthand and, after ten years of faithful attendance, realized that now I was eligible for a medal for being the slowest-witted, most-unable-to-be-taught and longest-attender-at-school-studying-one-subject.

I went to every night school in the city of Seattle, both paid and free, studied under expert teachers, but I couldn't learn shorthand. It had something to do with my coördination, I believe, because I was never able to learn arm-movement writing in school, either.

Mary, as I have pointed out, was never in favor of my attendance at night school. She thought it was a waste of time and she was right, but learning shorthand got to be an obsession with me, like swimming the English Channel. I bought a book of stories in shorthand and for years mouthed them out on the streetcar riding to and from work. But at my jobs the minute anyone ever said to me, "Take a letter," or "Get your notebook, Miss Bard," I would get such a case of buck fever I'd make wiggly little scriggles instead of smooth curves and little lines and would get far behind trying to remember whether "a" went on the inside or outside of the angles.

Night school differed from day school, I learned, not only in time of day but in atmosphere and type of students. Day-school students, who were usually young, career-conscious people, eager to get jobs and get started (the fools), exuded an air of cheerful self-confidence. Night-school students, predominantly young foreigners and old Americans suddenly faced with the necessity for earning their own livings, were even in times of great prosperity badly handicapped by language difficulties, the

wrong color of skin or old stiff fingers. Nevertheless, they zeal-
ously, gallantly tried, in spite of the inadequacy of their tools,
to carve their niches in the stone face of the business world.

The Public Evening School was housed in a large gray stone
building that smelled of stale sandwiches and chalk. My shorthand classes were usually from six to eight, which meant that I
could go right from work and eat dinner when I got home.
Sometimes, however, I would have to take the seven-to-nine class
and then, to kill time and to avoid the long trip home and back
downtown again, I took another subject from six to seven. Once
I took French, another time Speech and another time Creative
Writing.

The Speech woman, who wore a big brown felt tam and rough-
tweed suit, said, "Korrrrect speeeeeech is more eemportant than
korrect post-eur. A person is eemeejutly judged by hees speeech."
As she talked she rolled back her lips, swung them to the sides
or pulled them down so she looked like a red snapper. I used to
imitate her at home for the pleasure of the family.

Each session of the Creative Writing class was jam-packed with
frustrated people who wanted to be writers and live Bohemian
lives. Almost every student carried a large brief-case bulging with
manuscripts which either the publishers were too timid to publish, were too crooked to publish, or else had kept just long
enough to steal the idea and give it to some big writer.

In addition to their frustration, most of the students were
violently jealous of each other. The teacher, who confided to
me one night that trying to teach people with nothing to say
how to write it down was a sad business, had us write stories
and little articles and then read them aloud and invite criticism.

Before the unfortunate victim had read his last word, the stiff
upraised arms of the criticizers were as numerous as wheat stalks
on a stubble field. The criticism ran to: "I don't like your style
and nothing you said was true to life," "I don't like to say this,

honey, but your grammar is terrible," or "I don't think that fella would have married the girl after she treated him like that, I know I sure wouldn't have," or "I think the story wonderful and I don't think we should be so hard on our fellow authors because think how you're going to feel when you get up there."

A Scandinavian friend of mine at Writing class wrote personal experience stories, all very depressing, about how she was fired and not paid, about one place she worked where the woman was so stingy they only bought half a pound of hamburger for dinner for themselves and their two servants and about the time she slipped on the sidewalk and broke her hip and the city wouldn't pay her. She had a stack of rejection slips about nine feet high and couldn't understand why.

"I tell de trut," she said. "Dere is not vun vord I write dat is not de trut." I told her that I thought she should write about happier things, not be so sad, and cited Mark Twain as an example. She said, "You mean I should make yokes?" I said yes and so she went home and laboriously inserted Pat and Mike "yokes" here and there in her sad little manuscripts.

A little fat Greek man thought the idea behind successful creative writing was quantity not quality and he came staggering into each session with about a hundred pounds of badly written, greasy manuscript in pencil on scratch paper, about a moronic detective and an even stupider police captain who could never catch a big gang of killers and robbers who continually robbed a little Greek grocery store run by the cleverest little fellow ever to appear on a grubby piece of scratch paper.

The class criticizers were relentlessly cruel to him, so another student and I invited him to have coffee with us and we told him he was a genius. He said, "I got lotsa ideas. I write all night lotsa times." We told him that someday he would be famous and he was so grateful he brought us each a bottle of Metaxa brandy.

Mary was right. I never met any executives at night school,

and it didn't improve my shorthand much, but there were many times when I found it most comforting to look around a big class and feel that we were all failures together.

## CHAPTER 10

### *BILLS! BILLS! BILLS!*

A BILL is a thing that comes in a windowed envelope and causes men to pull in their lips and turn the oil burner down to 60 degrees and women to look shifty-eyed and say, "Someone must have been charging on my account."

A bill collector is a man with a loud voice who hates everybody. A collection agency is a collection of bill collectors with loud voices who hate everybody and always know where she works.

I could no more have a complete feeling of kinship with someone who has never had bills than I could with someone who doesn't like dogs. Owing money is not pleasant, but those of us who have grown wild with frustration trying to yank and pull one dollar into the shape and size of five have cringed with embarrassment at the stentorian voices of bill collectors, have been wilted by money lenders' searing questions; and have resorted to desperate dreams (in my case usually involving scenes where a beautifully dressed, charming, red-haired lady says to a lot of different people, "Your pleading just bores me — close my account!"), but emerge finally, if we are able, kicked and beaten into a reasonable facsimile of a human being and/or dog-liker.

The only person ever able, to my knowledge, to confuse completely bill collectors, credit managers and their ilk, is my mother. Mother, a truly charming and talented woman, has no more financial sense than a hummingbird. Arguing with her about money is like trying to catch minnows in your fingers and, worse, she adopts a reasonable attitude toward bill paying.

When a credit manager would call Mother and shout accusingly, "You promised to be down here on Monday and you didn't show up," Mother wouldn't cringe or get tears in her eyes but would say pleasantly, "I know, but I was busy with something else."

When the credit manager said, "Why didn't you come down on Tuesday, then?" Mother would say, "Would you mind holding the phone, the cat seems to have a fur ball in her throat?"

Eventually the hardest-boiled credit manager would give up. "Next Monday, then?" he'd finally ask wearily.

"All right, next Monday," Mother would say, adding after he had hung up, "if my primrose woman doesn't show up."

Mother employed the same infuriatingly reasonable tactics with Mary and me.

"Mother," I'd shout in exasperation, "I gave you $25 Thursday to pay the gas bill and they called me today and said it hadn't been paid."

Mother, intent on frosting an applesauce cake, would say, "Which man did you talk to?"

"A Mr. Ellsworth," I'd say.

Mother would say, "Is Mr. Ellsworth the one with that lump behind his ear?"

"I don't know about the lump," I'd say. "WHAT ABOUT MY TWENTY-FIVE DOLLARS?"

Mother would say, "Lower your voice. I gave it to the egg man."

"But I promised it to the gas company and the egg man isn't due until next week," I'd wail. "Why did you give it to him?"

"Because," Mother would say, gently, "his wife has arthritis. Now let's eat this applesauce cake while it is hot."

Mother, a strong believer in and supporter of small business, made keeping the household accounts more confusing than world government. Mother had an egg man, a bread woman, a rabbit man, a chicken man, a spice man, a slabwood man, an old-forest-growth man, a good plumber, a punk plumber who would come on Sundays, a primrose woman, five magazine men, a chimney cleaner, a bulb man, an orange man, a dahlia woman, an apple man, a regular manure man, a well-rotted manure man, a pots-and-pans woman, a moth-ball-and-pot-holder woman, a wire-toecover man, a little old needlewoman, a Christmas-wrapping woman and a downspout man.

All of these "at the doors" as we used to call them, had regular times to appear but because they all loved Mother and because her method of payment was so erratic, they dropped in whenever in the neighborhood. On payday they swarmed around the house like yellowjackets around a rotten apple.

Occasionally when Mary and I would try to bring order into our lives and live on a budget, we would gather the family together for strength and try to take Mother to task for her "at the doors."

"Can't you get rid of some of them?" we'd wail.

"I'll do my best," Mother would say. "Now which ones do you want to eliminate?"

"The pot-holder-and-moth-ball woman," we'd all shout together.

"Why?" Mother would say.

"Because," we'd say, "her pot-holders are no good, and her moth balls contain some sort of special breeding stimulant for moths."

Mother would set her lips stubbornly. "Mrs. Twickenham," she'd say, "makes mistakes in her crocheting because she needs new glasses which she can't afford. I know her moth balls are no good and smell horrible but I try to throw them right away."

So Mrs. Twickenham stayed.

"All right," we said. "What about that wire-toecover man? You know we've never been able to use one of his inventions."

Mother said, "I have. I'm using his egg basket to keep the dogs off my camellia cuttings."

"What about his butter slicer, his bread cutter, his fruit basket, his soap dishes, his lettuce bag?" we said. "None of them work."

Mother said, "Yellow Belly had her kittens in the fruit basket and anyway Mr. Muster's wife has TB."

When I came winging in from a chicken farm, where budgeting had been simply a matter of subtracting the feed from the eggs, adding the sacks, subtracting the gasoline, adding the potatoes, subtracting the buttermilk and adding the pig, I was unprepared to cope with a system where I was paid every two weeks, the main bills came once a month, Mother's little businessmen came every week or every day or by the seasons, insurance payments were quarterly, taxes were yearly, and no matter how many times we had macaroni and cheese there was always some creditor left over. Somebody who came at dinnertime and announced in ringing tones, "Collect for the *Times!* . . . Collect for the sewing machine! . . . Collect for the slabwood! . . . Collect for the Belgian hares!"

We all pooled our money and Mary and Mother and I distributed it to the best of our ability and Mother's reasons, but it was a losing game. Like climbing up a rock slide. We'd just get to the top and the front porch would sag, or the toilet would overflow or the downspouts would leak or Christmas would come and down we'd go to the bottom again.

Then, of course, there were things like the five green party dresses I charged in the course of one winter.

My darkest memories are of that spring after my first winter of charge accounts. For months, as I rode to and from work on the streetcar, I had been confronted at exactly eye level with advertisements that pleaded, "Use your credit! Don't go without!

Buy from US — take a year to pay! NEVER SAY HOW MUCH — SAY CHARGE IT!"

So one day I did. I opened a charge account at a large department store and bought a hand-woven tweed coat on sale for $15. "A charge account," I told the family, "really saves you money. This coat was a marvelous bargain and I never could have gotten it if I hadn't had a charge account. After this, we'll charge whatever we need and pay at the end of the month."

"Good idea!" "Sound reasoning!" "Oh boy!" said the family.

At first we were very careful and limited our charges to pots and pans, stockings, water glasses and bath mats. The small bills came in, I paid and said, "You see, a charge account makes life much simpler." So I opened a few more, and a few more and a few more and then came Christmas. "Charge it, charge it, charge it," I said all over town and if I hesitated the least little bit the clerks said, "Don't worry, honey, things bought in December aren't billed until February." In December, February seems as far away as July and so I staggered through the Christmas crowds, my arms loaded with rich gifts, the smells of fog and pine tingling my nostrils, certain disaster dogging my heels.

Then Christmas was over and so was my lumber job and bearing down upon me as surely and relentlessly as death was February 10th. Mother said, "Go down and talk to them. Explain that you have lost your job and won't be able to pay until you find something permanent." I said, "Yeah, something permanent that pays about $5000 a month. Somebody *must* have been charging on my accounts."

Mary said, "Pay each one a little bit. That's what I do. Even 50 cents lets them know that you intend to pay."

How could I give Mr. Beltz of the fishy eye, reluctant credit and five green party dresses, 50 cents? I said I'd handle it my way.

My way was to lie awake all night in the bed I shared with

Mary, flinching as occasional raindrops bounced from the sill of
the open window to my face, and watching the street light
make prison bars on the wall. My way was to toss and turn and
beat my brains and wail, "Why did I do it?" Five green party
dresses! What had I been thinking of? I must have been crazy.
I hardly ever went to formal parties and even if I did was there
any reason I always had to be in a charged green?

I finally got through February, which was a short month, but
I lost 12 pounds, was as jumpy as a cricket and had such circles
under my eyes I looked like a marmoset.

Then one day I was walking along the street and right up
ahead of me on a huge signboard was an awfully nice-looking
man. His outstretched hands were filled with ten- and twenty-
dollar bills and in a big white bubble to the right of his head he
was begging me to come on down to the Friendly Loan Company. "We want to help you," he said. "Stop worrying. Come
down and let us share our money with you."

I hurried right up to the small, dark office housing the
Friendly Loan Company.

"Whaya want?" said the friendly little lady at the desk, whose
mouth should have been set out in the woods to catch raccoons.

"I want to borrow some money," I said, adding with a gay
little laugh, "a lot of money."

Miss Friendly Loan looked at me coldly, threw her lips over
to the left and yelled, "Chawrlie! Customer!"

Chawrlie, who had close-set, pale green eyes and a small head,
took me into his office and shot questions at me for an hour. I
had intended to lie about my job, my salary, my bank account,
my bills, everything, but I found that I couldn't lie to Chawrlie.
He caught me up every time, picked the lie up in two fingers,
handed it back to me still wriggling and told me to keep it.

When I had finally told all, Chawrlie had me sign a note for
$100 and then handed me only 62. The other 38, he said, went for

carrying charges, upkeep, risk insurance and probably that great big advertisement. The interest was 12 percent and I was to pay $5 every two weeks. I thanked Chawrlie profusely and skipped out to distribute the $62 among my charge accounts and to make rash promises about future payments.

*An awfully nice-looking man*

When I got home, I bragged to the family about my great financial acumen, told them about darling old generous Chawrlie and that night slept soundly for the first time in weeks.

It was fortunate I did, because from then on my life became a living hell. My jobs were all temporary — a week here, a week or two there, and though I was almost always paid, there was something about that temporary money that made it seem as if I'd won it on a punchboard. I'd use my salary to buy little presents for the family, take us all to a show, pay Mother's "at the doors" and tell myself, "When I get a permanent job I'll start in on the big bills."

It was the other way around, of course; the big bills started on me. Each of my charge accounts had a collector, equipped apparently with second sight. They knew about my jobs before Mary had found them for me and would often be milling around the door before I'd been properly hired.

"Who in hell are all those people?" one of my short-term bosses asked me.

"Bill collectors," I told him humbly.

"All of them?" he asked in amazement.

"Yep," I said, "and I've more that haven't found me yet."

"And I thought I had troubles," he said, and was very kind about my shorthand.

I was ashamed of owing money. I was scared to death of all credit managers and I hated my bill collectors. I sneaked around town, jumping six feet if anyone touched me on the arm, getting tears in my eyes every time I was called to the phone and dashing for the rest room if a stranger came into my office.

But it wasn't until I got behind on the payments to the Friendly Loan Company that I learned what trouble really was. The Friendly Loan collectors were everywhere. They yelled at me in the lobby of movie theaters when I had dates, shouted at me on the streetcar, and the woman with the coon-trap mouth called me on the telephone three or four times a day no matter where I was working.

Then I went to work for the Government and the first week so many bill collectors came roaring into the office or called me on the phone that I expected to be fired. Instead my boss took me to the Federal Employes Union and they paid all my bills.

They paid the Friendly Loan exactly $27 — the difference between the $35 I had paid, which apparently had been credited to cleaning the rugs, new draperies, etc., instead of the principal, and the $62 I had received, and told them that if they didn't like it they could come into court and fight charges of usury.

In all my life I will never forget the deliriously free, terribly honest feeling I had the day the Federal Union notified me that all my bills had been paid and that from that day forward, except for a matter of several hundred dollars I owed them and was to pay back so much out of each pay check, I was solvent.

Is it any wonder that I don't mind paying my income tax?

## CHAPTER 11

### *BUNDLES FOR BARDS*

I READ the other day that some women solve the clothes problem by giving a designer $100,000 a year to dress them. All I can say for that designer is that he must be sewing together old hundred-dollar bills and using them for interlining.

If it is hard to be well-dressed on $100,000, imagine how hard it was to be well-dressed on nothing. Fortunately, we could all wear each other's clothes, but our wardrobe, even when combined, had nothing in common with the "early evening," "country living," "an afternoon at the museum" or "something for the symphony" categories depicted by the fashion magazines. Our clothes had categories but they were "clean," "dirty," "work," "date" and "terrible" (which we wore around the house).

Our biggest problem, next to getting something in the first place, was trying to keep it away from Alison and her high school friends. We threatened Alison with torture, we ordered her friends from the house, but it was all wasted effort and for Alison's four high school years, nothing Mother or Mary or Dede or I owned ever got really cool.

I would clean and press a dress and have it neat and ready for work in my closet, but when I went to get it, it would be gone and in its place would be a wrinkled, milk-shake-spotted tweed skirt and a blouse ripped under both arms.

"Alison," I'd yell. "Where is my brown dress?"

"Which brown dress?" Alison would say, her eyes shifting from side to side like a metronome.

"My office dress," I'd say. "It was brand clean and pressed and now it's gone."

"I haven't seen it," Alison would say, slipping through the front door and signaling to whoever had it on not to go past the house. That night when I got home the dress would be back in my closet, reeking with some musky perfume and still warm.

For a long time we bought our clothes at nice stores, waiting until they were marked down for the last time, which meant that we were just buying our summer clothes when the rest of the world was getting ready for snow. But "it's not your clothes but you yourself that counts," Mother told us and so we whetted our personalities and patched our petticoats and dreamed of the day when we'd be rich and beautifully dressed and dull.

Then Dede and I found the Bargain Mart, a funny little dark store with funny little dark clerks; store hours geared for musicians and gamblers; clothes that often bore, in addition to labels from other stores, traces of other occupancy, such as powder around the neck or a forgotten clip. Dede and I never could decide whether the Bargain Mart people merely bought up leftovers from other stores or were receivers of stolen goods.

The worst thing about the Bargain Mart was their boxes, which were bright magenta with enormous gold letters on both sides screaming BARGAIN MART at anybody within a radius of 12 miles who didn't carry a white cane. Dede and I loved the Bargain Mart but we certainly hated those boxes which were made of such punk cardboard that they tore when we stopped in the alley and tried to turn them wrong side out.

We didn't take Mary to the Bargain Mart because we knew that she'd be more interested in what they were doing in the back than in the good bargains, but we took Mother and she bought, for $17, a gray tweed coat with a "Made in England" label in the sleeve and a fountain pen in the pocket.

Mary didn't miss being taken to the Bargain Mart because she had her own ways of being well-dressed on no money. When asked to a cocktail party she would rummage in the trunks in the attic, grab the garden scissors and often emerge in an hour or two looking at least different. One Saturday afternoon she took our black taffeta evening dress with the huge full skirt and our white high school graduation dress and, by cutting off the sleeves and lowering the neck of one and removing the skirt from the other, evolved a very smart ankle-length black jumper dress with a white dotted-organdy blouse with enormous puffed sleeves, real lace on the collar and a demure little black velvet bow at the neck. Mary's only trouble was that she made so many major changes with pins that sitting down in one of her creations made you feel like one of those Hindus who lie on spikes.

One time a Mrs. Schumacher, a very rich friend of Mother's, met Mary at a cocktail party and admired her dress, and when Mary told her she had made it not ten minutes before out of some old portieres and a few pot holders, Mrs. Schumacher was so impressed that the next day she sent over a huge box of clothes accompanied by a note which said, "Some things I've hardly worn, and thought you and your brave little family might use."

"Hooray!" we all said, diving in, jerking things out and throwing them over our shoulders. But when we'd looked at everything, we knew that we would all have to be a great deal braver than we were to wear Mrs. Schumacher's hand-me-downs, which were big blouses and big party dresses, of chiffon, satin and beaded fringe, all orchid or fuchsia.

"Here," we said, tossing them to Anne and Joan and their friends for "dress-ups," and for years afterward we could hear them in the playroom quarreling and saying, "Now, Joan, Tyrone Power wouldn't wear a beaded Schumacher," or "How can I be Sonja Henie when you have the chiffon Schumacher?"

Last year at an autographing in southern California, a large woman in a beaded purple chiffon Schumacher came up to me and said, "I'll bet you'll never guess who I am," and I wanted to say, "I don't know who you are but I know what you've got on." But I said, "No, I'm sorry, I don't."

She said, "I'm Mrs. Schumacher from Seattle," and I said, "How wonderful! You're the woman who gave us all your old clothes during the depression," and to my surprise she wasn't at all pleased but got very red in the face, said, "I don't remember any such thing," and went flouncing off.

Shoes were also a depression problem. First, there were the children who delighted in greeting me at the end of a weary day by lifting a foot and displaying either a large new hole or a sole flopping up and down like a panting dog. "Not another pair?" I'd groan and they'd say, "Um, um, and my play shoes have come unsewed and my party shoes are too short." You could get very good children's shoes for $2.50 in those days, but $2.50's didn't grow on trees and I longed to bind the children's feet.

Mary and Dede and I got our shoes in cheap stores that carried pretty good imitations of Andrew Geller and I. Miller for $1.98 if you could stand the pain and didn't go out in the rain. The $1.98's required a great deal of breaking in, in fact almost complete demolition, before you achieved anything approaching comfort. I remember a pair of green lizagator pumps that took over two months of breaking in by the whole family before I could walk across the room in them without fainting.

We had a little shoemaker in our neighborhood who would do anything to our shoes, short of half- or whole-soling, for 15 cents and many's the morning we waited in our stocking feet while Anne or Joan or Alison ran up to Mr. Himmelman's with our shoes.

"There," Mr. Himmelman would say, polishing the shoes on his sleeve after he had sewed up the side or put on heel tips. "Just like new, eh?"

One time I bought myself a pair of brown suede shoes which looked very nice but were apparently made of suede-finished scratch paper because the first day I wore them it poured and my feet got soaked and the next morning when I went to tighten the laces of my new shoes the eyelets came out and hung on the lacings like little gold beads.

"Hurry and take these to Mr. Himmelman," I told Alison. "Tell him to bore new holes or something."

But Mr. Himmelman told Alison, "These are not shoes. Just imitation. Bah, no good. Tell your sis I'm sorry I cannot do a thing."

Last winter I bought a pair of real alligator pumps and though they are comfortable and have stayed sewed even in snow, I can't forget those old exciting days when a sudden storm might dissolve my brand-new pair of simu-calf pumps and leave me standing at a busy intersection in my stocking feet.

# CHAPTER 12

## "NOW LISTEN, MOTHER, IT'S ONLY A FIFTEEN-MINUTE-A-DAY PROGRAM"

During those years when we were all living at home, Mother managed to keep reasonably busy. She took care of my two children, did most of the housework, cut the lawn, gardened, fed and administered veterinarily to our household pets, which included at one time three dogs, four cats, a canary, two guinea pigs, a white rabbit and a mallard duck, and fed and administered homeopathically to her five children, our house guests who often stayed five years, and an adopted sister.

For recreation Mother helped with homework, heard long, often dull stories about jobs and lovers, listened to the radio, made sketches, grew primroses, read all the new books and almost every magazine published, attended family-night movies and entered contests.

For years we all saved wrappers and box tops and Mother wrote 25 words or less on Why I Like Ivory, Lux, Camay and Oxydol, and had gentle unselfish dreams of what she would do with the $10,000 or the new cars she would win. But not until the Old Gold contest came along and she accompanied her entry with a letter stating, "I am a little old grandmother who smokes two packages of Old Golds a day" (and coughs constantly) and won $50 and a flat tin of Old Golds, did she have any success.

We were tolerant about Mother's contests but we were not nice about her radio programs. "How can an intelligent woman listen to that stuff?" we'd ask. "Those serials are corny."

"I don't remember asking you for your opinion," Mother would say. "And I find them very relaxing. It's like having someone read aloud to me while I do my borish housework."

The one serial we didn't object to was "Vic and Sade," an extremely witty, very original little program that had none of the kidnapings, killings, trials, bawling, poisonings or dreadful little children that graced the other daily droolers. In fact, it was so clever and cheerful it was finally taken off the air.

Then there came the day when Mary switched from direct-mail to radio advertising and we were grateful for every minute Mother had spent with Ma Perkins.

As soon as Mary had launched herself in radio she started in on the rest of us. First, it was merely a matter of listening. Every afternoon Mary told Seattle housewives about good bargains in half-soling, denture cleaner and rat poison and every evening told her family that we were indifferent, uncoöperative, unappreciative and unprogressive because we forgot to listen to her. "Did you listen to my program?" she'd ask us at dinner, and we'd all say yes whether we had or not and then she'd check on us. "What was today's big bargain?" she'd ask and if we didn't know she'd slam her napkin down beside her plate and say, "How can I expect to reach the ears of a million housewives when I can't even get my own family to listen to me?" and we'd feel ashamed of ourselves and vow to do better. The one time we all did remember to tune in on Mary she said, "You must come down and see our imported English tin setter sweats," which fact we joyfully reported to her.

Then, through her own program, Mary got some singing spots for Dede, whose voice was so beautiful when she sang "Boy of Mine" in an attempt to get people to come down and buy boys' underwear on sale for 49 cents that we all cried, and Dede, who got seven fan letters, began wearing green eye shadow in the daytime.

Mary naturally turned next to her old stand-by, her most faithful jack of no trades and master of nothing, me. "Canada

Dry wants you to write them a terribly funny radio program," she told me one night at dinner.

"Why me?" I said. "I never drink ginger ale."

"Radio," Mary said, "is the greatest advertising medium of the age and offers magnificent opportunities to all talented people. For anybody to sit home and not take advantage of radio is so unbelievably stupid I don't even wish to contemplate it."

I said, "Who shall I talk to in Canada Dry?"

Mary said, "You won't have to see anybody in Canada Dry because they don't know about the program yet. We have a half-hour spot we want to sell them and I told our production manager that I'd get a program if he'd arrange the audition."

So I wrote two skits which were probably not very funny but were certainly not improved by the services of the two no-sense-of-humor "drahma" students imported for the audition.

"Hahnd me that cahn of peppah, Chollie," intoned the female drahma student speaking from her diaphragm and tossing her lips back from her clenched teeth. "Wheech cahn, deah?" replied her cohort, raising one eyebrow and stroking his pimply chin. If the Canada Dry people were there they were certainly nice about it and left quietly without any fuss at all.

Then one day Mary sold a large department store on the idea of a daily radio serial, to be cast from their employes, directed by Mary, and written by er . . . uh . . . er . . . Mother — Mary decided on the spur of the moment as she sold the program.

When the advertising manager asked to see the script, Mary said, "I left it at the office, but we'll start auditioning tomorrow morning and you can read it then." He said, "Fine, fine," and Mary rushed off to call Mother, who was raking leaves and exercising the mallard duck, which someone obviously not familiar with the family had given us alive and expected us to kill and eat.

Mary said, "Mother, could you write a 15-minute-a-day radio serial?"

Mother said, "Why, I don't know. I've never given it much thought."

Mary said, "Well, dear, I've just sold the program and I have to have a script tomorrow. All it needs is to be funny and have suspense. Will you do it, Mother?"

Mother said, "How much is 15 minutes' continuity?"

Mary said, "Gosh, I don't know. You're the one who listens to the daily droolers. Write the first episode and we'll all read and time it tonight. We can add or subtract what we need."

Mother said, "I wish we could afford to have the lawn mower sharpened. It just chews the grass off."

Mary said, "You write this program for me and you can afford to have it sharpened every day if you want to."

"Oh, am I to be paid?" Mother asked, cheering up considerably.

"Naturally," Mary said. "You'll get $25 a week."

"My," said Mother, "just like winning one of those $100-a-month-for-life contests."

So Mother laid aside her rake, put the duck in the basement, fed the children, put them down for their naps and then sat down in the breakfast nook and wrote the first episode of "Schuyler Square."

It was charming, it was funny and it had suspense. After dinner that night we read, Mary timed and Mother made the necessary changes.

The next day, the advertising manager signed the contract and for the next year, five nights a week, about ten or eleven or one or two o'clock, Mother would slide into the breakfast nook to drink coffee, to smoke millions of cigarettes, to cough and to write, in her absolutely unreadable handwriting, her 20 pages on both sides of radio continuity.

# CHAPTER 13

## "JUST LIKE FLYING"

I KNOW that most people think that the worst pitfalls in the path of a working girl are low salaries and sex. I don't. I think the worst pitfalls in the path of a working girl are shorthand and office parties.

Office work can be dull enough but office play is worse. Why don't people realize that it is as ridiculous to try to get all the people who work together to blend socially as it is to expect everybody living in one apartment house to be best friends?

All the office parties I've ever attended were either so proper they were stifling or so unleashed they were indecent. At the unleased parties little accountants, who during working hours never unpursed their lips and called fellow employes of 20 years' standing "Mister" and "Miss," invariably turned into the most rapacious of fanny pinchers; the primmest and most unyielding of all the office females got disheveled and hysterical; and the boss, who had always appeared gentlemanly and above average, turned out to have a wife who told dirty stories and insisted on fixing everybody "jusht one more lil drinkie".

For weeks, even months, after a real bang-up office party the involvees would go shamefacedly around apologizing and being tiresomely humble or else nursing little hurts and slights.

For a long time I worked in offices too small for any office get-togethers, but I was not spared, because my friends, Mary's friends, Mary, even my sister Dede, worked in bigger places where they had lots of parties. I was dragged to bank picnics, insurance dances, oil-company masquerades, construction-company country-club debauches, canned-salmon swimming parties, department-store dinners, radio-station free-for-alls, electrical-sales roller-skating parties, even ferryboat christenings. These were all distinguished by either an anesthetic dullness or a great deal of hysterical activity. Whether or not you enjoyed yourself depended on your idea of fun.

I remember the auto-parts Christmas party that the try-to-be-grand wife of the office manager had insisted be formal (which meant merely tuxedos and a dress any length below the calf) and at her home. Both guarantees of misery. How choked and stuffed the men looked. How overcurled and unsure the women.

There was a large blue Christmas tree in one corner of the crowded living room and as each couple was herded past it to be introduced, the uncomfortable wives remarked, "Oh, what a beautiful Christmas tree. My, I just love blue Christmas trees. They look so frosty," and each husband said, "I like a plain green tree myself," which elicited a dirty look from the manager's wife and a nudge or kick from his own.

There were little dishes of nuts and olives and a very few tiny crystal ash trays placed here and there. The nuts and olives brought forth, "Would you wish for some err-derves?" "No, thanks, I wouldn't care for some," or "Oh, thanks, don't mind if I do," and "My, it certainly is a lovely party. There's nothing like seeing folks all dressed up. I told Charlie, 'You can't wear overhalls all your life.'" "I'll just take one almond — I'm on a diet." "Oh, heavens, no more for me. I'm full up. But they're lovely err-derves."

As the room filled so did the tiny ash trays. The hostess apparently didn't notice this but several of the guests did and made self-conscious trips to the neat swept empty fireplace, lost their nerve and carried them back again. When a husband spilled ashes on the rug, his wife scrubbed at them with her best handkerchief, looked embarrassed and said, "Men!" As was inevitable after a while there was the unmistakable smell of burning wool and a frantic search which revealed the overflowing ash trays, some marks on the tables and one cigarette stub smoldering on the rug under the edge of the davenport. Immediately the host and hostess were down on all fours, rubbing at the burn, checking the burn, measuring the burn and making everyone in the room miserable. I fully expected them to dust for fingerprints. After a great deal of discussion but no confessions they let the case rest but I noticed nobody smoked after that.

About midnight some very small glasses of a raw sherry and several plates of a dry bready fruitcake were passed. Most of the men downed the sherry like straight shots, but they were not given refills. The wives sipped theirs, remarking, "What lovely sherry. I think fruitcake and sherry go lovely in the evening."

After the sherry, everybody started for the upstairs and their wraps and as each couple said good night I heard the host and hostess say, "Now don't you worry about that rug — accidents are bound to happen — and a Merry Christmas to you, too." I had a feeling that the minute the door closed on the last guest they were going to have a big fight about office parties and that burn on the rug and I was glad.

The other extreme was a construction-company party at a country club outside of town. We were a little late and when we drove under the porte-cochere it sounded as if we were entering an amusement park. "Help, somebody help me!" "Ohhhhhhhhhhhhh!" "Wheeeeeeeeee!" "Ouch! Georgie!" "Stop!" "Don't you dare, Hank!" "Oops, try again," sprang at us like "The News of the World" at movie theaters. "This is going to be quite a party," my escort said.

It was a come-as-you-please party, and suits and plain blacks mingled with beige laces and orchid taffetas as did pin stripes and plain browns with the two dinner jackets. There were two or three bottles of whisky on every table and several under them. Everybody danced every dance and deliberately bumped into each other on the crowded floor. "Hey, watch where you're going!" our partners yelled at each other, laughing as they clashed us womenfolk together like cymbals just for the hell of it. It was certainly lively. One man fell into and broke the drum, another punched the orchestra leader in the nose because he wouldn't let him lead the orchestra, another went around filling the men's pockets with seltzer water.

By the time supper was served everyone was at the wrong table, everyone was tight, the poor waiters were almost in tears and I seemed to be alone. My waiter, a small sad-looking man,

*They clashed us together like cymbals*

said, "What are they celebrating?" and waved his arm around to include all the staggering, milling, yelling crowd. "Being alive and having a job, I guess," I said.

A small girl with a thick white skin and half-closed eyes came over to the table, leaned down on her elbows and said, "Boo!" I said, "Who are you?" She said, "I'm the wife of blue prints over there but it doesn't make any differenshe, honey, I jusht came over to tell you that your nose is shiny. Here," she reached down her neck, drew out a large gray powder puff and slapped it briskly around on my face, covering my nice shiny make-up with a thick white powder. "Thash better," she said, putting her powder puff away and swaying as she tried to focus her eyes on me.

I went into the ladies' room to take off the powder and found it crowded and terrible. The first vice-president's wife had got sick and was sobbing, "I've been poishoned." A small drab girl in a plum-colored suit was sitting in a corner twisting her handkerchief, looking very green and saying nothing. Several girls were repairing their make-up and exchanging notes. "So what if you're married?" I says to him. "Who isn't?" One older woman was sniffing smelling salts. The colored attendant, who carried a sheaf of one dollar bills like a bridge hand, said, "Anything I can do for you, honey?" I said no, wiped off the powder and left. When I got back to our table my escort had returned and we went home.

I resolved never to go to another office party.

Then Dede announced that her office was giving a skiing party and would I go with her. I enjoyed the mountains in winter, the stillness, the deep blue shadows, the untouchedness, the thin tingling air — but I was not at all enthusiastic about skiing, and I saw no point in beginning now.

"No," I told Dede. "I don't know how to ski, I don't want to learn and I loathe office parties."

Mary, who had by this time married a Danish doctor and spent all her week-ends skiing, said, "Skiing is a wonderful sport. It is the closest you'll ever come to flying. You must go. It is very healthful, stirs up the blood, especially when you ram into a tree, and I think everybody in the family should learn."

I said, "But I'm no good at sports and I'll probably break my leg."

"Nonsense," Mary said. "Skiing is all a matter of relaxing and balance. Anybody that can bend their knees can ski."

I said, "How did Claire do last week-end?"

Mary said, "Oh, she broke her leg but it was a simple fracture of the tibio-astragalus so she'll be back on skis in no time."

I said, "How did Margaret make out?"

Mary said, "Well she was going up a steep hill and she had forgotten her climbers or slipped or something — anyway, she landed sitting down wedged in a hollow tree stump and she wasn't hurt at all but she was terribly mad. We thought she'd gone back to the practice hill and so we didn't look for her for about four hours."

"I can hardly wait," I said. "Imagine looking forward to spending next week end breaking my tibio-astragalus and being wedged in an old stump for four hours. Are you crazy?"

Mary said, "Betty, skiing is the coming sport. Everybody is learning, there are excellent instructors at the mountains and the air is wonderful."

I said, "No."

Then Alison, who loved skiing, was very fearless and at her first lesson had shot down the mountainside like a bullet, said, "Betty, you should go. It's so much fun, just like flying."

Dede said, "Oh, come on Betty. We haven't anything else to do and it might be fun."

So I asked Mary if I could borrow her skiing clothes and she said, "Of course you can. Oh, I know you'll love skiing.

There isn't anything as exhilarating as flying down the mountains in the early morning, your skis hissing through the powdery snow, your blood singing, your skin tingling. Now remember, the most important thing to do is to learn to fall, then remember to keep all your weight on the balls of your feet and your knees bent."

I said, "Just lend me your pants and your boots and keep the address of a good bone man handy."

So we went. All 40 of us to a lodge in the Cascade Mountains. The car Dede and I were in had no chains and after we passed the snow line the back end veered from one side of the road to the other so that one minute we were peering down over the edge of a thousand-foot precipice and the next were crouched against the bosom of a thousand-foot mountain. Everyone else in the car laughed loudly at these antics but Dede and I looked at each other grimly.

About dusk, the car stopped, we unloaded our luggage and skis and started through the knee-deep snow toward the lodge, which was leering down at us from a pinnacle in the distance. "Just like flying," Dede said bitterly as she ploughed along, her skis over her shoulder, her suitcase dragging in the snow.

Finally, we reached the inn, had coffee royals in front of a big fire and skiing began to seem like a pretty nice sport after all.

*"Track!"*

After dinner skiing and tobogganing parties were organized. Everyone was very eager and excited and soon the mountain stillness was threaded with a bright pattern of shouts, screams, laughter and singing. It seemed to make little difference to these true sports enthusiasts that the organizer of the tobogganing party had marked off a toboggan slide which crossed the ski run so that sometimes the skiers would have to jump the toboggan, sometimes they landed on the toboggan, their ski poles digging into the backs of the tobogganers, and sometimes the toboggans banged into the skiers, knocking them down if they were lucky.

After the first collision, Dede and I went back to the lodge and to bed. But from the screams and yells that persisted until almost morning, the danger of a collision was only the extra thrill that made these already dangerous sports even more irresistible to the other 30. The bed was hard, narrow and damp but at least it was stationary.

In the morning it was raining and the little red flags that marked the slalom course hung down wetly and sadly against the gray slushy snow. Occasional large icicles let go and silently disappeared in the drifts against the lodge.

The floor of the ski room was awash with mud and as each wet foolish skier came in to dry off, the fire hissed and spat and the air was filled with the smell of hot wool. "Oh, you must come out," the people who had been out said to the ones in front of the fire. "You don't notice the rain and it's so much fun."

Finally, uneagerly, Dede and I put on our jackets, caps and mittens, left the nice comfortable fire and went out. It was wet and slushy but the rain had relented to spitty gusts. I put on my skis, adjusted the clamps, gave myself a push and went sailing down a little hill and into a snowbank. "Hey, Dede," I called excitedly, scooping the snow out of my mouth as I brought my left leg over my right shoulder, "Come on, it's fun." We fell down hundreds of times but the snow was soft and it didn't hurt

When we came out again after lunch we found that the tem perature had dropped noticeably and turned the wet surface of the snow to a glare of ice. Now that *was* fun. We couldn't steer our skis at all and slid rapidly even on the level. "This is one sport I'm going to like and be good at," I thought exultantly as I slid off a boulder, swerved around a tree and waited for Dede.

When she caught up with me she said, "There's a hamburger stand over on the highway and it's within skiing distance if we can make it down that steep icy hill over there."

"That little thing," I said, confidently skiing over, "Why that's nothing," and shouting, "Track!" I gave myself a big push, but only one ski took off. The other stayed on the top of the hill and the next thing I knew there was a tearing pain and I found myself suffocating inside my waterproof parka. "Help, help," I yelled, tugging wildly at the parka. Everyone was laughing and pointing at me but no one offered to help.

"Help, I'm hurt," I yelled louder and a girl said, "Track!" and skied right over my arm. Finally a man in a white jacket, seeing me spread over the face of the hill and sensing trouble, undid my ski, helped me out of the parka and said, "Now, you've just turned your ankle. Get up and walk on it right away and you'll be skiing again in no time."

He helped me to my feet and everything went black. I came to to find him rubbing my face with snow and saying, "Just a little sprain and the best cure for it is walking."

So I scrambled to my feet and slowly and very painfully started up the hill to the lodge. The first steps felt as though my ankle were being crushed in a giant vise. "I simply can't stand this," I said, sitting down and starting to unlace my ski boot. Immediately several people rushed over and said, "Oh, don't do that. Never take off your ski boot, it supports the sprain and anyway you'll never get it on again. Just get up and walk on it."

"I can't," I said. "It feels like my ankle is crushed."

"Nonsense," said a tall man with a mustache, grabbing my foot with his big strong hands and pinching my ski boot to test for broken bones.

I screamed, "You're hurting! Don't touch my ankle."

He dropped my foot; I moaned in agony and he went away mumbling things about poor sports and only trying to help.

Fortunately, someone who didn't belong to our hardy group, and who knew something about skiing, told me I shouldn't walk on my foot and produced a toboggan to take me to the car.

When I got home Mother cut off my ski boot and sock, put my foot in a bucket of hot water and called Mary's husband. He came right over, examined my foot, gave me some codeine and said my ankle was broken.

"And I was relaxed and my knees were bent," I told Mary bitterly.

She said, "Nobody but a fool would ski in the rain. Terribly dangerous."

Mary's husband said, "Nobody but a fool would ski. Mary has the right idea. She doesn't risk her limbs in the snow. She stays in the lodge and plays the slot machines."

That was my last office party.

## CHAPTER 14

## *"HAND ME THAT STRAITJACKET, JOE— THE GOVERNMENT"*

ONE of the first things I learned and loved about the Government was that I wasn't the only bonehead working for it. There were thousands of us who didn't know what we were doing but were all doing it in ten copies.

I got my first Government job by falling down a flight of stairs. Mary and I had gone to a dinner party at the apartment of friends. I can remember that I didn't want to go. "I should be going to night school," I told Mary. She said, "Betty, you only live once. There will be some very charming people at this dinner party and we're going to a concert afterward. Now, for heaven's sake, let's forget night school."

So we went to the party and the people were so charming that I didn't look where I was going and fell down my host's small winding stair and ripped the knee out of my stocking.

"Oh," I moaned as they all hurried to help me. "No job and my only pair of stockings."

"Don't you have a job?" said a very shy man with a French wife.

"No," I said. "Not since yesterday."

"I'd like you to work for me," he said. "The Government. National Recovery Administration. It'll only be temporary for a while but then there should be some good permanent jobs."

"You see," said Mary later. "People like Mr. Sheffield don't hang around night schools. This time you're in on the ground floor and you can get to be an executive."

I'll always remember my first day with the Government. At 8:45 on a Monday morning in July, Cleve and his Cord convertible deposited me in front of the Federal Office Building. I flicked a speck of dust from my skirt, straightened my seams, adjusted my clean white gloves and went skipping up the marble steps. I was on the right side of the tracks at last. Working for the Government! What a firm ring it had. How pleasantly it would slide off my tongue when I applied for credit. I waved to Cleve, who, in spite of a gas tank that had registered empty all the way to town, was easing sleekly away from the curb accompanied by many envious glances, and pushed open the swinging door.

The inside of the building was as cool as a springhouse. The tiled foyer, crowded with people going to work and waiting for elevators, had a gay, relaxed atmosphere, a complete contrast to mornings in other office buildings where I had worked. Mornings marred by grumpy businessmen, shuffling their feet, glancing irritably at their watches as they awaited their chance to push into the elevator and be whisked up to where they could start doing something obviously distasteful to them.

Government people had a delightful "It'll keep until I get there" attitude. "What a day!" they said to each other. "When are you taking your leave, Joe? Looks like vacation weather." They exchanged morning pleasantries with the elevator starter and the operators and kidded a small colored man called Bill who loaded his car as though it were a train — "All aboahd for Evrett!" he shouted. "This cah's goin' to Evrett! Shake a leg, Colonel, youh julep's gettin' wahm waitin' foh you."

Several people looked at me, recognized me as a stranger and smiled. I smiled back and felt welcome.

I asked Bill where Mr. Sheffield's office was and he grinned and said, "Eighth floah. You startin' to work theah?" I said I thought so and he said, "Well, now, I'm real glad. We don't have any red hair in this building at all. It look mighty nice on cold mornings."

I said, "Maybe I won't last until winter."

He said, "You'll last all right. Don't worry about that. Evybody last with the Govment." As I got in, he winked and whispered for me to look behind me. A woman in a coonskin cap and sheepskin coat was leaning on the window sill eating doughnuts out of a greasy bag. "She lasted," Bill said. "She left over from Daniel Boone's time, he, he, he!"

Mr. Sheffield's office, on the top floor, was labeled Bureau of Foreign and Domestic Commerce but taped below the black lettering was a white cardboard bearing a large blue eagle and the letters NRA. I opened the door and walked into what might have been a receiving room at a terminal post office. Everywhere were bulging gray canvas mail bags and new confused employes.

I waited uncertainly by the door. Presently at the far end of the room, I noticed two young women seated facing each other at mahogany desks. They were opening mail, exchanging occasional remarks and exuding an air of stability and leisure that seemed to cut them off from the hurrying and confusion of the rest of the room as completely as though they were glass-enclosed. I knew instinctively that they were civil service — and had nothing to do with the new regime.

I was watching them enviously when a tall, dark girl came over, introduced herself as Miss Mellor and led me into another office where Mr. Sheffield, a slender, nervous man, was talking on the phone, running his hands through his hair and staring wildly at a stack of telegrams, air mail and air-mail special delivery letters that the office boy was adding to continually.

Obviously this room, with its comfortable mahogany furniture and thick rug on the floor, had once been a quiet, delightful place in which to write leisurely letters and reports and to contemplate the price of grain in Algeria. Now it was like a subway station. At long tables in the center of the room about 15 assorted people, old, young, male and female, all armed with letter openers, were furiously emptying canvas bags of mail.

I asked Miss Mellor what was in the mail sacks. She said, "PRA's — President's Re-employment Agreements. Everybody in business is supposed to sign one and promise that he'll pay his employes at least $14 a week and cut their hours to 40 a week. When he signs he gets a sticker like this to put in his window." She pulled from under the confusion on Mr. Sheffield's desk a sticker about five by eight inches with the letters NRA in bright red across the top and a picture of a fierce-looking blue eagle with one foot on some sort of gear. Miss Mellor said, "According to the National Industrial Recovery Act, you can't have Government contracts unless you have a blue eagle in your window. This is the district office for four states."

Just then Mr. Sheffield hung up the phone, jumped to his feet, and looked at me dazedly without a sign of recognition.

I said, "Remember me? I fell down the stairs Friday night and you offered me a job."

He said, "Oh, yes. Betty Bard." The telephone rang again. He picked up the receiver and began talking.

Miss Mellor, who drawled and appeared to be as unrufflable as slate, laughed and said, "That's enough. He recognized you."

She led me to the table, introduced me, gave me a paper knife and a stack of mail and I set to work at the first job I had ever had that really fitted my capabilities. Lift, slit, take out, unfold, lift, slit, take out, unfold, lift, slit . . . By 11 o'clock my shoulders ached and my slitting hand was cramped, so I got up and went down the hall to the rest room for a cigarette.

The rest room was deserted except for a slender girl with tinsely blond hair and gray eyes, who was smoking and staring pensively out the window. We looked shyly at each other and then she said, "Are you working for Mr. Sheffield?" I said I was and she said so was she, she typed.

I said, "I thought I would like a monotonous job but I'm already bored and tired."

She said, "This is my third day and by five o'clock I'm so tired I could die but I keep saying, 'Four dollars a day four dollars a day,' and going out for a cigarette whenever I can."

I said, "Is four dollars a day all we get?"

She said, "All? I think that's dandy. My last job paid eight dollars a week and I ran the whole company. As soon as we're put on a permanent basis, we'll get either $105 or $120 a month. Can you type?"

"Sure," I said, adding bravely, "shorthand, too."

"Better tell the office boy," she said. "He assigns the work and he needs typists."

She told me her name was Anne Marie Offenbach and that her mother was a friend of the Sheffields. I told her my sister Mary was a friend of the Sheffields, too. On the office boy's next trip I told him that I could type and take shorthand, so he sat me in another room, at a wiggly little table back of Anne Marie and had me type alphabetical lists of the PRA signers.

At 12 o'clock, Anne Marie and I went over to the grocery store which served lunch. As we ate she told me that she already hated most of the people working with us. She said, "A woman came over to me yesterday, gripped my arm and hissed, 'Don't work so fast. Make it last.'"

I said, "That's the trouble with big offices, if you're slow you get fired, and if you're fast everybody hates you."

She said, "Already there's a strained feeling in the office — everybody listening and watching to see who you know. Don't tell anybody you know Mr. Sheffield."

I said, "How can I? Nobody speaks to me."

She said, "That's because you came to work in that big cream-colored car. Somebody saw you and the word has already gone around the office that you're rich and don't need to work."

I laughed, told her that we were on our 63rd straight Sunday of meatloaf and I didn't see how we could be any poorer and that anyway Cleve had acquired the car by an elaborate series of trades dating back to his tenth birthday. Anne Marie said, "Well, if I were you, I'd have your brother let you off a block from the office, a lot of those people seem kind of desperate."

When we got back at one o'clock, I asked the office boy if he'd heard I was rich and he said, "Sure, that's why I like you," and winked. A woman across the room nudged her neighbor, whispered something to her and they both glared at me.

The afternoon was very hot, the minutes crept by and there

sprang into being that oldest and most bitterly fought of all
office feuds. No air versus fresh air. Anne Marie and I both sat
by windows which we had opened wide. When we came back
from lunch we found them shut and locked, the office stuffy and
thick with heat. We opened our windows wide again and immediately remarks, like little darts, went flitting through the air.
"Brrr, it's so cold I can hardly type," or "Pardon me a minute
while I get my sweater. Some people seem to have been raised in
the North Pole." "Would you mind if I put your coat around
my knees. It's so drafty."

At three o'clock, Anne Marie and I went over to the grocery
store for coffee. When we got back the windows were shut and
locked again and there was a note on my typewriter: "Listen,
you, type slower — you're working us out of a job."

I crumpled the note up and threw it in the wastebasket and
opened the window again. There wasn't any air either inside or
outside now, and my fingers splashed on the typewriter keys.
Noticing that several of the typists were hunt-and-peckers, I
tried to tell myself, "Look, that's their problem. They should
have gone to night school." But I knew that these people were
desperate for work and there wasn't going to be enough to go
around. One of the hunt-and-peck typists was as old as my
mother and had a gentle, most unbusinesslike face. I smiled at
her and she smiled back and just before we went home she gave
me a recipe for a one-egg cake. On the streetcar I prayed that
there would be some sort of a permanent filing job for her.

I stayed with the NRA until the office closed on December 31,
1935, and true to Mary's predictions I rose from a $4-a-day typist
to a $120-a-month secretary, to a clerk at $135 a month and
finally to a labor adjuster at $1800 per annum. To me, even bet-
ter than the money and security was the fact that I was on the
other end of the gun. Somebody else was worrying about getting
my thoughts down in her notebook. That to me was success.

My next Government job was with the Treasury Department, which I had to leave eventually for a year-long bout with tuberculosis. In the Treasury Department I found that I had to have an entirely different sense of values. The big issues were not that we were spending millions of dollars in an effort to rehabilitate Americans; nor, the fact that the money we were spending was actually our own and it was up to us to see that it was put to the best possible use. Instead, our major concerns were whether the files should be kept by purchase order number, by requisition number or by voucher number; whether invoices should be in six or three copies; or whether being late should be knocked off our annual leave.

I could tell the day I started to work there that the Treasury Department and I were worlds apart. In the first place they had people working for them *who had never made a mistake;* in the second place they chose to ignore all previous experience not gleaned in the department and started everyone, no matter who they were or what they had done, even brilliant former labor adjusters who had their own secretaries, at the very bottom, and in the third place they thought that all Treasury Department employes, even those crawling around on the bottom, should be at attention ready for a call 24 hours a day.

"We do not allow mistakes," I was told and so my hands shook and I made lots of mistakes. This was the Procurement Division of the Treasury Department and we were buying supplies and letting contracts for the WPA, which was a very large order.

Every day from 8:30 to 4:30 or 7:30 or 10:30 I entered names and prices on big sheets of paper, but we were always behind in our work and got many little penciled letters on lined paper, addressed to the Treasurer of the United States and pleading for money long overdue. "I can't buy no more oats and I need new harness. Please send me my money," Charlie Simpson would write and I would get tears in my eyes as I took out his file and found that we were returning his invoice for the fourth time because he had only sent one copy, or had not put on the certification or hadn't signed it.

For months I worked overtime and almost gave myself ulcers trying to make our contractors do things the Treasury way and trying to make the Treasury do things in a way not quite as frenziedly hurried as glacial movement but not quite as slow as the decomposition of ferns into coal.

Then I became resigned and became a regular but happier Treasury employe. When a pitiful letter came in pleading for long overdue payment, instead of getting choked up and running from department to department, I would callously toss it into the enormous ready-for-payment stack, say, "Old X-3458962 is screaming for his money again," and go out for coffee.

I had been working for the Treasury Department a little less than a year when it came time to make my Christmas cards. I drew a nice little design, bought an enormous stack of paper that would take water color, obtained permission from the office boy to use the office mimeoscope and styli, one stencil and the office mimeograph, and one night my friend Katherine and I stayed on after work and ran off my Christmas cards.

The next morning when I arrived at the office, flushed with accomplishment and bearing a painted sample of my art work, I was greeted by furtive looks and whispered conferences. "What in the world's going on?" I asked, thinking they had at least uncovered some enormous bribe or misappropriation of funds.

"Someone broke into the building and used the mimeograph last night," a frightened co-worker whispered. "They're holding a conference about it downstairs now."

"Well, I used the mimeograph," I said. "I got permission from the office boy. I'd better go tell them."

"I wouldn't if I were you," she said. "It's a pretty serious offense and everybody's very upset."

"Nonsense," I said. "I'm going right down."

Just then the office boy came tearing into the office. He was pale and frightened. "Don't tell them I gave you permission," he gasped. "Please don't."

"Okay," I said. "But why?"

"There's a big meeting going on downstairs," he said. "They're going to send for you in a minute."

They did and I went down and was confronted with the evidence — a spoiled Christmas card saying "Merry Christmas and a Happy New Year — Betty Bard."

"What do you know about this?" the officer in charge of mimeographing said.

I said, "It's my Christmas card. I stayed down here after work last night and ran them off on the mimeograph."

He said, "Betty, that mimeograph is Government property — it is against the law to use Government property for private use."

I said, "I asked permission to use the mimeograph — anyway I always used the mimeograph at the NRA to make my Christmas cards."

He said, "*That* was the National Recovery Administration. *This* is the Treasury Department."

I said, "Well, I'm sorry, I didn't know I wasn't supposed to."

He said, "Being sorry isn't enough."

I said, "Well, I'll pay for the stencil and the ink, then."

He said, "I can't accept payment because there is no proper requisition or purchase order authorizing you to purchase them from the Government."

I said, "Well, what do you want me to do?"

He was so solemn about it all that I thought for a moment he was going to hand me a pistol and tell me that he would leave the room while I took the only way out. He didn't though. He looked out the window. Stared straight ahead. Leaned back in his chair and jingled coins in his pocket and finally said to me, "Well, I'm going to forget the whole thing. I'm just going to pretend it never happened. But don't . . . ever . . . let . . . such . . . a . . . thing . . . happen . . . again . . . while . . . you . . . are . . . in . . . the . . . employ . . . of . . . the . . . Treasury . . . Department."

I took great pleasure in sending one of the Christmas cards to every single person in the entire Treasury Department, many of whom I didn't know. I could just see them burning them in ash trays and burying the telltale ashes in old flowerpots.

## CHAPTER 15

### *"ANYBODY CAN WRITE BOOKS"*

At the time Mary decided that anybody can write books, I was married, living on Vashon Island in Puget Sound and working for a contractor with cost-plus Government contracts, making a very good salary.

Then an old friend of Mary's arrived in town and announced that he was a talent scout for a publishing firm and did she know any Northwest authors. Mary didn't, so she said, "Of course I do, my sister Betty. Betty writes brilliantly but I'm not sure how much she has done on her book." (I had so little done on it I hadn't even thought of writing one.) The publisher's representative said that the amount I had done was not the important thing. The important thing was, had I talent? "Had I talent?" Why, Mary said, I had so much talent I could hardly walk. She'd call and make an appointment for him to just talk to me and see. She did, too. That very afternoon at five, and she called me at a quarter to five.

"Betsy," she said. "Forrest's in town and he is a publisher's representative and needs some Northwest authors so I've told him you were one. You're to meet him at the Olympic Hotel at five o'clock to discuss your new book." "My what?" I yelled.

"Your new book," said Mary, perfectly calmly. "You know that you have always wanted to be a writer and Betsy, dear, you've got great talent."

"I have not," I said. "You know perfectly well that the only things I've ever written in my life were a couple of punk short stories, some children's stories, 'Sandra Surrenders' and that diary I kept when I had TB.

Mary made noises of disgust. "The trouble with you, Betty, is that you have absolutely [she said "ab . . . so . . . lute . . . ly"] no sense of proportion. Instead of using your brain to write a book and make $50,000, you in . . . sist on getting a mediocre job with a mediocre firm and working yourself to the bone for a mediocre salary. When are you going to wake up? When?"

I said, "But I can't write a book."

Mary said, "Of course you can, particularly when you stop to think that every publisher in the United States is simply dying for material about the Northwest."

"I never noticed it," I said sullenly.

Mary said, "Betty, listen to me. We are living in the last frontier in the United States. The land of the great salmon runs, giant firs, uncharted waters and unscaled mountains and almost nothing has been written about it. If you told the people in New York that salmon leaped in our front doors and snapped at our ankles they'd believe it. Most of the people in the United States either think we're frozen over all the time like the Antarctic or that we're still wearing buckskin and fighting Indians. Now, personally, I think it's about time somebody wrote the truth."

"What time is the appointment?" I asked weakly.

"Five o'clock," Mary said, "You've only got five minutes."

As I put on lipstick and combed my hair, I told one of the girls in the office that I had to hurry as I was going to meet a publisher's representative at the Olympic Hotel to discuss my book. She said, "Gosh! Betty, are you writing a book?"

"Sure," I said with the casualness of great talent, "and this publisher's representative has come all the way from New York to talk to me about it."

"What's your book about?" she asked.

"About my experiences on a chicken ranch," I said.

"Oh," she said, with obvious disappointment.

Walking up to the hotel in the February rain, I decided that I would tell Forrest that I was writing a sort of rebuttal to all the recent successful I-love-life books by female good sports whose husbands had forced them to live in the country without lights and running water. I would give the other side of it. I would give a bad sport's account of life in the wilderness without lights, water or friends and with chickens, Indians and moonshine.

The publisher's representative, who was very friendly, liked my idea and told me to go home and write a 5000-word outline and bring it to Mary's dinner party the next night.

Having never written either an outline or a book, I was a little slow and found it necessary to stay home from work the next day to finish it. I called the construction office and told my best friend there that I had to stay home and write an outline for a book but would she please tell the boss I was sick. She said sure she would, wished me luck, hung up the phone and skidded in and told the boss that I was staying home to write a book and so I was fired.

When I told my husband and daughters that I was going to write a book they were peculiarly unenthusiastic. "Why?" they asked. And I couldn't think of any reason except that Mary thought I had great talent, so I said, "Because every single publisher in New York wants me to, that's all." A likely story, they told each other, as they tapped their foreheads.

During that long, long year between the conception and birth of *The Egg and I,* I sometimes got so depressed I put the book away in disgust and went into town and applied for and got dreary little part-time jobs that seemed much more in keeping with my ability than writing. Then, after a month or so, Mary would hear about it and call me up and demand that I quit.

One Monday morning during the summer, I was hanging out the last of a huge washing when Mary called and demanded over the long-distance phone, "Betty Bard MacDonald, are you going to spend the rest of your life washing your sheets by hand or are you going to make $50,000 a year writing?" It didn't leave much of a choice, so I got started writing again.

Toward the end of the summer, when the book was almost finished, Mary told me to write to Brandt and Brandt, literary agents, whose name she had gotten from the former editor of the Seattle *Times.* All successful writers have agents, she told me, and Brandt and Brandt are the very best. Mary said, "Be sure and tell them about the short stories, the children's stories and the TB book. Remember, nobody likes a one-book author."

From that day on until I wrote my second book, Mary waved that "Nobody likes a one-book author" slogan around like an old Excelsior banner. When I finished my second book she changed it to "Nobody likes a two-book author." Then three. But now the tables are turned because she has written her first book and I'm on my fifth.

Feeling exactly as though I were trying to join an exclusive club on forged credentials, I wrote to Brandt and Brandt and sent them the 5000-word outline I had shown the publisher's representative. In my eagerness to prove that I wasn't a stinking old one-book author I made it sound a little as though we had to wade through old manuscripts to go from room to room in our log house, and that I was a veritable artesian well of the written word. Much to my amazement and chagrin, Brandt and Brandt, immediately on receipt of my letter, wired me that they were delighted with the outline and to send every manuscript I had, which certainly wouldn't take long.

I called Mary and told her about the telegram and she said, "Now, bonehead, are you convinced that you're a writer or do you still want to work in some musty little office?"

We both laughed and then Mary said, "Of course, your book will be a best seller and they'll want you to go to New York and then to Hollywood."

"What's the matter with Europe?" I asked.

Mary said, "Just wait and see."

Before I could answer Brandt and Brandt's telegram, I got an air-mail letter from them telling me that the J. B. Lippincott Company, publishers, wanted to buy the book on the strength of the outline and would I accept a $500 advance? Would I accept a $500 advance? Huh, would I accept a 50-cent advance was more like it.

I was on my way to town and had stopped at the mailbox on the way to the ferry and there nestled among a pile of bills, was this long white important-looking envelope. My first thought, of course, when I saw the Brandt and Brandt on the back, was that it was a letter taking back the telegram. I didn't have time to open it on the dock, so I waited until I was installed in the Ladies' Cabin before ripping open the flap and removing with trembling fingers the letter that rocked my world.

I read it over and over and with each reading it became more wonderful. My book, that nebulous product of Mary's faith in me, had suddenly materialized into an actual thing. I was a writer and I had to tell somebody. I hurried all over the upper deck of the ferry but it was empty. I went down to the car deck but there were only trucks.

When we docked at the other side, I scanned the waiting cars for a familiar face and finally in desperation rushed over to a man and his wife whom I knew very slightly and told them that my book had been accepted and I was to get $500. They were as enthusiastic as though it had happened to them and I left them feeling very successful and terribly talented.

The next dandy thing that happened was the next spring when I was learning that the lowest period in a writer's life is that awful interval between acceptance and publication. I knew I was a failure, I knew the book was no good, I was sure I was going to get the manuscript back and I had spent all the advance.

I decided to go to town and look for a job. Preferably one involving the filing of the same card over and over and over day after day. I had found a reasonable facsimile of the job I had in mind and was making my weary way home along our trail, when Anne came running to meet me, calling, "There's a telegram for you and you're to call Seattle operator 28 right away." It's come, I thought. They have decided not to publish the book and they're demanding their money back. "Hurry, Betty," Anne said. "Find out what the telegram is." "No," I said. "I'm going to wait until after dinner. I'd rather get bad news on a full stomach."

After dinner I called the operator and Whispering Sam, who was at that time relaying all messages to Vashon before burning the only copy, read me a very long wire of which I got about ten words. Three of these were *"Atlantic Monthly"* and "serialization," which I knew must be wrong, as *The Atlantic Monthly* represented to me the ultimate in literary achievement and I was certain they couldn't be interested in anything I had written.

I called Mary and she immediately changed her tune from best sellers and trips to New York, to awfully important books, not very good sellers, and trips to Boston. She said she'd call Western Union for me and call me right back. She did in a matter of minutes and told me that I was to call Boston the next morning at eight o'clock and she thought I'd better get the next ferry and pick up a copy of the telegram which Western Union was reluctantly holding at the edge of their telegram burner. The next ferry left in 16 minutes, so I sent Anne and Joan up to my sister Alison's and I ran the mile and a half to the dock.

The main office of the telegraph company is located on a dark side street in the financial district in Seattle and as I got off the bus and walked in the rain across the deserted streets, I kept thinking, "This is the most important moment of my life. I must remember everything." I felt enchanted and as though I should be leaving a trail of light behind me. My steps made no sound and I was as light as a petal when I entered the telegraph office and asked for my telegram. I read it standing by the counter and then, stuffing it in the pocket of my raincoat, I floated out to my sister Mary's.

I told Mary about my strange enchanted feeling and she said, "You just feel successful, but imagine how I feel. All of a sudden my big lies have started coming true!"

*Betty MacDonald*

In 1945, an unknown redhead named Betty MacDonald stormed the best-seller list — and the heart of America — with a hilarious book of reminiscences called *The Egg and I*. Within a few months, the book made a fortune for the author and set hundreds of thousands of fans clamoring for more glimpses of Betty MacDonald's not-so-private private life.

Since then, Mrs. MacDonald has become something of an American institution. In *The Plague and I* she proved that even a tuberculosis sanitarium has its humor — if you know how to take it. In two children's books, she spread abroad some of the gaiety from her own large family. And in *Anybody Can Do Anything,* now happily sailing on the best-seller lists, she proves again that it is more fun to be Betty MacDonald than practically anybody in the world.

The daughter of a mining engineer, Mrs. MacDonald was born Betty Bard of Boulder, Colo. Her early childhood was spent in mining towns from Mexico to Montana until the big, cheerful Bard family finally settled down in Seattle. Betty married at 18 and started the chicken-farming career she immortalized in *The Egg and I*. Her subsequent adventures are recorded in *Anybody Can Do Anything.*

*Decorations by Henry Pitz*

# ELEPHANT BILL

*A condensation*

*from the book by*     LT. COL. J. H. WILLIAMS

*P*ACKED WITH dozens of amusing stories and little-known facts about elephants, *Elephant Bill* is the most absorbing animal book to appear in many years. Widely praised by reviewers all over the country, it appeared for months on the "specially recommended" list of the New York *Times Book Review*.

Lt. Col. J. H. Williams — "Elephant Bill" — spent 22 years in Burma as a specialist in "elephant management." With affection and deep knowledge he describes the varied personalities of different elephants, recounts their touching love stories and their care for their young, offers surprising examples of their intelligence, clears up the long-standing mystery of where and how an elephant dies, and gives the reader a memorable picture of Burma and its jungle people.

"The most delightful, most fascinating animal book in many a season."          —*Newsweek*

". . . the best book on elephants we have ever read . . . exciting and highly readable." — Sterling North, Post-Hall Syndicate

# CHAPTER 1

I HAVE always got on well with animals. I like them and, with one or two notable exceptions, they always seemed to like me. When I was a boy in Cornwall my first animal friend was a donkey. He had free range over the moors, but I always knew where to find him. During the World War of 1914-18, I was in the Camel Corps, and then, later on, Transport Officer in charge of a lot of mules. These experiences taught me much about animals, for both camels and mules are temperamental beasts; and mules have also a remarkable sense of humor, so that in dealing with them one gets plenty of exercise for one's own. That was valuable. My life has been spent east of Suez in places where if you lose your sense of humor you had much better take the first boat home.

Like millions of other fellows, when World War I was over I began to think about finding myself a job. A friend told me that he knew of a man who did something with elephants in Burma. This sounded as though it would be what I wanted.

My friend wrote to the fellow, introducing me as a candidate for elephant management, and I wrote to the head of the Bombay Burma Trading Corporation — the company concerned. It was 1920 before I got back to England, but my letter led to an interview and before the year was out I was in Burma.

My first vivid memories of Burma are not of the pagodas and rice fields and all I had read about, but of my first "jungle salt," Willie, the man under whom I was to begin my training.

I met him at his camp on the banks of the Upper Chindwin River, Upper Burma. He was, in his own words, down with fever, but he was sitting at a table, about midday, outside his tent, drinking a whisky and soda and smoking a Burma cheroot.

His welcome was icy, and I immediately guessed that he jealously resented anyone sharing his jungle life. About four o'clock in the afternoon I asked for a cup of tea — and was laughed at for not drinking whisky and soda. I vowed, privately, that I would see him under the table later on. About five o'clock seven elephants arrived in camp and were paraded in line for inspection. Willie did not speak to me as he walked off to inspect them. However, I followed him, uninvited. Judging by appearances, there was one worn-out animal which looked as though it might be the mother of the other six. Each animal was inspected in turn and Willie entered some remark about each in a book. This took up about half an hour, during which he did not address a single word to me. I was careful not to ask any questions, as I saw that I should only be called a damned fool for my pains. However, when the inspection was over, Willie turned on me, saying: "Those four on the right are yours, and God help you if you can't look after them."

For all I knew, I was supposed to take them to bed with me. The next evening, when Willie told me to inspect my own four and to see that their gear was on their backs comfortably, I followed a lifelong rule when in doubt: I trusted to luck.

After the inspection that first night, as my tent had been pitched near his, I joined Willie at his camp table. On it were two bottles of Black Label — one of his and one of mine.

After half an hour or so Willie thawed sufficiently to ask me, "Are you safe with a shotgun?" — not "Do you shoot?" as is more usual.

Silence reigned after my answer. Willie emptied and refilled his glass several times. At last he opened up and, passing his empty bottle to me, remarked, "I drink a bottle a night and it does me no harm. There are two vices in this country. Woman is one and the other the bottle. Choose which you like, but you must not mix them. Anything to do with the jungle, elephants and your work you can only learn by experience. No one but a Burman can teach you and you'll draw your pay for ten years before you earn it. Tomorrow I'll give you some maps and the day after you must push off for three months on your own. You can do what you damned well like — including suicide if you're lonely — but don't come back until you can speak some Burmese."

After this speech he walked off to his bed without even saying good night.

After four and a half years' service in the army I believed I was past the age of adventures; but leaving on my first jungle trip, two days later, I experienced a new thrill. With four elephants carrying my kit, a cook, two bearers and two messengers, I was on my own again. My life in charge of elephants had begun.

I had been on the march less than two days when the ancient female elephant known as Ma Oh (Old Lady) was discovered dead an hour before I was due to move camp. Willie had, I now know, somewhat unscrupulously palmed her off on me — and his terrible words, "God help you if you can't look after them," now rang in my ears. Seeing her enormous carcass lying in the jungle — just as she had died in her sleep — was a terrible sight, and it was awful that she had died within a few days of my being made responsible for her. How on earth, I wondered, should I get out of this mess? Willie's reception of me, the dead elephant, and his threat ringing in my ears combined to fill my cup with bitterness. "At the worst," I thought, "I can only lose my job. I'm damned if I'll buy them a new one!" It was a bad business but as I had no one to help me out I had to help myself, and I decided that the best thing I could do was to hold a post-mortem.

The Old Lady was scarcely cold before I was literally inside her, with her arching ribs sheltering me from the sun. I learned a good deal about elephant construction from her. Her carcass proved to be a cave full of strange treasures such as the heart, the gizzard and the lungs. The only snag was that I could not find any kidneys, and I was almost tempted to conclude that she must have died for lack of them. However, when I came to write out a report that evening I decided that "no kidneys" might not be an acceptable cause of death — so in desperation I left it at "found dead" and did not even mention my Jonah's journey.

Ma Oh's load was easily divided among the remaining three animals, and on I went. My instructions were to march to a certain village in the Myittha Valley, where I was to meet a head Burman named U Tha Yauk. I was on foot with my messengers and the two bearers and we had outdistanced the elephants by several miles by taking a short cut up the bed of the creek. U Tha Yauk had come some way out of the village to meet me and was squatting on a rock beside the creek up which we were traveling.

I greeted him with my three words of Burmese and laughed because I could say no more, and he laughed back; we marched on in single file until we came to a clearing around which there were about ten bamboo huts, all standing on bamboo stilts and thatched with grass. A Burmese girl dressed in her best, with a pretty little white coat and a flower in her hair, came forward with a cane basketwork stool for me to sit on. Three men came up with green coconuts and, cutting them open at one end, poured the juice into a cup of hand-beaten copper and gave it to me with the reverent gestures of priests administering the Sacrament.

Directly the elephants turned up, the crowd moved off to help unload them, and my cook was at once installed in his hut. My kit was soon piled up in one corner of my hut, which was divided by a bamboo matting wall into my bedroom on one side and my living room on the other.

In a quarter of an hour the room was furnished — with a ground sheet covered with bright-blue cotton *dhurries* on the floor, my camp bed, camp tables and camp chair. My bedding roll was undone and the mosquito net put in position. Meanwhile other Burmans were filling my tub in a bathroom at the back of the hut with tins of water from the brook. After dismissing the other helpers, my personal servant unlocked my basket packs and took out photographs to arrange on my dressing table and put my revolver under my pillow. Then when all was ready he asked me to come in. As soon as I had looked round and sat down he took off my puttees and boots and disappeared. In the bathroom I found a Burmese boy, who poured two buckets of hot water into my tub and swirled it around, giving me a smile, as though to say: "Bath ready, sir."

I bathed, and by the time I went back into my hut I found the table was laid with a spotless white cloth, and that flannel trousers, socks and white shirt were spread out on my bed, but that my perfect valet had once more vanished.

My dinner was ready, and as I finished each course hands of unseen attendants passed up the meat and vegetables, the sweet and savory, to my valet, who stood silently behind my chair as I ate. While I drank my coffee, he drew down the mosquito net and tucked it in and then gave a graceful bow saying, though I could not then understand him: "By your leave I will now go."

Left alone, I was overcome by a great homesickness. The overpowering kindness of the Burmans was too much for me and I asked myself what I had done to deserve it. It never dawned on me that the Burmans wanted to show their sympathy with me in my loneliness and in my ignorance of their language and of all the difficulties that lay ahead.

# CHAPTER 2

NEXT MORNING a new life began — my life as a pupil of U Tha Yauk.

With the aid of a good map of the Indaung Forest Reserve, he made me understand I was to go on a tour with him from the valley, crossing five parallel creeks flowing from east to west into the Myittha River. On the sides of each of the watersheds he had a camp of elephants, ten camps altogether, each with an average of seven elephants, or 70 working animals all told. Judging from the map, the distance between the camps was six to seven miles, with hills 3000 to 4000 feet high between.

At the first camp we reached I found about 20 Burmans, including a carpenter of sorts, erecting a set of jungle buildings. It was explained to me that this camp was to be my headquarters during the coming monsoon months. I soon realized that the elephant was the backbone of the Burmese teak industry.

The history of the Bombay Burma Corporation went back to the time of Burma's King Theebaw, when a senior member of the firm who visited Burma appreciated the great possibilities of the teak trade and was able to obtain a lease of certain forest areas. Sawmills were established at the ports, a system of rafting teak logs down the creeks and rivers was organized, and elephants were bought on a large scale.

Teak is one of the world's best hardwoods, partly because of the silica it contains. As it grows best in country inaccessible to tractors and machinery — steep, precipitous terrain 2000 to 3000 feet in elevation — elephant power is essential for hauling and pushing the logs from the stump to the nearest stream.

In the early days, the Bombay Burma Corporation bought some of its elephants from Siam, some from India, but the majority were obtained by capturing wild elephants in stockades and breaking them in. This process is known as "kheddaring."

When the Bombay Burma Corporation had built up considerable herds of elephants, it realized that elephant calves born in captivity could be broken in and trained more easily than captured wild elephants. Finally when the Corporation's herds had reached a strength of nearly 2000 animals it was found that births balanced the deaths and that new supplies of elephants were required only on rare occasions. The kheddaring of wild elephants, on any extensive scale, thus came to an end.

The health, management and handling of the elephants in this enormous organization impressed me as the factor on which everything else depended. The routine work of elephant management in camp consisted in checking up gear making, getting to know the "oozies," or elephant riders, inspecting elephants and dressing any galls caused by gear rubbing, wounds caused by bamboo splinters in the feet, and other common injuries.

For my early training in all these tasks I am indebted to U Tha Yauk. After our first trip we spent several days in camp. I mixed with everyone, forever asking questions and being given answers packed with information I had to remember. One day, going back to my hut for lunch, I first watched a most fascinating sight.

About 100 yards below my hut was a large pool in the brook. Two elephants, each with her rider sitting behind her head, entered the pool, and, without any word of command that I could hear, they lay down in the water. The riders tucked up their *lungyi* skirts so that they were transformed into loincloths, slipped off their mounts into the water and began to scrub their respective elephants from head to tail with a soap which lathered freely. Then they washed it off the elephants, splashing water over them with their hands. The soap they used turned out to be the soapy bark of a tree. Soon I was stand-

ing on the bank of the pool and from there I watched five elephants being washed in the same way. Two of them were cows with young calves which rolled over and over and played in the water like young children. There were also two large males, with gleaming white tusks which were scrubbed with handfuls of silver sand.

After they had all been washed and dried off, the elephants were paraded for inspection—all drawn up in line abreast, each rider dressed in his best.

U Tha Yauk advanced with

military precision and, after bowing instead of saluting, handed me a set of books, all ragged and torn. On the cover of each an elephant's name was written.

I looked at one book and called out the name of the elephant; and the rider, hearing me, rode it up to me at a fast, bold stride. Both rider and elephant had a sort of natural magnificence. The oozie halted the animal just before me. He was a splendid beast with his head up, his skin newly scrubbed but already dry in the sun, a black skin with a faint tinge of blue showing through it which seemed to make it so alive. The white tusks, freshly polished, gleamed in the sunlight. The motionless rider appeared to be sitting on one leg while the other dangled behind the elephant's ear. On his face was an expression of intense pride — pride in his magnificent beast.

Suddenly, he gave an order and the elephant swung round to present his hindquarters, on which there was a brand, made with phosphorous paint when the animal was six years old.

I opened the book and read a number of entries, each with the date when he had been inspected during the last ten years. On the front page was the animal's history with his registered number and other details — such as that he had been born in Siam, bought when he was 20 years old, badly gored by a wild tusker, but had fully recovered after being off work for a year.

Thus I inspected each of the animals in turn and read their histories. As each inspection was finished the rider and elephant left the clearing and disappeared into the jungle.

When they had all gone I was taken round the harness racks — just a row of horizontal branches of trees on each of which hung the gear of one of the animals. All the harness except the heavy dragging chains was handmade by the riders. There were great cane basket panniers, woven breast straps of fiber, wooden breeching blocks, padding from the bark of the banbrwe tree, ropes of every kind twisted from the bark of the sha tree.

In those first three months on my own I did most of the things worth doing in Burma. Tha Yauk helped me to achieve my ambition — to shoot a wild bull elephant. My main reason for shooting him was not to secure the tusks, much as I coveted them, but to carry out a post-mortem to see what the organs of a really healthy elephant looked like, and to make another attempt to find the kidneys. This second post-mortem taught me a good deal about what had been wrong with Ma Oh. In fact, it showed me half a dozen reasons sufficient to explain her death.

After three months which passed all too soon I returned to Willie, having learned a great deal. When I arrived I got the greeting I expected: sarcastic remarks about my having let one of my elephants die in the first two days — no doubt by having overloaded her with all my blasted new kit.

I replied that I was surprised that she had lived as long as she had: her liver was riddled with flukes and her heart was as big as a football.

"How do *you* know how big an elephant's heart ought to be?"

"I shot a wild tusker that was 40 years old, and I did a post-mortem on him to see how the organs of a healthy elephant compared with hers. His heart was only the size of a coconut."

Willie's whole attitude to me changed after I said this. What pleased him was that I had shot an elephant, not for its tusks, but in order to learn more about elephants. For Willie, like most men who live long in the jungle, hated big game being shot. He felt far more sympathy with any creature which was part of his jungle than with any new arrival armed with all his new kit.

That evening I became a companion with whom he could enjoy rational conversation instead of an interloper who had to be bullied and kept in his place. His great ambition had been to get someone who would take up the subject of elephant management seriously and it seemed to him that I might be the man he wanted.

Before I left him two or three days later, he had advised me to take up elephants and to make them my chief concern and my life's work. I thus owe a great debt of gratitude to Willie.

The job of extracting teak and delivering it a thousand miles away has many branches, and up till that time none of the European Assistants had specialized in trying to improve the management of elephants. Most of the details had been left to the Burman.

The average European Assistant joining any of the large teak firms in Burma was put in charge of a forest area bigger than an English county. In it were scattered a total of about a hundred elephants, in groups of seven. By continually touring during all the seasons of the year, he might be able to visit every camp about once every six weeks. Under such conditions it would be a long time before he learned to know his elephants even by name, still less by sight; and it would be a very long time indeed before he knew their individual temperaments and capacities for work.

I was more fortunate, as I was responsible for 70 elephants, all working in a fairly small area. I was thus often able to visit my camps twice a month and to spend a longer time in each of them.

What follows is largely the result of my having the luck to start in conditions that enabled me to get to know my elephants really well.

## CHAPTER 3

I T IS impossible to understand much about tame elephants unless one knows a great deal about the habits of wild ones. The study of wild elephants usually entails shooting a few of them at some period either deliberately, for sport or ivory, or in self-defense. Most men who have shot elephants come afterward to regret having done so—but "to hunt is to learn."

Wild elephants normally live in herds of 30 to 50, and during the year cover great distances, chiefly in search of fodder. During the rainy monsoon months—from June to October—they graze on bamboo in the hilly forest country. After the monsoons are over they move into the lower foothills and the swamp valleys, feeding more on grass and less on bamboo.

It is at this time that the full-grown male tuskers join the herd, though they seldom actually enter it, preferring to remain on its outskirts. At this season they do their courting and mating, in the course of which an older bull often has to fight some youngster who is pursuing the same female.

Wild elephants hate being disturbed on their feeding grounds but they do not usually stampede suddenly, like many other herds of big game. With an uncanny intelligence, they close up round one animal as though they were drilled, and their leader decides on the best line of retreat. He leads and they follow irresistibly, smashing through everything, like steam rollers.

Most wild-elephant calves are born between March and May. I believe that if the mother elephant is disturbed she will carry her calf during its first month, holding it wrapped in her trunk. I have seen a mother pick up her calf in this way.

For many years I could not understand the bellowing and trumpeting of wild elephants at night during the hot weather when most calves are born. The fuss is made by the herd in order to protect the mother and calf from intruders—in particular from tigers. The noise is terrifying. The herd will remain in the neighborhood of the maternity ward for some weeks until the new arrival can keep up with the pace of a grazing herd. The ward may cover an area of a square mile and all day the herd will graze all over it, surrounding the mother and her newly born calf, and closing their ranks round her at night. The places chosen are on low ground where a river has suddenly changed its course and taken a hairpin bend. These spots are thus bounded on three sides by banks and river. The kind of jungle found in such places is always the same. They are flooded during the rains, but during the hot weather — the normal calving period — they are fairly dry with areas of dense kaing, or elephant grass, eight to twelve feet high, with an occasional wild cotton tree giving shade. They are eerie spots and to explore them is an adventure. Wild pigs breed in the same type of jungle and harbor their sounders of sucking pigs under huge heaps of leaves and grass which in size resemble ant heaps four feet high.

It is common practice for a Burman oozie to ride his elephant silently up to such a "pig's nest" of leaves and grass and, silently controlling the elephant by movements of his foot and leg, to instruct him to put a forefoot gently on the mound. Squeals and snorts usually follow from the old sow, and three or four sucking pigs join her in a stampede.

It is a peculiar thing that the elephant, which becomes so accustomed to man and has such confidence in him once it has been trained, should be so afraid of him in its wild state. Owing to this fear of man, they do surprisingly little damage to village crops, considering the thousands of wild elephants in Burma. They much prefer their own deep jungles and seldom leave them. The damage that they do has been greatly and most unfairly exaggerated. Solitary animals may, however, do great damage and become bold enough to drive off any human intruder. They do this almost as if it were a joke. Such animals, however, are eventually declared rogues and are killed.

Ordinary fences around crops are no good as a protection against elephants. The Burma Posts and Telegraphs know only too well that an elephant has merely to lean against a telegraph post in order to push it over, or to grip it with its trunk and give a heave to pull it up with ease. The only effective fence against elephants is what is called the punge. This is often used as a trap, and it was a godsend during the war to the 14th Army, which often employed it instead of barbed wire. The punge fence, or trap, is made of a series of sharpened and lightly roasted, or smoked, bamboo stakes of varying lengths. One end of each is stuck into the ground at an angle of 30 degrees, with the point upward and facing outward. On the outside of the fence, concealed in the undergrowth, are very short stakes, protruding only three or four inches out of the ground, and behind these are stakes gradually increasing in length, the longest stick· ing out four or five feet. The depth of the fence may be as much as eight or ten yards.

I have seen wild boar stampeded down a track across which a punge fence had been erected. They were killed outright, skewered through the chest and out between the shoulder blades.

If an elephant charges a punge fence, a stake may easily pierce right through the foreleg. Once I had to extract such a stake, gripping the point with a pair of blacksmith's tongs and pulling it right through the leg. For, like a barbed fishhook, a piece of bamboo cannot be withdrawn by the way it has entered.

Pit traps, which occur so frequently in books about elephant hunting, are very uncommon in Burma. I think the Burmese elephant is too intelligent to fall into them. An effective and heinous trap which killed one of my own elephants was a spear, about the size of a light telegraph pole, heavily weighted and suspended in a tree over a game track. The release was by means of a trip-wire rope, and the spear came down with such force as to transfix the elephant, smashing his ribs and piercing his intestines. It must have taken at least a dozen men to erect this trap. I never traced the culprits. When I tackled them on the subject, all the villagers within a hundred miles round would only say that the tree must have grown like that!

Wire ropes of all sizes have become common in the jungle, and the simple wire noose can be very dangerous and terrifies elephants, as the trunk is often caught. If an elephant's trunk is seriously injured it will die of starvation, since everything it eats has to be torn down or pulled up and handled by the trunk.

The mating of wild elephants is very private. The bull remains, as usual, outside the herd, and his lady love comes out where she knows she will find him. She gives the herd the slip in the evening and is back with them at dawn. Sometimes a rival tusker intervenes and a duel ensues. This is why elephant fights are always between two bulls. There is never a general dogfight within the herd.

Elephant bulls fight head to head and seldom fight to the death without one trying to break away. The one that breaks away, however, frequently receives a wound which turns out to be mortal, for, in turning, he exposes the most vulnerable part of the body. The deadly blow is a thrust of one tusk between the hind legs into the loins and intestines, where the testicles are carried inside the body. It is a common wound to have to treat after a wild tusker has attacked a domesticated one.

Some males never grow tusks but these tuskless males are at no disadvantage in a fight. From the age of three all that the animal gains by not having to grow tusks goes into bodily strength, particularly in the girth and weight of the trunk. The trunk becomes so strong that it will smash off an opponent's solid ivory tusk as though it were the dry branch of a tree.

From the time that a male calf is three years old there is always interest among the oozies as to whether it is going to be a tusker with two tusks, or a tai (with one tusk either right or left), or a han (a tuskless male but with two small tushes such as females carry), or a hine, which has neither tusks nor tushes.

One of the most delightful myths about wild elephants is that the old tuskers and females eventually go off to die in a traditional graveyard. This belief has its origin in the fact that dead elephants, whether tuskers or females, are so seldom found.

I shall try to explain away the myth by describing what really happens. Take the case of a fine old bull that has stopped following the herd at about the age of 75 and has taken to a solitary existence. He has given up covering great distances in a seasonal feeding cycle and remains in the headwaters of a remote creek. His cheeks are sunken, his teeth worn out. Old age and debility slowly overtake him and his big, willing heart. During the monsoon months, fodder, chiefly bamboo, is easily gathered and he stays up in the hills. As the dry season approaches, fodder becomes scarcer and he moves slowly downhill to browse on the tall grass. Then, as the hot season comes on and there are forest fires, he is too tired and too old to go in search of the varied diet he needs and his digestion suffers. Fever sets in as the showers of April and May chill him, and he moves to water. Here, by the large pool above the gorge, there is always green fodder. He is perfectly happy, but the water slowly dries until there is only a trickle flowing from the large pool and he spends his time standing on a spit of sand, picking up the cool sand and mud with his trunk and spraying it over his hot, fevered body.

One sweltering hot evening in late May, he hears a mighty storm raging ten miles away in the hills, and he knows the rains have broken. Soon the trickle will become a raging torrent of broken brown water carrying trees and logs and debris in its onrush. Throwing his head back, with his trunk in his mouth as he takes his last drink, he grows giddy. He staggers and falls. He is down — never to rise again — and he dies without a struggle. The tired old heart just stops ticking.

Two porcupines get the news that night and in spite of the heavy rain attack one of his tusks, gnawing it as beavers gnaw wood. They have eaten only half through the second tusk when the roar of the first tearing spate of the rains drives them off.

A five-foot wall of water strikes the carcass — debris piles up while the water furiously undermines and outflanks this obstruction. At last the whole mass of carcass, stones and branches moves, floats, and then, swirling and turning over, goes into the gorge down a ten-foot waterfall and jams among the boulders below. Hundreds of tons of water drive onto it, logs and boulders bruise and smash up the body, shifting it further, and the savage water tears it apart. As the forest fires are God's spring cleaning of the jungle, so the spates of the great rains provide burial for the dead.

By dawn the floods have subsided and the porcupines have to hunt for their second meal of tusk. Other jungle scavengers have their share. But the spate comes again the next night and in a week all traces of the old tusker have disappeared.

## CHAPTER 4

I ARRIVED in Burma just as a determined effort had been started to improve the management of elephants and their calves. In order to do this, it was first necessary to improve the conditions of the oozies, who must be considered as part and parcel of the Burmese timber-working elephant which they ride. These men are born with a knowledge of elephants. Their homes are in camps in the most remote parts of the jungle. They can sit an elephant from the age of six, and they grow up learning all the traditional knowledge, the myth and legend, the blended fact and fiction which is attached to this lovable animal. At the age of 14 the average boy in an elephant camp is earning a wage. He starts life as a paijaik — that is, the man who hooks the chains to the logs — a ground assistant of the oozie.

It is a proud day in that boy's life when he is promoted to oozie and has an elephant in his own charge. There is no more lovely sight I know than to see a 14-year-old boy riding a newly trained calf elephant of six. The understanding between them is equaled only by that of a child with a puppy, but the Burmese boy is not so cruel to his elephant as most children are to puppies. The Burman oozie has a pretty hard life. In the first place, he has to catch his elephant every morning and bring it to camp. Catching his elephant involves tracking the animal a distance of about eight miles, starting at dawn through jungles infested with all types of big game. That in itself is a lonely job, and to do it successfully the oozie has to become one of the jungle beasts himself — as alert and as wary as they are.

He knows the shape, size and peculiarities of his own elephant's footprints with complete certainty. Once he has picked up the trail, he sets off following it. While he is doing so he notices many things: he finds the spot where the animal rested in the night, he observes its droppings, and can tell from them that his elephant has been eating too much bamboo and for that reason will probably have headed for a patch of kaing grass that grows on the banks of the creek over the watershed.

When he has gained the ridge he will halt and listen, perhaps for ten minutes, for the distinctive sound of his elephant's kalouk, or bell, which the oozie made himself. Elephant bells are made with two clappers, one on each side, hanging outside the bell, which is made from a hollowed-out lump of teak. No two bells ever have the same note and the sound of 15 or more can only be compared to the music of a babbling brook.

As the oozie approaches his beast he begins to sing so as to let her know that he is coming. Then, instead of bursting through the kaing grass that stands nine feet high, he sits down on a boulder beside the creek and fills his homemade pipe and lights it. Between the puffs he keeps calling: *"Lah! Lah! Lah!* [Come on! Come on! Come on!]." But no sound comes from where his elephant is grazing, so he changes his words to *"Digo lah! Digo lah!* [Come here! Come here!]." And he will sit and smoke and call some 15 minutes without showing impatience. He gives her time to accept the grim fact that another day of hard work has begun for her. If he hurries her, she may rebel.

Presently the elephant emerges from the kaing grass, and, chatting away to her, he says: "Do you think I've nothing else to do but wait for you? You've been eating since noon yesterday."

Then his voice rings out with a firm order: *"Hmit!"*

Dropping first on her haunches and then reposing with all four legs extended, she allows him to approach her.

*"Tah!* [Stand up!]," he orders, and she does so, keeping her front legs close together. He then bends down and unfastens her hobbles and throws them over her withers. Then the oozie orders her to sit down, climbs onto her head and away they go.

When they reach camp the oozie has his first meal of the day, washes his elephant in the creek, and then harnesses her for work. Their job for the day is to climb a ridge 2000 feet above the camp and to drag a log from the stump to the creek.

When the oozie reaches the log with his elephant and his paijaik, he will trim it of knots so as to make it easier for dragging and fasten chains round it securely. After that there begins the wearisome task of dragging a log 29 feet long and six or seven feet in girth — that is to say, over a hundred cubic feet of timber, or four tons dead weight. For a mile the path follows the top of the ridge. "Patience! patience! patience! *Yoo! Yoo! Yoo!* [Pull! pull! pull!]," calls the oozie. As the elephant takes the strain, she feels what power she must exert besides that of her enormous weight. The ground is ankle-deep in mud, and there are dozens of small obstructions which must be leveled out by the log's nose — sapling stumps, bamboos, rocks.

The elephant puts out her first effort and, bellowing like fury, pulls the log three times her own length and then stops. She rests then to take breath, and her trunk goes out sideways to snatch at a bamboo. It is her chewing gum as she works but it earns her a sarcastic comment from the oozie: "My mother, but you are forever eating!" However, his patience is quite undisturbed. The elephant takes her time. *"Yoo! Yoo! Yoo!"* calls the oozie, but there is no response. *"Yooo! Yooo! Yooo!"* Then the elephant pulls again, but this time, as it is slightly downhill, she pulls the log six times her length before she halts. So it goes on until they reach the edge of a precipice — a 400-foot drop. The elephant knows the exact margin of safety, and when the log is ten feet from the edge she refuses to haul it any closer.

The chains are unfastened, and the elephant is moved around behind the log. The oozie gives his orders by kicks and scratches with his bare feet behind the elephant's ears. So he coaxes her

to bend down her massive head in order to get a leverage under the log with her trunk. Working like that, she moves it first four feet at one end, then rolls it from the middle, then pushes the other end until she has got it onto the very edge of the cliff, almost trembling on the balance. She will then torment her oozie by refusing to touch it again for ten minutes. Finally, when the oozie's patience is almost at an end, she puts one forefoot out as calmly as if she were tapping a football, and the log is away — gone. There is a crash in the jungle below, and then a prolonged series of crashes echoing through the jungle as the log tears down bamboos until it comes to rest 400 feet lower down, leaving the elephant standing on the edge of the precipice above, with a supercilious expression on her face, as though she were saying: "Damned easy."

Half an hour later elephant and oozie have reached the log again, having gone round by a circuitous game track to the foot of the precipice. Once down there, she has again to drag the log with the chains along a ledge. Dragging a log weighing four tons while negotiating a narrow ledge is a risky business, for the log might roll. But the elephant can judge what is safe to the inch — not to the foot — and she works with patience, patience, patience. Both oozie and elephant know that, should the log start to roll or slide over the edge, all the gear and harness can be got rid of in the twinkling of an eye. The elephant has only to whip round in her tracks, step inside her chain, and bend down her head for all the harness to peel off over her head as easily as a girl strips off a silk slip over her shoulders. For this reason it is very rare indeed for an elephant to be dragged over a precipice by a log suddenly taking charge.

After negotiating the ledge, there is an easy downhill drag for half a mile to the floating point on the side of the creek. By that time it is about three o'clock in the afternoon. The oozie unharnesses his elephant, puts on her fetters, slaps her on

her backside and tells her that she must go off in search of
food. For neither of them is their day's work really over. The
elephant still has to find her fodder, not only to chew it but to
break off, pull down, or pull up, every branch, tree, creeper or
tuft of grass that she eats. The oozie has to repair his gear,
trim logs or weave a new laibut, or breast strap, of bark. This
bit of harness takes the full strain of the elephant's strength when
dragging and has to be made accordingly.

Living under such primitive conditions, not only the oozie
but also his wife and family need frequent medical attention,
and they have no one to look to but the European Assistant who
lives nearest. Apart from all the diseases, accidents are constantly
occurring in the jungle; the Assistant has to be ready to take
decisions which would make an ordinary medical man's hair
stand on end. One may come into a new camp and find sick
people down with beriberi — two women with their breasts
split like ripe tomatoes from the swelling characteristic of that
disease — and one has to decide at once what to do. One has
to be ready to treat a girl with an afterbirth hemorrhage or a
man scalped by a bear. Malaria is more common than head colds
in England. Dysentery and even cholera and smallpox epidemics
are all liable to break out in the jungle. I am convinced that life
in such conditions would be unbearable if it were not for the
elephants, which exert a fascination over the Burmese, a fascination which Europeans soon begin to feel as well.

## CHAPTER 5

DURING the war I was talking about elephants to two war
correspondents, one American and the other Australian.
The latter asked me: "Is it true that elephants are very shy about
their actual love affair?" Before I could answer, the American

chipped in with: "Of course they are; aren't you?" The mating of elephants is a private affair, and even the oozies of the tusker and the female concerned may not know that it has taken place. Often they know, but regard it as none of their business.

Europeans tell and even believe the most fantastic tales about the mating habits of elephants, but the love-making of elephants as I have seen it seems to me more simple and more lovely than any myth. It is beautiful because it is quite without the brutishness and the cruelty which one sees in the matings of so many animals.

Without there being any appearance of "season," two animals become attracted by each other. The average female first mates between the ages of 17 and 20. She shows no sign of any particular season but apparently feels some natural urge. Days and even weeks of courtship may take place. Eventually the mating is consummated, and the act may be repeated three or four times during the 24 hours. For months the pair will keep together as they graze and their honeymoon will last all that time. After the day's work they will call each other and go off together into the jungle. My own belief is that this close relationship lasts until the female has been pregnant for ten months — that is, until she has become aware that she is pregnant.

The companionship of the male is then replaced by that of a female friend or "auntie." From that time onward they are never apart and it becomes difficult to separate them. Indeed, it is cruel to do so. Their association is founded on mutual aid among animals, the instinctive knowledge that it takes two mothers to protect a calf elephant against tigers which, in spite of all precautions, still kill 25 percent of all calves born.

Gestation lasts 22 months. After the calf has been born, the mother and the auntie always keep it between them as they graze — all through the night — and, while it is very young, during daylight hours as well.

To kill the calf the tiger has to drive off both the mother and auntie by stampeding them. To do this he will first attack the mother, springing on her back and stampeding her; then he returns to attack Auntie, who defends the calf, knowing that in a few moments the mother will return. On many occasions I have had to dress the lacerated wounds of tiger claws on the backs of both a mother elephant and her friend. A baby calf follows its mother at heel for three or four years, being suckled by the mother from the breasts between her forelegs.

This position, between the forelegs, affords the calf perfect protection. At birth the calf's trunk is a useless membrane growing rather to one side so as to allow the calf to suck more easily through the mouth. It does not become flexible and useful for three to four months. When the sacred white elephant of Mandalay Palace was a calf its mother died and it was suckled by 20 young Burmese women daily as wet nurses, and so reared.

At the age of five or, at most, six years, the calf has learned to gather its own fodder and gradually gives up suckling its mother. Female elephants have an average of four calves in a lifetime. Twins are not uncommon and two calves of different ages following their mother at heel is quite a usual sight. Larger families are not uncommon.

After weaning, young elephants go through an awkward stage, becoming a bit truculent owing to the desire for independence — much like human boys and girls.

At 15 or 16 they become very much like human flappers and young stalwarts. Young male elephants do a lot of flirting with the females from the ages of 16 to 20, sometimes being most enterprising. But the average animal does not show any signs of musth until the age of 20. A male elephant will mate when he is not "on musth," in fact he usually does. But when he is on musth all the savage lust and combative instincts of his huge body come out.

From the age of 20 to 35 musth is shown by a slight discharge of a strong-smelling fluid from the musth glands near the eye, directly above the line of the mouth. In a perfectly fit male it occurs annually during the hot months, which are the mating season. It may last about two weeks, during which time he is very temperamental.

From the age of 35 to 45 the discharge increases and runs freely, eventually dribbling into his mouth, and the taste of it makes him much more ferocious. He is physically in his prime at that age, and unless he is securely chained to a large tree while on musth, he is a danger to his oozie and to other elephants. His brain goes wild, and nothing will satisfy him.

From 45 to 50 musth gradually subsides. Tuskers that have killed as many as nine men between the ages of 35 and 45 will become docile during musth in their later years. But no elephant on musth can be trusted unless he is over 60 years old.

Poo Ban was normally a friendly animal and would let me walk under his tusks, but he went on musth in the Taungdwin Forest area, killed his oozie and another man, then killed two female elephants and attacked all men on sight. Finally he entered villages, tore rice granaries open and became the terror of the valley. I offered a reward of 300 rupees for his capture and decided to destroy him if he could not be captured.

He was marked down in a dense patch of bamboo jungle in Saiyawah (the Valley of Ten Villages), four marches away. With Kya Sine, my gun boy, I set out, lightly loaded with two traveling elephants as pack. The evening before I was to tackle Poo Ban I was testing my rifle when Kya Sine begged me to let him go ahead and attempt to recapture him without shooting, so that he could earn 300 rupees. Unfortunately I gave in and before dawn he had gone on ahead. I arrived at 3 p.m. next day to be met by men who said, "Kya Sine is dead." Poo Ban had killed him during his attempt at recapture.

That night I bivouacked in an open place which had at one time been paddy fields. It was a brilliant moonlit night and before I went to sleep I made my plans to recapture Poo Ban. I intended to wound him in the forefoot, break his spirit and then heal the wound.

I was asleep, lying in the open, when I was wakened by a clank! clank! clank! Luckily for me, a piece of chain had been left on Poo Ban's off forefoot. Two hundred yards away, in the open, a magnificent tusker was standing, head erect in challenge, defiant of the whole world. He was a perfect silhouette. I did not dare move an eyelid, and while I held my breath he moved on with a clank, clank, clank, which at last faded away like the far sound of the pipes over the hills.

At dawn I tried to put my plans into action. When he had been located, I took up my position, while 20 Burmans with four shotguns among them tried to drive him past me.

At last Poo Ban came out of the jungle with his head held high. He halted, and then made a beeline across my front, traveling fast over the open ground.

Kneeling, I took the shot at his foot on which my plans depended. The bullet kicked up a puff of dust in front of his near forefoot as he put it down in his stride. I had missed!

Poo Ban halted and swung round to face me, or the bark of my rifle which he had heard. Then he took up the never-to-be-forgotten attitude of an elephant about to charge, with the trunk well tucked away in his mouth, like a wound-up watch spring. As he charged, I took a chest shot at 25 yards. His tusks drove nine inches into the ground, his head dropped. For a few seconds he balanced and then toppled over dead.

I dropped my rifle and was sick, vomiting with fear, excitement and regret. Poo Ban was dead, and I had failed to catch him alive. There was no court of inquiry. My report was accepted and I was given the tusks as a souvenir, a souvenir of a double failure that I bitterly regretted, and of the death of the finest and bravest Burman hunter I have known.

## CHAPTER 6

THERE IS undoubted cruelty in breaking the spirit and train-ing wild elephants after they have been captured by kheddar-ing. The ideal age at which to capture a wild elephant is usually considered to be from 15 to 20, as it is then only a few years before it is sufficiently mature to do heavy work and to earn its original cost. But the spirit of a youngster of that age, whether male or female, takes a lot of breaking. It often takes a matter of weeks, while it is tethered to a tree with chains, and its con-tinual struggling and fighting to break free cause the most shocking galling of the ankles and neck. Food is thrown to the animal, but insufficient and unsuitable food leads to great loss of condition. The wounds it receives are almost impossible to treat, and they become flyblown and ulcerated.

In the end the young animal becomes heartbroken and thin. Finally it realizes that it is in captivity for the rest of its days and, after the last heartbreaking struggle, will put up with a man sitting on its head.

But a calf born in captivity is far more easily trained. From the day it is born until it leaves its mother at five years old it is in contact with its mother's oozie. It flirts with him like a child, it pretends to chase him, then runs away again. But though so playful, it seldom trusts him much beyond accepting a tidbit of fruit or a handful of rice from his hands.

In November of its fifth year the calf is weaned and from that moment becomes more independent. Five or six calves are trained at a time in one camp. An area of 100 yards square is cleared, except for a few trees to give shade. In the middle a "crush," or triangular-shaped pen, is built of logs of about the height of the average five-year-old calf. The logs of which it is built are fastened with wooden pegs; no nails are used. The bark is stripped from the logs, which are rubbed smooth and smeared with grease — all precautions against galling the calf's hide. In camp, in addition to the calves with their mothers, is an elephant known as the koonkie (schoolmaster). This animal is usually a tuskless male between 45 and 50 years of age, chosen for his docility and patience.

On the morning when the first calf is to be weaned, the mother and the calf are brought into the clearing and made familiar with the crush and its surroundings. Once the calf has been lured into the crush with a bit of fruit (or butted into it by the koonkie), the attendant Burmans quickly slip two stout bars in behind its hindquarters. It will usually struggle and kick for about two hours. Then it sulks and finally it will take a banana from the oozie out of sheer boredom and disgust.

Meanwhile, the calf's future rider has been attached to a pulley a few feet over its head. Two men on the ground, on either side of the crush, control this pulley and on a signal from the rider he is lowered slowly onto the calf's head.

"Damn you, get off!" screams the calf, bucking like a bronco. The would-be oozie has soon to be hauled up again, but no sooner has the calf quieted down and accepted another banana than the rider is lowered once more — and so on, until the poor little calf seems to say, "All right. Sit there if you must."

When it has finished the bananas it will buck again, but directly it starts eating, down comes the oozie once more.

So far so good. The poor calf is tired, but the Burmans, stripped of all but their tucked-up lungyis, are thoroughly enjoying the game, though they are dripping with sweat.

Suspended from another pulley above the center of the calf's back is a heavy block of padded wood. This is also lowered onto

its back and provokes more bucking-bronco antics. A moment or
two later the block is lifted, but directly the calf stands still,
down it comes again. Once more there are determined struggles
to get free. And so it goes on, and all the while the calf is
being offered food and spoken to with kind and soothing words.
Finally, in utter disgust the calf sits down with its front feet
straight out, hoping that it will get rid of the pests.

A cheer goes up from the Burmans, a cheer which soon becomes a chant of, "*Tah* [Get up]! *Hmit* [Sit down]!" As the
weight is lifted, the calf gets up and all the Burmans chant,
"*Tah!*" As the weight comes down, and the calf sits, all of them
chant, "*Hmit!*" in chorus.

After a time the rider, still attached to the pulley, remains
comfortably seated on its head. By evening, unless the calf is
a really obstinate young devil, the rider can turn and, putting
his hand on its back instead of the log of wood, order the calf
to sit down by pressure and by saying, "*Hmit.*"

Once that is possible, the calf is considered broken. Often
it takes less than 12 hours with no cruelty whatsoever. Sometimes, however, in dealing with obstinate and truculent young
tuskers, the game has to be kept up, by the light of bamboo
torches, far into the night. Occasionally it may last even till
the next morning. But however long it may take, the Burmans
never give in and never give the calf any rest until their object
is achieved. The great lesson is that man's will power is stronger
than the calf's and that man will always get his way.

Before the calf is taken out of the crush on the following
morning it is hobbled with well-greased buffalo-hide thongs,
and it is then tied to a tree for 24 hours, being caressed and
cajoled all the time by its future rider. He makes it sit down
each time he approaches. He mounts on its head, remains there
ten minutes, orders the calf to sit again and dismounts, and sometimes keeps it in the sitting position for five or ten minutes.

Extraordinary patience is needed throughout. Once the Burman starts, he goes on until he gains his point. He never lets the calf win a victory, however temporary.

The calf is then taken for its first walk, attached to the koonkie by a buffalo-hide girdle. The koonkie thinks the whole thing a bore but he stands no nonsense. If the calf jibs, sits down or lags, he gives him one wrench that pulls him along. On occasion he will give him a real welt with his trunk.

It soon becomes a decorous walking out and at a later stage the koonkie can manage two calves — one on each side of him.

From the age of breaking, young elephants are kept under training until the finishing age of 19. For about two years they remain in the camp nursery, merely being caught daily and taught the simple words of command and the "aids" of the rider, as well as by foot control behind their ears.

The "aids" are simply movements of the rider's body by which he translates his wishes, almost instinctively, to his mount. Thus an intense stiffening of his limbs and leaning back will be at once understood as halt. A pressure on one side will be understood as turn to the left, on the other as turn to the right. Leaning forward and forcing downward will mean stoop or kneel. A dragging up on the right side will be correctly interpreted as lift the right foot — on the other, as lift the left.

At about eight years old, young elephants carry their first pack and become "travelers," accompanying a European Assistant when he tours the forest. They thus become accustomed to going over mountains and down streams, carrying light weights, such as camp cooking pots or light bed rolls.

During the early years the elephant never really earns its keep or does enough to pay the wages of its oozie but it is learning all the time. Up to the age of 19 or 20 it will have cost about a thousand pounds, when the wages of the oozie, training costs and maintenance are added up. But thereafter the elephant has on the average a working life from its 20th to its 55th year.

Each working year consists of nine months' work and three months' rest, necessary both to keep it in condition and on account of the seasonal changes. Each month consists of only 18 working days and 12 rest days, animals working three days in succession and then resting two. Thus, during the nine months of the working year there are only 162 working days. Each day averages about eight hours. Thus an elephant works 1300 hours a year. During this time an average animal delivers 100 tons of timber from stump to a floating point in a creek.

## CHAPTER 7

BY THE TIME it is 25 years old, a well-trained elephant should understand 24 separate words of command, apart from the signals or "foot aids" of the rider. He ought also to be able to pick up five different things from the ground when asked. That is to say, he should pick up and pass up to his rider with his trunk a jungle dah (knife), a koon (axe), his fetter or hobble chain, his tying chain (for tethering him to a tree) and a stick. I have seen an intelligent elephant pick up not only a pipe that his rider had dropped but a large lighted cheroot.

He will tighten a chain attached to a log by giving it a sharp tug with his trunk, or loosen it with a shake, giving it the same motion with his trunk as that given by a human hand.

An elephant does not work mechanically; he never stops learning because he is always thinking. Not even a really good sheep dog can compare with an elephant in intelligence.

If he cannot reach with his trunk some part of his body that itches, he doesn't always rub it against a tree; he may pick up a long stick and give himself a good scratch with that instead.

If he pulls up some grass and it comes up by the roots with

a lump of earth, he will smack it against his foot until all the earth is shaken off, or if water is handy he will wash it clean. And he will extract a pill the size of an aspirin tablet from a tamarind fruit the size of a cricket ball in which one has planted it, with an air of saying, "You can't kid me."

Many young elephants develop the naughty habit of plugging up the wooden bell they wear hung round their necks with good stodgy mud or clay so that the clappers cannot ring, in order to steal silently into banana groves at night. There they will have a whale of a time, quietly stuffing, eating not only the bunches of bananas but the leaves and indeed the whole tree as well, and they will do this just beside the hut occupied by the owner of the grove, without waking him or any of his family.

I have personally witnessed many remarkable instances of the quick intelligence of elephants, though I cannot claim that they equal the famous yarns which delight all of us, whether we are children or grownups — such as that of the circus elephant who saw a man who had befriended him sitting in a sixpenny seat and at once picked him up with his trunk and popped him into a three-and-sixpenny one!

But the following incidents seem to me to denote immediate brain reaction to a new situation rather than anything founded on repetitive training.

An uncertain-tempered tusker was being loaded with kit while in the standing position. On his back was his oozie, with another Burman in the pannier filling it with kit. Alongside on the flank, standing on the ground, was the paijaik attendant, armed with a spear which consisted of a five-foot cane, a brightly polished spearhead at one end and a spiked ferrule at the other. Another Burman was handing gear up to the Burman in the pannier, but got into difficulties with one package and called out to the paijaik to help him. The latter thrust the ferrule of the spear into the ground so that it stood planted upright with the spearhead in line with the elephant's eye. Then he lent a hand. The oozie, however, did not trust his beast, and said in a determined voice, "Pass me the spear." The tusker calmly put its trunk round the cane at the point of balance and carefully passed it up to his rider. But unthinkingly he passed it head-first. The rider yelled at his beast in Burmese, "Don't be a bloody fool — pass it right way round!" With perfect calm and a rather dandified movement, the elephant revolved the spear in mid-air and, still holding it by the point of balance, passed it to his oozie, this time ferrule first.

One of the most intelligent acts I ever saw an elephant perform occurred one evening when the Upper Taungdwin River was in heavy spate. I was listening for the boom and roar of timber coming from upstream. Directly below my camp the banks of the river were steep and rocky and 12 to 15 feet high.

I was suddenly alarmed by hearing an elephant roaring as though frightened and, looking down, I saw three or four men rushing up and down on the opposite bank in a state of great excitement. I ran down to the edge of the near bank and there saw Ma Shwe (Miss Gold) with her three-month-old calf, trapped in the fast-rising torrent. She herself was still in her depth, as the water was about six feet deep. But there was a life-and-death struggle going on. Her calf was screaming with terror and was afloat like a cork. Ma Shwe was as near to the far bank as she could get, holding her whole body against the raging torrent and keeping the calf pressed against her massive body. The swirling water kept sweeping the calf away; then, with terrific strength, she would encircle it with her trunk and pull it upstream to rest against her body again.

There was a sudden rise in the water and the calf was washed clean over the mother's hindquarters. She turned to chase it, like an otter after a fish, but she had traveled about 50 yards downstream and crossed to my side of the river before she had caught it and got it back. For what seemed minutes she pinned the calf with her head and trunk against the bank. Then, with a really gigantic effort, she picked it up in her trunk and reared up until she was half standing on her hind legs so as to place it on a narrow shelf of rock five feet above the flood level.

Having accomplished this, she fell back into the raging torrent and she herself went away like a cork. She well knew that she would now have a fight to save her own life, as less than 300 yards below where she had stowed her calf in safety there was a gorge. If she were carried down, it would be certain death. I knew as well as she did that there was one spot between her and the gorge where she could get up the bank, but it was on the other side from where she had put her calf. By that time my chief interest was in the calf. It stood tucked up, shivering and terrified, on a ledge just wide enough to hold its feet. Its little, fat, protruding belly was tightly pressed against the bank.

While I was peering over at it, wondering what I could do next, I heard the grandest sounds of a mother's love I can remember. Ma Shwe had crossed the river and got up the bank and was making her way back as fast as she could, calling the whole time — a defiant roar, but to her calf it was music. The two little ears, like little maps of India, were cocked forward listening to the only sound that mattered, the call of its mother.

As darkness fell, a torrential rain was falling and the river still separated the mother and her calf. I decided that I could do nothing but wait and see what happened.

At dawn Ma Shwe and her calf were together — both on the far bank. The spate had subsided to a mere foot of dirty-colored water. No one in the camp had seen Ma Shwe recover her calf but she must have lifted it down from the ledge in the same way as she had put it there.

Five years later, when the calf came to be named, the Burmans christened it Ma Yay Yee (Miss Laughing Water).

Just before the war, experiments in the use of local anesthetics and even of general anesthetics on elephants were carried out. No doubt these will be resumed one day. But up till the time of the reconquest of Burma, after the Japanese invasion, all elephant surgery was on old and somewhat primitive lines.

It needs confidence to walk under an elephant's jaw and tusks, armed with a heavy knife in one's left hand and a six-pound wooden club in the right hand, and then to tell him to hold up his head while you drive the knife up to the hilt into a huge abscess on his chest with one blow of the mallet.

One blow of the mallet is all you can get; if you try another you must look out for squalls. But if you do the job properly and make a quick and quiet getaway to his flank, he will let you go back ten minutes later to clean out the abscess and then syringe it with disinfectant.

Wounds caused by tigers, most often received by mother elephants protecting their calves, are exceptionally difficult to heal and often do not respond to modern antiseptics.

The Burman has cures for all the ills that may befall an elephant. Some are herbal, some are mystic spells and incantations, and some of them have had to be vetoed as being definitely harmful. But I have so far found no treatment for tiger wounds that comes up to the traditional Burmese method of plugging the wounds with sugar. The Burman also used maggots to clean up gangrened wounds for centuries before the method was rediscovered in modern surgery.

It has been quite truly said that once an elephant goes down, due to exhaustion or severe colic, he has only a 25 percent chance of getting onto his legs again unaided. Any method of keeping him on his legs improves a sick elephant's chances of survival. The Burman will do this by putting chili juice in his eye — a counterirritant that must be agony. But it is effective and about doubles the animal's chances of recovery. No matter how far modern veterinary research goes, we shall always rely to a certain extent upon the Burman's knowledge.

I know without question that an elephant can be grateful for relief given to it from pain and sickness. For example, I remember Ma Kyaw (Miss Smooth, an expression often used to describe any Burmese girl with a strikingly good figure). She had fearful lacerations on the barrel of her back from tiger claws, and I treated her for them every day for three weeks. In the early stages she suffered great pain, but although she made a lot of fuss she always gave way and let me go on. When she was sufficiently healed I sent her back to camp under a reliable Burman with instructions that she was to be given light dressings of fly repellent on the wounds. Two months later I was having a cup of tea in camp outside my tent while seven elephants were being washed in the creek near-by, preparatory to my inspecting them. The last animal to come out of the creek was Ma Kyaw. As she passed me about 50 yards away, with her rider on foot, I called out, "How is Ma Kyaw's back?"

Her rider did not reply, as he had not caught what I said, but Ma Kyaw swung round and came toward me.

She walked straight up to where I was sitting, dropped into the sitting position and leaned right over toward me so as to show me her back. Having patted her I told her to "*Tah* [get up]," and away she went, leaving me with the agreeable conviction that she had come to say thank you.

## CHAPTER 8

ELEPHANTS are good swimmers and are extremely buoyant. When the oozie is going to cross a large river, such as the Irrawaddy, with his elephant, he fits a surcingle under its belly and over the withers, kneels on the animal's back and grips the rope in front of him, using a stick to signal his "aids."

For a time the elephant will swim along gaily with a rather lunging action. Then, all of a sudden, he will submarine into 15 feet of water. The animal, for pure fun, will keep submerged almost to bursting point, trying to make his rider let go.

But the oozie knows that an elephant can only stay underwater for the same length of time as a man. So he holds on. The elephant, meanwhile, is doing a fairylike dance on tiptoe along the bottom, while the poor old oozie is wondering if the animal will ever surface. Suddenly both reappear, blowing tremendously and taking great gasps of breath.

When elephants have to be moved long distances by water they are frequently taken on rafts, or barges, towed alongside a paddle steamer. Getting elephants onto such flats needs endless patience. First one has to find a leader which the other beasts will follow, and then one has to camouflage the gangway with tall grasses or palms on either side of it to a height of 12 feet.

Once I had to ship two flat loads of 20 elephants from a river station on the Irrawaddy. I was assisted by a very capable Anglo-Burman and we started work at dawn, but had only got one flat loaded by noon. The irate old skipper of the paddle steamer was due to leave at 2 p.m. By 5 p.m. we got the last elephant on board the second flat and the skipper's temper was just like mine. Just when I thought my job was finished and the skipper's had begun, he blew the steamer's siren — of all the damn fool things! And at the same time the enormous side paddles started to churn alongside the loaded flats full of elephants, on either side of the steamer.

The captain's shock was greater than mine, as 16 elephants trumpeted and roared, drowning every other sound. I think he thought half of them had broken loose and were boarding his steamer after his blood, whereas sheer terror kept them in their places. He had to reckon with me, however.

We eventually got the animals settled down and under way and put in an hour's steaming before tying up for the night. Leaving my Assistant to check on the chains, I made for the saloon to make it up with the skipper over a peg.

At midnight I was still yarning with the skipper when my Assistant arrived to say that a young tusker had collapsed. His doing so had caused little commotion. As far as I could discover, he had collapsed dead-beat from fatigue. To get anywhere near him, one crawled through a forest of elephant legs.

After I had given him half a bottle of brandy without results, I decided there was nothing more I could do but let him lie and wait for the dawn. I had gone to my cabin when my Assistant came back, looking very shy, to say that the Burman oozies wanted to put a temple candle for each year of the elephant's life round the prostrate body and might they try it?

The theory was that when all the candles were alight, but before they burned out, the animal would rise. My reply was, "Yes. Buy 21 blinking candles but don't set fire to the ship!"

That was the last I saw of him that night, but at dawn he came to my cabin to say, "It's worked, sir. The animal is up. But you were one year out in his age. We had to do it a second time and use 22 candles!"

He was so sincere that I did not like to say what I thought, which was that the elephant was a young animal which liked sleeping with the light on.

As regards sleep, elephants are rather like horses. They get most of it standing up and they will only go down when they think that, for a brief period at night, all the world is asleep. The time is never the same, but it is always at that eerie hour when even the insects stop their serenades. It never lasts longer than half an hour if the animal is fit, but while it lasts he sleeps very soundly. For an hour previously the elephant stands absolutely motionless without feeding. Then he seems satisfied that all is well, and down he goes in a slow, silent movement, as if overcome by some unseen jungle god. In bright moonlight it is a most beautiful but uncanny sight.

Elephants and ponies do not get on together. The elephants sometimes become so scared of ponies that a whole train of them will stampede at the sight of one, with the result that oozies are injured and gear is smashed. This feeling is exceeded only by their hatred and fear of dogs. In fact, a dog is one of the few animals at which an elephant will lash out with its trunk, and I have never known a dog and an elephant to make friends. This hatred cannot easily be explained. It is possible that elephants are afraid of dogs biting their trunks, or it might be an instinctive fear of hydrophobia, which is the dread of everyone who keeps a dog in camp, Burman and European Assistant alike.

Nevertheless, practically every European Assistant keeps a dog. The elephants hate them and one is always losing one's dog, owing to leopard, tiger, bear and snakes. It is easy to ask why, under such conditions, one keeps a dog? But I know of no other existence where a dog is so necessary as a companion to share every moment of one's life and to drive away loneliness.

A dog usually sleeps in one's hut or tent, but even so it is a great worry. For only if it is fenced in behind chairs and boxes under one's camp bed can one feel reasonably sure that a leopard will not take it while one is asleep.

One Assistant had his cocker spaniel snapped up by a leopard when it was sleeping chained up beside his bed in his bamboo hut. He did not wake until it was too late to do anything. The chain was broken and both had vanished. He was determined on revenge, so the next night he borrowed a dog from the elephant men and tied it up to his office box beside his bed. Then he put out his lamp and sat up in an upright chair in one corner of the room, prepared to wait all night if need be.

The familiar babble of chatting ceased in his servants' camp,

the glow of the fires died down. At last the hour of stillness
arrived, when all sounds seemed to cease. Then there was a
sudden tension in the room and he could feel his heart pounding. The dog suddenly tore at his chain, pulling the heavy specie
box to which it was tied across the bamboo floor.

The Assistant raised his loaded shotgun, and switched on his
torch, and on the bamboo steps in the doorway stood a leopard,
blinded by the light. The Assistant fired both barrels and it fell
dead. In a moment the camp was stirring with lights and his
servants were uttering exclamations of delight. One of them
ripped open the white belly of the leopard and pulled out a black
knot of the curly coat of his master's beloved spaniel.

This was too much for my friend, who turned away and
ordered his people back to bed, telling them to take the terrified

camp dog with them. He told me that he cried himself to sleep that night and that he thought it had done him good.

While we were talking later after a day's work an oozie and his wife approached. The man was holding a baby honey bear in his arms. It was about the size of a coffeepot. They squatted down side by side in front of us, she with her shoulders bare and her tamain tucked across her breasts.

"Would you like to have the baby, *Thakin Galay?*" the man asked my friend, for they had heard of the loss of his spaniel.

It was a charming expression of sympathy which they did not put into any other words.

"No," my friend and I both said together.

The little bear seemed to understand and began to make queer babyish squeals and fumble about — and, with a perfectly simple, natural movement the Burman passed it to his wife, who put it in her lap, untucking her tamain from across her breasts. Then she lifted up the little bear and began to nurse it.

When we had thanked them again for the offer of their pet, they rose, bowed and departed with the bear cub still at her breast. She had been feeding it three or four times a day, filled with all the Buddhists' pride that they were doing something of importance in their lives by preserving life and convinced that their action would put them on a higher plane in nirvana.

There was nothing unusual in this. The jungle women will suckle baby fawns and any young creature which inspires them with pity. "It deserves pity," are words often on their lips, and their pity at once moves them to succor and keep alive the orphan. Thus they will adopt newborn tiger or leopard cubs, and bears, not hesitating to save the lives of the hated enemies of their menfolk which would become dangerous if they were reared. There is a wonderful gentleness in these jungle people.

The Burman has no sympathy, however, with any eccentric European who keeps a snake as a pet.

I have been told the story of one "jungle salt" in the Pyinmana Forest who did keep such a pet. She was a 17-foot python whom he called Eve. She had a silver collar and chain, and he took her on all his tours in a basket carried on one of his elephants.

Eve did little except sleep and eat at longish intervals. She lived in his hut or tent, finding warmth during the day between the blankets of his bed, and at night getting warmth from her master. But he kept her lying outside his bedclothes.

In the end familiarity bred contempt of danger. One cold night when her master was asleep, Eve glided under the bed-clothes, and lay beside him, seeking warmth. While he slept she gradually twined her coils around his body. The Assistant woke to find his legs and hips in a viselike embrace. The more he struggled, the tighter Eve drew her constricting coils. His yells for help brought his camp servants running to his bedside, but he was not released until Eve had been cut into several pieces.

The Burman who told me the story gave it a moral twist of his own by saying that women are safest on the other side of the blanket and that snakes are best dead.

Elephants are not usually frightened by natural phenomena without very good reason. They do not mind thunderstorms in the way that dogs do, and they remain calm in the face of forest fires. I have only once seen elephants really frightened by nat-ural phenomena, and that was due to their realizing that they were in a gorge where water was rapidly rising in a spate.

Rain was coming down as though it would never cease. I had decided to take a short cut through the Kanti Gorge. I was traveling with eight young pack elephants, and it would save us a climb of 2000 feet from one watershed to another. After pass-ing down the gorge, I meant to move up a side stream. My spirits were high, the oozies were singing, and our circus was traveling in Indian file down the hard, sandy bottom of the stream.

Both banks of the gorge were sheer rock, to a height of about

30 feet. The gorge was three miles long, and the stream was about ankle deep when we started down it. By the time we had gone a mile one could hear the unmistakable sound of a heavy thunderstorm breaking in the headwaters of the stream. The elephants showed their nervousness by half turning round. The bore of water eventually overtook us, and it was soon lapping under the bellies and round the flanks of the smaller calves.

By some instinct not shared by man, the elephants knew there was more water coming down. They began what would soon have become a stampede if they had not been hindered by the depth of the water and kept under partial restraint by their riders. It became a terrifying experience, as there was no possibility of turning back and no hope of getting up the sides. During the last mile all the elephants began bellowing; that, with the sound of the torrential rain and the raging, muddy water around, made it seem a pretty grim situation.

I never knew a mile to seem longer. Bend after bend came in view, with never a sign of the mouth of the creek I knew, which would provide for our exodus from the black hole in which we floundered. Logs were floating past and, though I had no time to be amused then, I noticed how the elephants' hindquarters seemed to have a magnetic attraction for them. Just as a log was about to strike its hindquarters, the elephant would swing its rear end to one side, giving the log a glancing blow so that it caromed off like a billiard ball from the cushion and passed on to the chap in front—and so on all down the line.

We were fortunate, really, as the smaller animals were just afloat when we went round the bend to go up the side creek. The water was up to my armpits, and I was holding my rifle in both hands above my head. The side creek came down in spate only half an hour after we had started up. If we had met the combined spates at the confluence, all our kit would have been lost.

The elephants scrambled up the first feasible bank after turning in off the main river, and at a general halt they seemed to look at me as if to say: "And you call yourself a jungle man!"

## CHAPTER 9

Savage elephants are as rare as really wicked men, but those that are not savage sometimes give way to moments of bad temper. Their most tiresome and dangerous habit at such moments is to pick up a large stick or stone with the trunk and throw it with great force and accuracy at some onlooker. One has to be prepared to jump when this happens.

Of course, during the musth period all males are of uncertain temper. My interpretation of musth is that it is an instinctive desire in the male elephant to fight and kill before mating. The mere act of mating does not cool his passion. He would rather fight for his chosen mate before he won her, driving off and killing an intruder during the time that he is making love.

The great majority of cases in which oozies are killed by their elephants take place when their charges are on musth. For some unknown reason, the animal may then suddenly attack his rider, first striking him with tusk or trunk, then crushing him to death with a knee when he is on the ground.

Strange as it may sound, there is very little difficulty in finding a new rider for such an animal. Many riders take pride in riding an elephant known to be dangerous. Such men find life easy; they care nothing for anything or anyone. They are usually opium eaters, but in spite of that they work well.

In addition to the rider, a dangerous animal has a really good type of spearman attached to it as an attendant, whose duty is to cover every movement of the rider when he is entirely at the mercy of the elephant — undoing his fetters, for example. Although the spearman carries a spear, the secret of his control is by the eye. He keeps his eye fixed on the elephant's. The two men are usually sufficient to control a savage elephant.

I have known one case of what seemed like remorse in an elephant. He was a tusker who killed his rider. But he guarded the body and would let nobody get near it for a whole week. He grazed all round it, and charged in mad fury at anyone who came near. When the body had quite decomposed he wandered away from it; ten days later he was recaptured without any difficulty and behaved quite normally. He was not on musth.

The wickedest elephant I ever knew was called Taw Sin Ma (Miss Wild Elephant). She was about 25 years old when I first knew her, and there was nothing in her recorded history which gave any explanation of why she should just loathe every European she saw. Even at inspection she had to be chained to a tree and when one was 100 yards away she would begin to lunge and strain at her chains in order to attack.

I had a nasty experience with her, when she first attacked me and then chased me, following me by scent for four miles.

I met her by chance when I was walking from one camp to another. I came on her suddenly and she went for me at once. I raced off, not knowing for two miles whether I was on the right track back to the camp I had left. There would have been no hope for me if her hobbles had snapped or come undone, unless I had found refuge up a tree. As she was hobbled, my pace was a little faster than hers. She wore a brass danger bell around her neck (docile elephants wear wooden bells). Often it sounded from the bell as though she were nearly up to me.

I dropped a haversack, hoping she would halt and attack it, but I heard no check in the sound of her clanking bell. When I had climbed to the top of a ridge I halted for a few moments to locate her. Then on I plunged, trying to act on the law of the jungle that one must never hurry and always keep cool. Once one breaks that rule every thorny bush that grows reaches out a tentacle to impede one, to tear and scratch. My relief was great when I met two men, busy with a crosscut saw on a fallen teak tree. But I had only to shout out the words: "Taw Sin Ma!" and they joined me in my flight without asking questions. They soon took the lead and, as I followed, I at least had the satisfaction of knowing I was on the right track to camp and safety.

One of them got into camp well ahead of me and gave the alarm on my account. When I got in I met a chattering group of elephant riders and their families, all of them doubled up with laughter or smacking their hands on their hips in mirth at the sight of me — all, that is, except Maung Po Net (Mr. Black as Night), who prepared to go out and meet his "pet."

There was no alternative but to join the Burmans in their joke — for I often wanted them to share in mine. So I joined in their laughter and their hip smacking.

Within an hour a rider came back with my haversack, quite undamaged and not even trodden on, and Po Net rode Taw Sin Ma back into camp. The expressions on both their faces seemed to indicate that the same incident might be repeated next day. It did not, as I at once issued 25 feet of chain for Taw Sin Ma to trail behind her whenever she was at large grazing.

Some riders teach their charges tricks that give a wrong impression of the animal's real disposition. Bo Gyi (Big Man), a young elephant, always charged his rider as soon as he appeared to catch him and bring him to camp. But at ten paces the animal would stop dead and sit down for his fetters to be undone, as gentle as a lamb. Any other rider would bolt.

The secret — that it was just a matter of standing one's ground — was only discovered after the rider who had taught him the trick had been killed by a bear. The elephant was at large for a month after his rider's death; nobody would face him. Finally a reward of 300 rupees was offered for his recapture.

A young village lad turned up one day, saying he could capture him. Two days later he came into camp riding the animal and smiling gaily and was paid his 300 rupees. Two of my own men had gone with the lad and had watched the whole procedure from a hiding place near-by. The secret had come from a young Burmese girl, a former sweetheart of the dead rider. The young lad was her new lover and no doubt boy and girl found the 300 rupees a useful start in life.

Young calves, if they have not been properly trained, are apt to get savage if not well-handled afterward. One particular calf named Soe Bone (Wicked Bone) delighted in chasing me whenever he got an opportunity. We decided he was not too old to learn his manners. "Shoot him in his toenails with roasted rice," was the suggestion. So I emptied two cartridges and, after filling them with rice instead of shot, I wandered out of camp to find Soe Bone. He was in a sandy creek throwing wet sand over his body and was under a bank only three feet high.

"Hullo, little chap!" I said, greeting him.

"Little chap to you," he seemed to reply, and charged.

I stood my ground and gave him a left and right in the forefeet so as to sting his toenails. Did it stop him? I nearly lost my precious shotgun as I made my getaway. He was up that bank with his fetters on almost as quickly as I could turn to run. And he did not love me next time he saw me either.

We decided to put the little devil back into a crush and cane him. A substantial crush was made, and into it he was enticed and trapped. My head Burman came to fetch me, carrying in his hand a six-foot whippy cane. At least a dozen Burmans were there to witness the caning of this naughty schoolboy, as even Soe Bone's own rider had no use for his chasing game.

I was asked to give him the first 20 strokes. And what a behind it was to whip! I went to his head first and showed him the cane. He showed me the whites of his eyes as if to say: "Wait till I get out of here," but I changed his mind for him, and he squealed blue murder. Then everyone present, except his rider, was ordered to give him half a dozen, whereas his rider was permitted to stay behind and give him tidbits after we had all gone.

I saw him next morning, being loaded with some light kit as we were moving camp, and he looked rather ashamed of himself. Suddenly he saw me, carrying a stick, and instead of pricking his ears as he did when he was going to chase me he gave one shrieking trumpet and bolted into the jungle.

One of the most remarkable incidents I ever had with savage elephants concerned a young Shan woman of about 20. I was sitting in my hut near the camp one evening, very worried over a seriously injured spearman, Maung Chan Tha, who had been gored that afternoon by an elephant named Kyauk Sein (Jade Eyes). Maung Chan Tha had been trying to save the life of the rider, Maung Po Yin, who had been killed instantaneously by the elephant; the beast had then attacked the spearman. The animal had gone on musth and was at large in the neighborhood.

I was discussing the case with my head Burman when suddenly, quite unannounced, a tall, fine-looking girl walked into my bamboo hut and I immediately recognized her as the widow of the dead rider. She was not wailing or weeping, or carrying her youngest child, which is the custom on such occasions. She just stood erect and in a firm, unemotional voice said: "May I have a dismissal certificate from you for my husband, Maung Po Yin, who was killed today by Kyauk Sein?"

"Yes," I replied. "And your compensation, if you will wait till tomorrow, as I am busy arranging to get Maung Chan Tha to hospital." I added how grieved I was and, in sympathy, asked her if she had any children.

My head Burman answered, instead of her, that she had none, and then, addressing her as though he were most displeased with her for coming to see me in such an unceremonious way, said: "You can go now. I shall be coming back to camp soon."

She moved quietly out of the room, a tall and graceful figure.

When she was out of earshot I turned to my head Burman and asked, "Is that Po Yin's wife?"

"Yes," he replied. "She takes more opium than Po Yin did and that is the reason why she has no children."

I was very much surprised, as it was the first time I had ever heard of a Shan girl taking opium. Then my old Burman said in a quiet voice, "Give me ten ticals of opium tonight, and she will recapture Kyauk Sein tomorrow, because she has often caught him for Po Yin when he was in a heavy opium bout."

I gave him the opium he asked for, but I went to bed that night with a very disturbed conscience. To add to my troubles, Chan Tha died before dawn.

About ten o'clock, my old Burman came to me saying:

"Kyauk Sein is coming in with Ma Kyaw riding him."

I could scarcely believe my eyes: Kyauk Sein was passing through the camp with the Shan girl riding him, oblivious to everything, her eyes fixed straight in front of her. Her long black hair was hanging loose down her back and she wore her blue tamain girdled above her breasts, leaving her beautiful pale shoulders bare. I did not interfere and was soon informed that Kyauk Sein was securely tethered to a tree.

That evening Ma Kyaw was brought to me to receive the compensation due to her. She was dressed in her best, wearing a multicolored tamain, a little white coat, and a flower in her jet-black hair. She knelt and bowed low three times and then sat down in front of me. She kept her eyes lowered.

After paying her the compensation due to her for the loss of her husband, I gave her an extra bonus for recapturing Kyauk Sein. When I told her this, I could see a wisp of a smile at the corners of her mouth. I then wrote for her a certificate such as is customarily made out for all men killed in accidents. These certificates are for the benefit of the jungle Nats (gods), who require them before admitting the spirit of the dead rider to their domains. The certificate ran, "I hereby give leave to Maung Po Yin, rider of Kyauk Sein, to go where he wishes, as he has been dismissed from my service," and I signed it.

When I had risen from my table and given the money and the certificate into her hands, she wiped away two crocodile tears, got up and went quietly out into the dusk.

Next day, when I asked my old Burman about finding a new rider for Kyauk Sein, he told me:

"Oh, that is all arranged. Maung Ngwe Gyaw is an opium taker, too. He has taken on (not married) Ma Kyaw, and they tell me that the biggest opium taker of the lot is Kyauk Sein, the elephant. Another ten ticals of opium would be useful." By that time I would willingly have given him 20 if he had asked.

I do not believe to this day that the girl took opium, but she was a resolute character and the elephant Kyauk Sein knew her well enough to take opium out of her hand. I think she completely stupefied the animal before she caught him.

The ways of the jungle are strange, but all is not savage, hard and cruel in it. For every savage elephant that attacks or kills his rider there are 99 that are docile and friendly.

## CHAPTER 10

I FIND IT hard to realize now, after living for 25 years in the jungle with the most magnificent of all animals, that for the first three and a half years my eyes were blinded by the thrill of big-game shooting. I now feel that elephants are God's own and I would never shoot another. However, I can still live over again the thrill when I was young enough to take any opportunity that offered which gave me even chances of life or death.

I remember how for two whole months I spent day after day near the mouth of the Manipur River trying to get a solitary wild bull elephant — and every day was hard, and ended in disappointment. He was well known by the name of Shwe Kah, which my elephant riders had given him.

Shwe Kah had gored two of my tuskers badly and had continually worried my elephants. Many of my riders had seen him and they described the dimensions of his tusks outside the lip, by stretching both arms out horizontally to show their length and by encircling their legs above the knee with the outstretched thumbs and forefingers of both hands to indicate their girth.

I had numerous opportunities to bag other wild elephants at that time, but I was set on getting Shwe Kah. I saw him twice but not in a position for a shot. I then went on leave for a month, knowing I should be back in the same area during May, the best month in Burma for big game.

One night during my leave I met a very pleasant major who told me he was more than keen to bag an elephant before he left Burma. I said, "I'm going back on the 25th for a tour of jungle camps, during which I hope to get in some big-game shooting myself. Can you get a month's leave?" He jumped at it. I explained that I would do all I could to put him on to the track of a decent wild tusker, but that Shwe Kah was to be mine only.

He joined me on the appointed date and we set off, poling up the Myittha River in a country dugout. Shortly after we reached Sinywa (Wild Elephant Village), a Burman arrived to say there was an enormous wild tusker, believed to be Shwe Kah, not 300 yards from their camp, a mile away.

Without any hesitation I was off. My companion candidly admitted that he was far too tired to leave camp. By 3 p.m., under a sweltering tropical sun, I had got near enough to this wild elephant to hear an occasional flap of his ear. There was no other sound, as he was browsing in elephant grass 12 feet high, through which I had ventured, following up his tracks. I knew that the river bank could not be far to my left. I stopped and took a quick swallow from a water flask, as that was probably the last refresher I should get.

I was suddenly alarmed by realizing that my presence had been detected by the elephant, probably, as so often happens, by scent. There was a never-to-be-forgotten noise of the animal cracking the end of his trunk on the ground—it makes a sharp, clear, metallic, ringing sound, owing to the trunk being hollow. Then there followed an awful silence. I had no alternative but to stand my ground. Both of us were left guessing, but the elephant broke first and made away from where I was standing, whereupon I made direct to where I imagined the river bank to be. Not many seconds passed before I heard a tremendous splashing, and through the tall grass I saw a magnificent tusker elephant crossing the river 50 yards below me, moving fast.

Without hesitation, I jumped down the eight-foot bank, landing in three feet of water but sinking into the mud to the tops of my boots. I was bogged. It was now or never. I decided on a heart shot, as he was moving quickly, and I was unsteady.

Crack! He was quite 75 yards away when I fired. He stumbled a bit, recovered, and then swung round like a polo pony and came back, not 25 yards below me. He was wild with rage — so wild that he did not see me. I was stuck and had no hope of regaining the bank. As he climbed up where he had slid down before, I realized that he was mortally wounded and noticed that his tusks did not appear as big as those of Shwe Kah.

I gave him another heart shot and there was no mistake this time. He collapsed stone-dead against the top of the bank. Before I had extricated myself from the mud, my gun boy, who had remained behind in a tree on the bank, went off to inspect him and came rushing back to me yelling: "*Amai* [Oh, Mother]! *Amai!* You have shot a Kyan Zit."

I was far too excited and occupied to appreciate what he meant. It was about half past four in the afternoon and sweltering hot. I well remember my feelings when I realized that I had not bagged Shwe Kah, as I could not now get a license to shoot another wild elephant for a year. However, all my disappointment vanished as soon as I saw the head of the magnificent beast I had shot. For he was something very rare and was already causing great excitement among all the elephant riders who had come rushing along from their camp.

"Kyan Zit! Kyan Zit! Kyan Zit!" was all they could repeat.

I could not have been more astonished if I had shot a unicorn. The words "Kyan Zit" describe a rare type of elephant tusk that has grown in rings or corrugations like the sections of a piece of sugar cane. The Burmans speak of such an animal as such a rarity as to be almost mythical, a king of elephants to whom all other elephants do obeisance, in terror of his strength.

Long discussions followed among the riders standing round and admiring the rare tusks. A head man arrived from camp to supervise their removal. Then the women of the camp arrived with children and babies in arms, all to be shown Kyan Zit.

Up to this time I had not allowed any of them to touch him, as I knew that once they started on a dead elephant they combined the qualities of souvenir hunters and vultures after flesh.

I then heard someone yelling my name. It was my guest, who on hearing my two shots in camp had hopped off his camp bed and, without waiting to put on his shoes, had come along with two or three of the men from my camp.

"Lord, how magnificent!" was his only remark, as he opened up his camera and took several snapshots. Then we settled down to supervise the removal of the tusks.

The human vultures now began operations. Whole baskets of meat were carried off to camp to be dried in the sun. There was enough to last them many months. It was my Burman hunter's perquisite to have the coveted aphrodisiac snips, which consist of the triangular tip of the trunk and the big nerves out of the tusks, which are also a native medicine for eye troubles.

By the time we had removed the tusks and the forefoot it was almost dusk. More men and women from Sinywa Village had arrived to carry away meat.

That was my last elephant, and I never shot big game again. Nevertheless, though I dislike it now, I have no regrets in regard to those early years. For it was those years that laid the foundations of a love and understanding of the jungle and the elephants in it. I shot four elephants, but on the other side of the account is all I have tried to do for hundreds of their fellows.

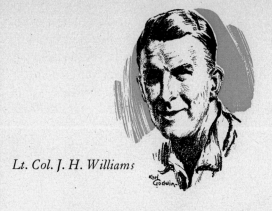

*Lt. Col. J. H. Williams*

THE VOLUMINOUS elephant lore which John Howard Williams ("Elephant Bill") accumulated during half a lifetime in the Burmese teak forests proved invaluable when World War II came. Commissioned a lieutenant colonel, Elephant Bill organized Elephant Company No. 1 for the 14th British Army and served for three years in the Burma Campaign. At one time he had 1000 elephants working under him. Not only did they haul army lorries out of the mud and build roads and bridges (270 bridges on the Burma Road alone, where bulldozers couldn't operate), but they also served as transport for evacuees. On one memorable trek engineered by Elephant Bill, 45 elephants plodded for 20 days, carrying 64 women and children over the mountains from Burma through Assam to India.

At the end of the war, Col. Williams with his wife and two children returned to England and addressed himself to the gentler pursuit of growing daffodils. Not for long, however, did he enjoy the quiet life. An opportunity to become managing director of a company that makes insecticide machines for sale throughout the world proved too attractive. "I hope to kill half the insects that have bitten me," he says of this job. "That is a very large undertaking."

*Decorations  by  Lyle  Justis*

# SIGNAL
# THIRTY-TWO

*A condensation of the book by*

MacKinlay Kantor

*W*HILE peaceful citizens sleep, the world of crime awakens and goes about its business — and the cop in the prowl car meets this world in nightly warfare. This powerful novel tells the exciting story of a rookie New York police officer in the city's toughest Precinct.

It is the story of young Dan Mallow, of Ellie, who loved and married him despite her fears, and of Ellie's brother, Blondie, whose flexible morals put all their lives in jeopardy. *Signal Thirty-Two* is told with all the skill and mastery that has made MacKinlay Kantor one of America's favorite writers.

"Stamped with authenticity . . . a memorable piece of writing." — San Francisco *Call Bulletin*

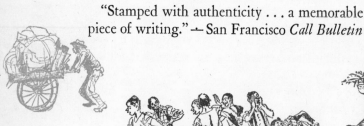

# CHAPTER 1

*Two-three Precinct. The address: Two-One-Two East One-Hundred-and-Tenth Street — in the basement — a Signal Thirty-two. . . . Twenty-third Precinct. The address: Two-Twelve East One-Hundred-Tenth Street — in the basement — a Signal Thirty-two. Four-Eleven a.m. WPEF Six-Four. . . .*

Of all the signals he had heard during his 16 years in the cops, with time out for war, Joe Shetland would remember this signal because it came across the air on the night when Daniel Mallow first worked with him. He would remember how Dan reacted to this, his initial job of any consequence.

As a patrolman of long standing, Shetland was pleased to see that Mallow gave a favorable impression immediately. Dan was of average height with a thick but muscular torso and long strong arms that he managed with an easy grace. His step was light for a young man so solidly built. His eyes were brown and keenly observant, with quick lights in them, his mouth sensitive but determined. His hair shone thick and shiny with natural waves. Quite the glamour boy, Shetland thought; but he might make a good cop if he did not allow himself to be spoiled by his own jauntiness.

At 42 Joe Shetland himself was not at all handsome. Well over six feet in height, he had been better-looking when he was younger, before he lost most of his hair. He lived in solitary fashion but he had much resource within himself. In his middle 20's he had suffered through a frustrated and tragic love affair (a secret passion for the wife of a friend) and had found himself sunk in despair when he realized, after two years of doubts and self-abnegation, that nothing could come of it.

Later he had other loves but never felt the compulsion to

marry. At 26, while casting despairingly about for an interest, a physical peril and thrill to occupy himself, he stood in a crowd one night and watched firemen performing miracles atop their ladders as four people were carried down from a smoldering hotel. There would be a pride here, a dangerous satisfaction in such work . . . his mind was made up that moment.

Shetland went to study at a trade school where people were trained for preliminary approach to the Fire Department and for other civil-service lists. Affected by the testimony and ambition of fellow students, he switched after a month or two and concentrated on police courses. A year later he got on the List, and knew that he had made no mistake; he knew it from his very first hour in blue.

Joe Shetland had lived now for many years in a rooming house west of Times Square near Ninth Avenue. He read a great deal. He would have been surprised if he had been told that by this time he was a well-educated (if self-educated) man. He had absorbed with slow and eager retention a solid ration of biography, history, some philosophy and a good deal of verse.

The world in which he moved was a worrying, splintering mass of human wretchedness. But Shetland was honestly proud —assuredly proud—of his accomplishment in the police department.

On his Forty-eight (the 48 hours of liberty which follow a six-day tour of duty for patrolmen, unless strikes or elections or similar disasters intervene) it was Shetland's custom to go out to the home of his married sister, Mildred, in Jackson Heights, await the return of his small niece and nephew from school, fondly watch them bathed, brushed and garbed for revelry, and then escort them to Times Square, the automat and a movie, and back to Jackson Heights again. Usually both children slept on the subway before they reached home. They slept, leaning against their uncle, small faces pale and pink . . . frail soft hair, and runny noses sometimes. . . . He sat erect, gazing coolly ahead; sometimes people smiled and thought what a complacent father he seemed to be. These excursions were a substitute for the frustrated affections of his earlier years.

Shetland loved, in memory, the woman who had overpowered his affections when he was young. He venerated a number of war-vanished friends deified by the mere ugly accident of their death. Collectively also he loved his fellow patrolmen, but scarcely in any case individually. There was no fit peacetime comrade to enlist affection from him until Mallow came along.

*Two-Three Precinct, an alarm of fire at Park Avenue and One-Hundred-and-Twelfth Street — Box 1348. Cars 789, 713 and 930 respond. Authority TB. One-thirty-two a.m. WPEF Six-Nine. . . .*

As Shetland had done in 1931, so nowadays Dan Mallow watched firemen at their task while he served as a Police-Department probationer. He did not mislead himself with fancies of any satisfaction to be attained in hose-hauling or axe-wielding or the composite acridity of smoke, dust, heat, steam and fumes. Dan knew very well just why he had gone on the cops, even while fighting the dissuasion presented by an attractive girl with whom he was fervently in love.

Clearly as Dan recognized his own motive, he would still have had a hard time putting it into words for a layman to appreciate. . . . Few of the probationers who stood before the mayor, when Mallow's class graduated from the Police Academy, could have become openly articulate about their purpose. Yet they all felt it in one form or another; they stood rooted in the same weird incentives that prompted Dan to give up the job in which he was engaged — that of driving a newspaper delivery truck at night, carrying bundles of the *Daily Record,* a glaring tabloid, around the city.

His recollection went back, as it did frequently in moments when he was relaxed and off duty, to the important day when changes had been instigated in his life. The previous night had been dirty with rain, later perilous with sleet; Dan tried to beat the red lights on Lexington Avenue and was yapped at by traffic patrolmen.

Dan drove from station to station, ridding himself of his cargo . . . forever the bundles, the great weight of colorful comic-wrapped slabs on Saturday night, the lesser freight with murderers and strip-teasers staring on ordinary nights.

Mallow had longed to become a newspaper reporter. In bull sessions overseas he had said sometimes: "Sure. I think I'll be a reporter when I get back. I always did like to mess around that way — you know, go to fires and things. Every time some joker would get run over in the street, I was always about the first one there. Maybe it's just because I like excitement. But I used to do sports reporting for my high school paper . . . covered all the basketball games the last season I was in school. . . ."

He could say nothing of the deeper compulsion that ruled him. He felt it sometimes with a cutting edge: the impulse to observe an intimacy, the desire to soil his hands and his spirit in tragedy. Thus secretly Dan dramatized himself to himself: a seeker after other people's lives, a watcher just beyond the threshold, who truly preferred to stand inside.

When he came back from Europe he went bashfully from big office building to big office building. He was perturbed by busy gabbling knots of men and women who thronged on and off the elevators; people who belonged there, or knew just where they were going and why. Dan was greeted in turn with politeness and a kind of remote blinking pity. One personnel chief said: "I'm afraid you'll find it too difficult. You see, most of the newspapers had a considerable percentage of their personnel in the armed forces during the war, and many of those men —

like yourself—are just coming home now. Most of them will be wanting their old jobs back. Without previous experience or tenure, I'm afraid you will find it too difficult." Indeed Dan Mallow had found it so, though stubbornly he visited six offices in Manhattan, one in Newark, one in Brooklyn.

A cousin operated a fair-sized trucking line in Bridgeport, and Dan went there at last. He qualified as a chauffeur, got his license and spent nearly six months guiding his heavy vessel through the current of New England. The pay was good. There was at times a spice of peril while groaning through the drizzle on mountain curves. Dan tasted the camaraderie of other drivers, some of them Red-ball Express veterans of the ETO. He found a little bleached-haired girl in a Providence cafeteria who considered him the answer to her momentary prayer.

But what he missed more than anything else was New York itself . . . endless trickle of light blending in the disorganized power of its streets' own rivers. Dan came to Manhattan for a holiday, and finally made up his mind in a club car on the New Haven Railroad.

Good-bye to ten tons and trailer, good-bye to the platinum babe. This time he got a job on his second New York interview. Since he might not write for a newspaper at least he could be a newsboy. His soul grinned when at last he was wrenching along Third. Each pillar of the El was a challenge—each traffic lamp a foe to be conquered; he feuded satisfyingly with late-fleeing taxicabs. The tumult of stained humanity itself lapped around the wheels of his vehicle. . . . The neon signs winked a welcome. Dan was in the region he knew and loved — the smutty wilderness to which he truly belonged.

Then came the morning of meeting, the day of beginnings which could not be recognized at the moment they occurred.

Dan had finished his night's work. He strolled into a garish restaurant—one of two or three where he ate more from habit than from choice. Mechanism clicked . . . he had his check in his hand, and slowly he approached the bright-gleaming counters, his gaze wandering through lists of foods and prices beyond.

Blondie Dunbar yelled aloud and rushed upon Dan Mallow, coffee splashing from the cup in his hand.

The last time they saw each other? They tried to reckon it, but they could agree only on March — late March it was, 1945 — the date didn't matter. Their squadron was housed alongside the village of Genicourt, and they were making preparations to move to a base in Belgium . . . that place in Pontoise — what was the name of it? Drinking champagne on a rainy afternoon . . . they remembered. Blondie Dunbar's eyes went to Dan's old B-10 jacket with disapproval, and well they might. It was smeared with everything from engine oil to printer's ink, though Dan wore a neat flannel shirt and bright necktie under it.

"Don't look now," Dan told him, "but I'm driving a truck for the *Record*."

"I thought you were going to be a reporter."

"This was just as close as I got."

Blondie wore a blue chalk-striped suit. Folded on the chair beside him was the richness of a camel's-hair topcoat with a glossy new hat atop it. He sat debonair and snowy-shirted.

"You look like you were in Wall Street, Blondie."

Dunbar offered his ready smile. A native mixture of scorn and impishness shone as always in his gay hazel eyes. "Want to guess? You'll guess wrong."

"Tell me all."

"I'm a detective."

Dan's laughter made people look up from near-by tables. "I can't believe it. You wouldn't be able to keep your mouth shut long enough."

Blondie brought out his wallet and produced a card. *The Alliance Investigating Corporation. We work while others sleep.*

Down in the corner it said: *R. Emmett Dunbar, Investigator.*

"I'm always reading about guys like you in the papers I peddle," Dan said. "Your business is following husbands and wives around to see who they're sleeping with."

Blondie arose. "Come on. You're coming to breakfast."

"I was just going to order my breakfast when I ran into you."

"Oh, not this slop — this is Sunday morning, toots. What do you think I've got a sister for? She always invites me to breakfast on Sunday morning, and now I've invited you."

Dan pleaded that he was dirty . . . he had not shaved since the night before . . . the beat-up jacket, the ink, the grease from the truck . . . it was hard to say no to Blondie Dunbar. He had known Blondie for less than two years of his life; but under certain circumstances 20 months in the 495th Bomb Squadron might be like a decade somewhere else. A great many men had died, a great many men had survived, and two of these were Dunbar and Mallow. Theirs might be an association founded on tragic solidity, although they had no real mutual trust and only a one-sided respect — Blondie did indeed respect Dan. . . . There were certain girls with whom Blondie had been very selfish; there were fellow officers whom he had enraged. But with all deference to the spotty character of R. Emmett Dunbar, Private Investigator, in this hour he represented the 495th Squadron to Dan. He would have gone along to breakfast with Blondie no matter what he was wearing. On seeing Blondie he heard the taxiing airplanes, the eternal trucks bowling across a desolate landscape from Norman ports. He tasted Calvados again and watched clear ice forming on the gun sight beyond his instrument panel. Thus Dan allowed himself to be persuaded into a cab and they went up to a small apartment on Third Avenue near 63rd Street, and there he met Ellie Dunbar.

# CHAPTER 2

AUTUMN: the Spiks were thinning off the streets even on Friday and Saturday nights. The tropical warmth of New York's jungle cooled steadily week after week. It was truly fall, though the afternoons might be hot . . . there would be an Indian summer haze for those who rode on the Four-to-Twelve Tour, but the Indians were long gone from upper Manhattan, and new and incredible savages had come to take their place.

On the first day that Shetland and Mallow had met, Joe had gone over to the board and looked at the designation of assignments. To his disgust he saw Bertenelli's name X-ed out on the carboned list, and the name *Mallow* put there instead. He asked Lieutenant McClusky what had happened to Bunch. "Oh," said McClusky, "he went sick, I guess."

Someone else came out of the Ninety-five room and said, Yes, that was it: Bertenelli had some infected teeth and they were all swollen up. "The hell," said Shetland, "I knew they were bothering him last night, but I didn't know they were that bad." He didn't even ask about Mallow. It was obvious . . . seven new rooks had come into the precinct the week before; undoubtedly Mallow would be one of those.

Back in the locker room Joe passed the second line of greenish steel cabinets and turned to the left; his was at the end of the row. He unlocked the door and opened it. He took off his brown flannel suit and hung it carefully; he took off his shiny brown shoes and got out the black ones.

Joe put on the pants of his uniform and laced his shoes. He had been carrying a short-barreled .38 in his civilian clothes; now he took the other gun with its regulation barrel. Since Shetland had no family to spend money on, except his nephew

and his niece, he could spend for ammunition with a clear conscience. He fired often on the range . . . silhouette targets, he
liked those best. He had 11 Commendations, five of which had
involved shootings or the necessity for shooting. People in the
Department were always trying to persuade him to work his
way up into regular match play and possibly appear on a winning pistol team. That did not interest him at all. He liked guns
only insofar as their practical application was important.

He fastened on his nippers, his pen-and-pencil holder, the revolver and ammunition and all other appurtenances at the belt.
He looked at his good blouse, wondering whether to wear it . . .
no — he could make the old one do a while longer, if Sergeant
Hanahan didn't make too many snide remarks about savers.

He was just beginning to pin his shield upon the shabby
jacket, when another patrolman wandered toward him between
the lockers. This, it turned out, was Daniel Mallow, Shield 6483.

"Hello. My name's Dan Mallow. Are you Shetland?"

"Yes," and Joe stuck out his hand.

"I guess I'm riding with you tonight."

"That's right," said Shetland.

"What happened to your partner?"

"He went sick. Bad teeth."

"Oh, that's too bad."

"It's his own damn fault. I told him to have them yanked. An old guy like him can't afford to fool around with bum teeth."

Mallow stood there, properly attentive. "How many years has he got in?" he wanted to know.

"Twenty-two."

"That's a lot of years."

Shetland went on pinning the shield, taking a long time about it, studying Dan. This rook was very well set up — just slightly on the thick side around the chest and shoulders, not as gawky-looking as some. God knew it wasn't like the old days. Most of these modern boys were combat veterans; they had worn uniforms of quite another kind. They had known strife, peril, heartbreak, ignominy, filth, disorder and extensive pain of other varieties than those now commonly found in this precinct. It had done them a lot of good, man for man: they made better cops than the rooks who used to come along before the war. Long ago, if you wanted to be on the cops, and your uncle had a waving acquaintance with the alderman, and you could stand up supported by a wall, you were as good as on the cops.

Joe inquired abruptly, "Where did you study before you got on? Delavan's?"

Mallow nodded. Shetland wanted to ask him how well he did in that 176-yard run with the 70-pound weight, but thought better of it.

"How long have you got in now?"

Mallow smiled. "I don't know from nothing. I'm the greenest rook you ever saw. Just got assigned here last week. My name isn't yet dry on the book . . ." and right away Shetland had an instinctive feeling that Mallow was his boy. He was certainly smart-looking, all trigged out, eager and earnest.

"Well, what did they have you doing?"

"Fixed post on Lexington."

"How was it? Quiet?"

"Oh, yes, quite quiet."

"You been in a car before?"

"No, sir," said Mallow. Shetland wanted to tell him that you don't call another patrolman "sir," no matter if he is nearly old enough to be your father and has 16 years on you, but again he thought better of it.

"Wait a minute until I get this old saver slicked up and I'll go down with you."

"Saver?" echoed Dan politely.

"That's what we call an old blouse," Shetland explained. "You ought to get one. They discourage wearing savers but, believe me, they save! . . . Look — this isn't so bad. I paid three and a half bucks for it. You know — secondhand."

"Where do they come from?"

"Oh, guys retire and what not. There are some dealers down by Center Street that sell a lot of secondhand police stuff. I'll give you an address if you're interested."

"Thank you, *sir*," said Mallow with emphasis.

By this time the locker room was resounding with gabble and talk, alive with the last-minute scurryings of people who had been late in getting to the House. They went down, Shetland and Mallow, and within three minutes Sergeant Hanahan was turning out the platoon. He rattled through the assignments. There were two or three jobs for men on fixed posts. One job for Sector One. . . . He told them to keep a tight eye out for purse-snatchers; there was a gang of young kids operating again. . . . People up in Sector Five watch out for indications of race trouble, especially around 112th and Lex. Anybody whose name I haven't called? . . . Right face. Forward, march.

The brief ranks formed on the sidewalk. "Take your posts." They were off. The Avenue car always came in on 104th around the corner from Lex, and to this destination Joe led Dan Mallow. Two sector cars were already there but the Avenue car was a while in coming. . . . They talked a little. Joe asked if Dan were married. No. . . . "Better get married," said Joe. "It's no fun being an old bachelor like me." Dan laughed; he told Joe that he didn't look so old. Then the Avenue car came in with Dow and Galloway aboard. They got out and hailed Shetland loudly.

"I see you got a new partner, Joe."

"Yeh, Bertenelli went sick on me. How was it tonight?"

"Oh, quiet. We had one homicide about five o'clock. Nothing much else. We haven't had a run in three hours."

Shetland walked slowly around the dirty green Plymouth, inspecting it for fresh injuries, but he could find none. He checked the mileage and handed out the flashlight which Galloway had forgotten on the floor beside the seat. "O.K., Dan," he said to Mallow, and Mallow climbed into the recorder's seat. The boy sat stiffly, his hands twisting the thong of his stick. "You better put that stick out of the way," said Shetland, and Mallow started to turn around. "No, that's not so good. Hang it there from the handle on the door, right next to you. Maybe you'll have to shorten the thong a little. It's better that way; then you can grab it easily if you have to get out fast."

"You seem to be expecting trouble."

"There's always trouble up here. Or maybe it's in this car . . . you'll see how it is with an Avenue car; we get more runs than the rest. We go right through Sectors Two, Four and Six — Fifth and Madison Avenues. We get all three, and of course any of the other stuff that's on the air, unless we're — well, specifically instructed not to respond."

"Why would they do that?" Mallow asked in wonderment.

"Oh, some reason or other. But anywhere we get out, be sure and grab that stick."

"Gosh," said Mallow, "I'm sure glad I haven't had to hit anybody yet."

Shetland glanced at him briefly but intently. "Oh, hell," he thought. He said, "I don't know what you ran into up on that fixed post, but I guess it wasn't much. A lot of these characters you're going to get around the bars on upper Fifth and Madison every now and then — if you don't want to get cut, and don't want to shoot anybody, you've got to beat them. That's better than killing a guy, isn't it?"

"Why, yes, I guess so," said Mallow humbly.

They drove east past the House. The sergeant stood there on the curb, talking with one of the Brains from upstairs as the little parade went past . . . green Plymouths, one brown coupé . . . "Car 930 O.K.," and the sergeant waved them on. Thus they began their first tour together: there would be many more.

The specified district for the operation of this car was, as Shetland had described it to Mallow, along the western border of the three west sectors. Sector Two, on the whole, could be disregarded: they called it The Merry-Go-Round, because you rode around and around, hour after hour, day and night, and almost never did anything happen. You didn't even catch a brass ring. . . . Once in a while there was a purse-snatching when some lone cook walked home through late shadows; once in a while a traffic accident at a corner on Madison or Fifth. Sometimes, rarely, the patrolmen visited an expensive apartment, high and neat, boxed in 15 stories above the street; they were propelled upward by a frightened elevator operator unused to the proximity of blue uniforms in his sedate cage; they found perhaps a disappointed lover or a bankrupt, lying across his bed with a bottle emptied of sleeping pills beside him. . . . Sector Four, above 96th Street, was a little better, especially along Madison Avenue (or worse, depending on how you figured it). Sector Six, above 116th Street, was throbbing with a busy viciousness.

Shetland pursued a southerly course under the El pillars, intending to turn west on 96th.

"That woman," said Mallow. "She's trying to signal us."

"Yes, I see her."

Joe brought the coupé to a halt near the 99th Street intersection. He backed up slowly. A lumbering young Negress stepped from the curb and came to the door on Mallow's side.

"Policeman," the girl said in a low tremulous voice, "please!"

The faucet of pity bubbled remotely in Joe Shetland's heart as he saw the flat brown face smeary with tears. "Well, kiddo, what's the trouble?"

"My mamma," said the girl.

"What's the matter with your mamma?"

"I'm afraid to go up there."

"What do you mean, sister? You mean you're afraid to go up to your apartment? Where do you live?"

The girl turned and pointed. "One-five-six — the top floor. . ."

"God," said Shetland, "it's always the top floor, Mallow. You'll find that out if you ride in these cars long enough. . . . O.K., sister. So you're afraid to go up to your apartment. You're afraid of your mamma. What's your name?"

"Lusilla."

"Lusilla? That's one for the book. How do you spell it?"

The girl spelled self-consciously: "L-u-s-i-l-l-a."

"Lusilla what?"

"Lusilla Boyd." She began to cry again.

"Look," said Shetland, "you can't tell us what the trouble is if you keep crying like that. Now just get hold of yourself, and tell us what's the matter, and maybe we can help you out."

"She beat me!" the girl wailed. "She hit me with a pan — a dustpan. I got sore places all over my backside."

"How old are you, Lusilla?"

"Seventeen . . . my mamma she whip me last night because I said I wanted to leave home and go and live with my aunt."

"You haven't got a boy friend you want to go and live with?"

"No, no," the girl sobbed, "just my aunt. My two aunts. My one aunt by marriage and her sister."

"Where do they live?"

"Up on 127th. I don't want to stay home with my mamma any more because she so cross and she drink so hard. She just getting to be a regular wino, and she have men around all the time, and a nice girl — she just can't stay nice in such surroundings."

They kept talking gently, and finally Lusilla could speak expressively enough for them to understand the situation. Her aunt had offered her a home. Lusilla worked — she went out by the day and did housework, and she was very fond of her uncle's wife and the younger sister, too: Aunt Kate and Aunt Ranny, that was what she called them. She had come down to get her clothes and take them back to 127th Street, but fear overwhelmed her. She was afraid that she might receive another beating. She had been standing in the street for three hours, she said, just walking up and down, afraid to go upstairs. She had telephoned neighbors of Aunt Kate and Aunt Ranny, but nobody had yet come to help her.

Shetland ordered, "Walk back over there and meet us in front. We'll go up with you and see what we can do."

He parked the car near-by and drew out the keys. "See this? Always take the keys. I mean when we both leave the car."

"Roger," said Mallow.

They got out and stood on the sidewalk; Lusilla came toward them slowly. The party climbed the outside steps. The banister was broken in places and greasy all along its surface. They went up, flashlights guiding on through landings where the bulbs were out, until they reached the top floor. Lusilla crept out of the stair well behind them and began to sniffle loudly.

"You hush up," Shetland said in a low voice. "Don't say a word. Just stand quietly in the hall here beside this other officer. Which door is it?"

The girl pointed toward the short hall at the rear. Shetland moved along until he found the door; he tapped with his stick on the smudged panels. There had been a faint murmur of conversation inside but now it was terminated.

"Who is it?" demanded a throaty female voice.

"Police. Open the door."

There was a shuffling; the door opened narrowly and a black face peeked out.

"Listen," said Shetland, "I told you to open up." He forced the aperture wider but retained the knob in his hand so the door could not be flung wide enough to reveal the girl. Mallow, sensing the senior patrolman's tactics, moved closer in order to shield Lusilla. Shetland pushed the door halfway open.

It was a kitchen; two men were there, one naked to the waist. Beside a dirty kitchen table sat a mighty Negress in a cheap blue nightgown. "What you want?" she demanded malignantly. "We aren't having no trouble here; we been real quiet tonight."

"I didn't say you were having any trouble," said Shetland. "I just want to ask you a few questions. Is your name Boyd?"

"That's right." The woman put her chin in the air. "*Mrs. J. V. Boyd,*" she said.

"Who are these men?"

"Just some friends of mine. Can't I have friends in to call?"

"Sure you can," said Shetland, "and to take a drink, too. You can put that big glass jar of Sneaky Pete back on the table if you want to — the jar you hid behind your chair."

One of the men tittered weakly.

"We're not trying to raid you," said Shetland. "Have you got a daughter named Lusilla?"

The woman's small wicked eyes twitched in their sullen caverns. "What's the matter? She ain't had nothing happen to her, has she?"

"You got a sister-in-law living up on 127th?"

"Yes. Her name's Katherine Smith."

"It's just this: we heard you had a little trouble here last night. Did you beat your daughter?"

"No, I didn't beat her," she snarled. "I just chastise her."

"All right — chas*tise*, then; whatever you want to call it."

"A lady has got a perfect right to chastise her own daughter!" The woman bobbed her head defiantly.

Shetland was beginning to realize now how drunk she really was. "We won't go into the right or wrong of the matter," he said. "Do you know where your daughter stayed last night?"

"I guess she must have stayed up at Kate's," the woman said, after some thought. "She ran out of here; she just no good, officer! She won't mind her mamma. That sister-in-law of mine — you know what she's trying to do to me? She is trying to get me into court. I got a summons. She trying to get my daughter away from me!"

"Oh, I get it," said Shetland. "Children's Court, huh?"

The two colored men stood motionless — one in a clean yellow shirt marred by a splotch of wine on the front, the other half-naked with pearls of sweat showing above his hairy breast.

"O.K.," said Shetland, "when is your summons for?"

"Next Tuesday. I got to go to court. Leastways," she mumbled, "that's what they tell me."

"Would you object to your daughter's staying up there with your sister-in-law until the court decides where she shall live?"

The woman considered, staring at dirty dishes in front of her on the table. "No, I guess I wouldn't have no objection."

"You would let her come in here then—freely," persisted Shetland. "Let her take her clothes and things—let her come and go, freely, to get her things?"

The woman said nothing. The bare-breasted colored man cleared his throat. "You ought to do that, Julia," he said. "This policeman just trying to avoid trouble. You don't want no more trouble with Lusilla."

"Yes," the woman whispered, "I would let her come — freely."

"That's all I wanted to know." Shetland shoved the door open to its full width. "O.K., Lusilla," he said, "go in and get your clothes."

The girl seemed rooted to the floor.

Shetland touched her arm. "Come on," he said. "We're here with you. Don't be afraid."

In the kitchen the mother arose with a yell: "You dirty double-crossing policeman! You didn't tell me you had my little girl with you!" She seemed to be reaching around for things to throw, and Shetland cautioned her grimly as both Negro men moved to subdue her.

"You take it easy, lady. You promised. Don't start a row now, or I'll have to lock you up."

Between them the two colored men managed to wrestle the mother back into a chair. She put her head down on the table, knocking off a glass and breaking it; she sobbed heavily all the time her daughter was moving around in the one room behind the kitchen, gathering up her clothes.

On the stairs going down, Shetland said to Dan, "Do you see why we handled it that way? If we had taken the girl right in, her mother wouldn't pay any attention to us. She would have started bawling out the girl, and maybe there would have been a fight. The idea was to get her to promise that Lusilla could go in and get her clothes without any trouble, and then make her stick to what she said. You'll see the way it goes; every one of these family cases is different, and yet somehow they're all alike. Alike — in that they require common sense. You keep your temper, and you think things out before you try to lay down the law, and you can't go too far wrong."

In the lower hall they met two nervous colored women.

"That's her!" one of them shrieked. "Lusilla, honey, we came as quick as we could!"

"Are these your aunts?"

The girl nodded; the two frenzied women were smothering her with embraces.

"No telling what that woman might do to her," shrilled the eldest of the two. "She's a very bad woman, officer, very bad indeed! Did she have anybody with her?" she asked of the girl.

Lusilla hugged her shabby little zipper bag and a paper-wrapped parcel. "Yes," she muttered, "Cutty was there."

"Did he bother you?"

"No, he was very nice."

"That man Cutty!" the aunt yelled.

"Come on, lady, take it easy! Keep quiet; it's late."

"I don't care how late it is! That man — he been sleeping with her mother, and last night he tried to get Lusilla."

"Well," said Shetland, "she's got her clothes. Go on home. Take care of her; live happily ever afterward; but be sure to go down to court on Tuesday and tell the judge about this."

"We sure will," cried the aunts. They herded Lusilla ahead of them out onto the street and moved away.

"What do we do now?" Mallow asked. "Do we go back up-stairs and lock that guy up for contributing to the delinquency of a juvenile, or — "

"No," said Shetland, "we don't lock anybody up. Come on, let's get to work. We've messed around on this thing too long already. No, if you started arresting people for that, you'd have everybody in this neighborhood in jail."

"Might not be a bad idea."

"Not enough jails. Or people to look after them, or money to feed them. Come on — let's travel."

In the patrol car they jogged south to 96th and west toward Madison. The radio box above Mallow's knees buzzed steadily; static made a scream when the car passed near neon signs of a certain type, and eased into a softer stutter when they were past.

Shetland asked, "How about the signals? You know those?"

Dan wrinkled his forehead in thought. "Let's see. A Signal Thirty. That's an armed felony, isn't it?"

"That's right. Usually a stick-up or something like that. Signal Thirty-one?"

"That's a felony in relation to a motor vehicle — maybe a stolen car or — "

"O. K. What's a Signal Thirty-two?"

"Well, it's an Assist Patrolman. . . ." The younger man's voice trailed off. He seemed hesitating about a Signal Thirty-two, and with his heart and soul Joe Shetland wished to enlighten him. He had lived with enough awareness to realize that nothing is ever learned secondhand. Nevertheless he liked Mallow in this first acquaintanceship and wanted to help him. . . . If I could give you (he thought in a violent second) one tenth, one hundredth, one iota of the sternness I have learned, it would benefit you immeasurably. Oh, no, my friend, a Signal Thirty-two is not invariably a summons to assist a patrolman in the performance of his duties; rarely enough it's that. What about the two hopheads we found in the vacant schoolhouse yard, fighting tooth and claw, jaw and fingernail, and one of them had already bitten through the other's jugular vein? What of the torn blouse, the shredded slip, the scratches on the bare shoulder, the broken clock, the smashed holy pictures — the white girl trying to kill her yellow-faced mother-in-law? Ah, yes — and that truck that came weaving down Duffy's Hill on Lex, and then it began to jackknife, and it smashed all along the line of parked cars and then into that door stoop where those three women and the children were sitting innocently, trying to keep cool.

The middle-aged psycho with her head in the oven, and enough gas in there to blow up half the block. The old man exhibiting himself on a Fifth Avenue bench next to Central Park; and the butcher who went to work on his girl friend with a cleaver: it was a Signal Thirty-two where we couldn't get there in time, no matter how eerily the sirens wailed.

Shetland said quietly to Dan Mallow, "Well, a Signal Thirty-two can be just about anything."

## CHAPTER 3

THE accidental meeting with Blondie Dunbar, and later with his sister at breakfast, had done things to Dan Mallow. He thought of it now as the car rolled up the Avenue. Ellie Dunbar's fine gray eyes; the kind, laughing compassion of her voice; the wonder of the full bosom, the very slim waist; the swelling hips . . . yes, even the way she moved spelled perfection to Dan. Dan stood determined to have her for himself the moment he met her, no matter what difficulties might be waiting.

Dan knew from Blondie's talk that there had been dire poverty in Ellie's early life. Their father died when the Dunbar children were small; nothing much was ever said about him. There was talk of a high-tempered, complaining mother, who had died suddenly in middle age while Blondie was overseas. Ellie had always worked, it seemed: in high school, checking food at a neighborhood grocery store from four to six p.m., clerking in a near-by delicatessen afterward. Through this self-discipline, through other determined struggles that followed through the years, Ellie had educated herself. She had graduated from a good secretarial school in record time, and was now private secretary to a man named Hadley who owned the controlling interest in a publishing house that issued several trade journals.

On that first Sunday morning, Blondie had called before they left the restaurant, only at Dan's insistence. In his naturally heedless fashion, bullying and fattening off those who loved him for one reason or another, Blondie would have escorted half a dozen friends to Ellie's quarters with aplomb, and demanded that she cook breakfast for the tribe, and she would have done it.

"Whoa there!" Shetland said. Mallow jumped. The car was forging ahead with sudden speed. Shetland swung left at 111th and stepped harder on the gas.

"What is it?" asked Dan. "I didn't see — "

"One-way street. They just crossed Fifth Avenue headed east; this is westbound. We'll get them."

The car ahead was a medium-sized black sedan and had no taillights. They could see, as the car halted momentarily at Madison Avenue and then turned north, that there were several men in the sedan; both front and back seats were filled. Shetland switched north after them. "I don't like their looks. Pull your gun when we get out." He hauled on the siren briefly and brought the black sedan to a halt near 113th Street.

They got the men out. There were five; one had been slumped down asleep. They had a Connecticut license plate — all were Spiks; only the driver could speak a little English. The men jittered in surprise, real or feigned; they were voluble until Shetland barked them into silence. Dan kept the group covered while Shetland went over them one by one. Mallow searched the last man himself and was rewarded by finding a horn-handled pocketknife with a four-inch blade.

"What's this elegant little tool for?" Joe demanded.

Dark eyes brooded at him. *"No hablo inglés."*

"No," said Shetland, "you probably can't unless you really want to. I suppose you keep this little item to clean your nails," and the man nodded vigorously. Shetland tossed the knife back to Dan. "If you've got a kid cousin who's a Boy Scout, give him that, and tell him not to cut his head off out in the woods. Come on, Chico — leave us see ze license and ze registration."

Driver's license and registration appeared to be in order. They searched the car thoroughly. There were no guns or other contraband material hidden behind cushions or in the trunk. The driver explained haltingly that he had never driven in New York before; he was confused by one-way streets. Shetland gave him a brief but pointed lecture; he told him where to stop to have his taillights fixed immediately and waved the party on their way.

"Shouldn't he have had a ticket?" asked Mallow.

"Sure he should, but no use making it out. The guy would be to hell and gone up in Connecticut. As a matter of fact, I believe his story about not realizing that was a one-way street. There wasn't any other traffic, was there? These out-of-town folks — you might as well go easy on them, even when they're Spiks."

"I didn't know they had any Puerto Ricans in Connecticut."

"They've got them everywhere. I know we've got 240,000 right in this neighborhood, and more coming on every ship and every plane."

In front of 84 East 116th Street an old man stood by the curb, trying to whistle at them. He could make only sucking, whispering sounds. Shetland halted the car promptly.

"You want us, Pop?"

The old Negro, a sickly creature in a ragged Navy pea jacket, pushed his face into the car. "*Policía!* Trouble!"

"What ze trouble, *padre?*"

The old man pointed at the building behind him.

"Eighty-four. Is that it?"

"*Sí, sí —*"

"What floor?"

The man counted laboriously on his fingers. *"Uno, dos, tres —"*

"I'll bet it's the top again," said Mallow.

*"Cuatro!"* said the old man.

"Fourth floor, huh? Front or back?"

He made wild gestures.

"Rear. What have you got up there — a fight?"

He shrugged. "Me hear noise. Me —" He hesitated, and then got the word. "Me neighbor."

"We'll come up and take a look."

They climbed resounding staircases, night sticks dangling. The old man followed but retreated into a front apartment and closed the door hastily when they reached the fourth floor. Joe and Dan stood outside the rear apartment, listening. There was a ragged mumble beyond the door. Someone was sobbing.

"They're up, all right," whispered Shetland. "Probably just a husband and wife got in a row. But leave us see." He knocked firmly on the panel. *"Policía!* Open up."

Inside, the conversation was shorn off abruptly; several people shifted their feet. Someone approached the door and jabbered in rapid Spanish.

"I don't get you," said Joe and rapped more decisively with his stick. "Police!" he called again.

The door was opened; they entered the room, a kitchen once more. Most of these rear tenement apartments had the kitchen for an entrance hall; bedrooms lay beyond.

Two dirty women . . . one was gray with age . . . a thin young girl huddled on a kitchen stool . . . two teen-age boys . . . brown faces frightened even in their impassivity. Glowering across the kitchen table sat a hulking young man with shiny black skin marred by pink scars on one cheek. He wore a black felt hat with a crumpled brim.

"What's the trouble?"

The people looked at one another; only the young man did not look up. Moodily he regarded the can of beer gripped in his huge fist.

"Well, come on, give," said Joe.

The eldest woman cleared her throat. She shot a nervous glance toward the towering Negro at the table. "No trouble."

"The neighbors are complaining. What goes on?"

The young girl (she was pretty, and pale now for all her color) leaped suddenly from the stool and scooted into the room beyond, bursting into hysterical tears as she fled. Shetland inclined his head slightly and Mallow followed her.

"What makes with the babe?" Shetland called to him.

"I don't know." Dan came back into the kitchen. "She threw herself down on the bed and hid her face."

"Did somebody hurt her?" Shetland demanded of the group.

No answer.

"Looks to me like she's frightened," said Dan.

"Let's get to the bottom of this. Whose *habitación* is this?"

The frail woman in the soiled gingham dress touched her bosom. *"Mi casa."*

"What's your name? *Qué nombre?*"

"Gonsalez."

*"Señora?"*

*"Si.* Alicia—"

"O.K., Alicia. Is that your daughter went in there?"

The woman nodded; again her restless, fearful eyes hunted toward the giant at the table. Shetland didn't know whether the man was drunk or not; he was certainly acting stupid enough, and sullen, too. The others, according to Alicia Gonsalez, were all members of her family.

"Right. Now who's *he?*"

No one said anything. The man's heavy lids flicked up at last, revealing angry cat eyes underneath . . . gray eyes they were. He had more white blood than appeared from the color of his skin.

"My name's Williams," he said thickly.

"Do you live here, too?"

He did not reply. Señora Gonsalez uttered a nervous whinny. "No. He no live here."

"A friend? *Su amigo?*"

She nodded in fearful affirmation.

"Looks like a hell of a friend to me," said Shetland. "Get up, you."

The big man did not stir. Before Mallow could realize what was coming, Shetland had stepped swiftly forward and slapped Williams with the broad flat of his hand. Williams lurched half off his chair.

"Get up, you big bum," said Shetland. "I want to go over

you. Williams, huh? I think I remember you; I remember this place now. We were up here last year."

Williams arose reluctantly and lifted his hands. Dan went over the man carefully from the back. "He's clean."

"Maybe," said Shetland, "but take a look at that hat. They carry stuff there, too. And — oh yes, Dan — here's one for the book: if they happen to be wearing a cap, take a good look at the bill. They sometimes have a razor blade in the bill."

Mallow jerked off the man's sweaty hat and turned back the inner band. Two razor blades, naked and gleaming, the type with the blunt rim of steel along one side, flickered to the floor.

"Yeh, yeh," said Shetland. "What have you got those for?"

"That's my brother's hat," mumbled Williams.

"Oh, yeah?" said Joe. "Now listen, Williams. What's your front name?"

"Emerald," he muttered.

"What? Oh, is that a honey! I remember you now, Emerald Williams." Joe turned swiftly to the mother of the family. "Lady, don't you remember? One of the young kids ran down and phoned for the police one time; I was up here with my partner, the fellow I usually work with. A big fat fellow — old guy. We tossed this bird out of here. Remember?"

There was a flash of recognition in the woman's face. She nodded violently.

"You don't want him around here, do you?"

"No. Please." Alicia Gonsalez regarded the shambling Negro with loathing. "Make him go 'way!"

"What does he want up here, anyway?" asked Dan.

"He wants the babe," said Joe. "O. K., Emerald. Here's your hat; get going. And if you want a solid top on that head of yours don't ever come back again."

Williams muttered something under his breath.

"What did you say?" demanded Shetland.

"Didn't say nothing." Emerald Williams stalked out furiously, slamming the door hard. Dan tightened his grasp on his stick and took a step toward the door, but Shetland shook his head.

"O. K., folks. That was the trouble, wasn't it? He comes up, hanging around after her? He wants your little girl? Right?"

They murmured in relief. The other woman went into the bedroom where she could be heard soothing the girl, talking rapidly in Spanish.

"If he comes back again," said Shetland, "you call the *policía* and we'll break him in two. *Buenas noches.*"

"*Buenas noches,*" they chorused.

Outside in the hall, Shetland sprinted toward the stairway. "Come on, quick," he gasped over his shoulder. Williams could be heard far below them, stamping his way down the stairs.

Mallow was amazed to see Shetland descend the stairs with such speed; he had a hard time keeping up with him. Two or three flights below them Emerald Williams quickened his own pace; perhaps he sensed what was coming. There was the crash of his falling once, then he picked himself up and hurried on. They overtook him in the outer vestibule.

"Come here, you," said Shetland.

The big fellow — he was a good three inches taller than Shetland — glowered back in defiance. "I'm just going my way. Doing what you told me. . . ." He began to resist, but between them the two patrolmen hauled him into the darkened rear of the first-floor hall. Shetland pushed Emerald up against the wall.

"So you did what I told you to do, did you? Like hell you did. Remember what we told you last year — to stay away from that family — not to bother that girl?"

"You never told me —" the man began in surly defiance. The breath blew out of his mouth as Shetland punched him in the stomach. He doubled forward, clutching at his middle. "Oh — oh," he gasped. Shetland dropped his night stick. With lightning swings of both hands he slapped: left, right, left, right. Emerald sobbed and wailed; his hat fell off.

"This is nothing," said Shetland, slapping again, harder. "If you so much as set foot in this building again, I'll use the stick. I'll open up your scalp so wide they'll have to cut you a new one at the hospital. We should have done this last time! Now, what are you going to do?"

Williams had folded down into a bulking pile; he was squatting, sustained by the wall.

"You hear me? Are you going to stay away?"

"Yes, yes," sobbed Emerald. "Don't hit me again."

Shetland grabbed the man's collar and hauled him to his feet. He spun him into the center of the hall and drove the flat of his shoe against Williams' rear. The huge man went staggering forward, out through the vestibule doors.

"One of those cute little characters from the 25th," said Shetland, on the street. "Well, Dan, I guess you won't find that in any of the books. They don't give you that stuff at the Academy."

Mallow did not reply. They climbed back into the car and Shetland put the keys in the lock. Without starting the engine, he turned and looked at Mallow.

"*Qué pasa?*" he asked. "So what's the matter with you? The cat got your tongue?"

Mallow was too angry to look at him. "No." He struggled to control his rage.

"Well?"

"It's simply that you employed a lot of brutality you didn't have to employ. I've heard about stuff like that; that's how cops get a bad name, isn't it? If that was part of the deal, wouldn't they teach us?" Now he could face Shetland, though he was glaring. "You asked me. All right, I'll tell you: I'm just a rook, a greenhorn. You've got all these years in the job — "

"Oh, God," said Shetland.

"Well, you asked me what I thought and I'll tell you. I think it stinks! You didn't have to beat up that guy. Oh, he was big — he could take it — that's not the point. You could have got him on a lot of counts. Maybe unlawful entry, disorderly conduct, impairing the morals of a minor — attempted rape, for all I know. You could — " Dan bit his lip and stopped speaking.

Shetland said quietly, "Are you through? Let's drive."

They went south down a market street lined with smashed crates and blowing papers, reeking with its smells of fish and rotten vegetables. Shetland drove west to Madison and then turned south. Dan sat stiff and silent beside him.

"Dan," said Joe, "mind my saying that I like you? You're a good little baby, but you've got a lot to learn. I think you'll make a good cop, honey bunch. Now let papa talk. You were right about the possibility of arrest. There were several charges that could have been made — obvious ones. So what would happen? He would try to jump the girl eventually. If the family was around there might be a fight; maybe her mother would struggle to try to save her. I don't think those rats of brothers of hers would lift a hand, but I guess the old girl would have tried. So then Emerald would bop her on the head, or heave her out of the window, and we'd have a homicide."

Dan turned quickly and seemed about to speak. Even in the dim light Shetland could see that Mallow was flushing.

"Don't look at me," Joe said curtly. "Do your job. Watch your side of the street; I'll watch mine, but I can still talk while I do it. Remember what I said earlier about not enough courts and not enough cops — not enough jails to hold the people? That still goes. We can't collar every one of those bums, Mallow — only the very worst ones. Chances are that before you're through with this tour tonight, you'll see half a dozen cases that seem to require arrest. If we pinched them all, where would we be tomorrow? In court, testifying. If other cops did the same, every one of them in New York City would soon be in court, awaiting disposal of the collars he's made. There wouldn't be a cop on the streets. That's if we went by the book. . . . It's pretty near time for us to ring again, isn't it?"

Dan looked at his wrist watch. "Yes, I guess so."

"We'll call in here at 106th." Joe swung the car in a wide U-turn. Another car was at the curb ahead of them; Murray Hirschhorn was up at the box, ringing.

"Don't get out for a minute," said Shetland. "Let me tell you this, Mallow. Any cop who didn't do what I just did wouldn't be worth his salt in the 23rd. I gave the big bum a mild beating and one hell of a scare. He won't be back there — not for a long while at least; they'll have a little peace. They've got some self-confidence now. Chances are the next time Emerald shows his face on that fourth floor, somebody will yap about the *policía* and he'll take off, but fast. It usually works, Dan, believe me. . . . You want to ring? Murray's left the box now."

He leaned out and yelled at Hirschhorn, "Hey, Fat Stuff, *qué pasa?* Look out you don't get mugged."

## CHAPTER 4

Now, and many nights afterward, Dan Mallow learned the true loneliness of the late tour. Chilly streets stretched brown and bare, sometimes not even the shadows moved. A blight persisted over avenue and side street. When you were parked and the motor was not running, you could hear near-by signs creaking if the wind came strong . . . you were bored and tired before your time. You drove wearily, in catalepsy from which you might be compelled to bound at any split second, jagged out of your torpor by the cry, the tinkle of glass, the radio summons, the metallic thud of colliding automobiles or the barely glimpsed, half-imagined specter of a running figure smeared across a distant intersection. Sometimes Dan and Shetland talked together with the remote, deliberate intimacy of soldiers on isolated combat posts. Yet there were times when they did not choose to talk, when each was busy with his own thoughts, and only the dull lights of the coupé's dashboard — the round owl-eye of the radio's green light and the hissing from the amplifier — only these entities were earnest and vibrant.

Dan viewed in retrospect the series of events which led him on the cops. Some of these things he told to Joe, some he could never tell to a soul and dared not even reiterate too frequently to himself. Everything began on that day when he encountered Blondie and was taken to Ellie's apartment. Ellie lived with a girl named Sharon Gurtz, who was a professional leg model. Sharon's face was fat and homely; she had a queer little button of a nose and her eyes glimmered bulbously behind great harlequin spectacles. But her legs were so beautiful as to seem unreal. Those were her legs and dainty feet, enshrined on glossy, stilted shoes, that you saw in so many of the ads; her legs lent purpose to the twin arts of photography and nylon; the delight of her knees and calves was pictured constantly in *Vogue,* in *Harper's Bazaar.*

The apartment she and Ellie shared was on Third Avenue, one flight up from the green-painted front of a small delicatessen. The windows of the living room commanded a bleak view of the elevated structure, but the place had two cozy fireplaces — one in the living room, one in the bedroom — and the girls had repainted and repapered it into an attractive home.

Ellie had made popovers, or was preparing to bake them, by the time Blondie and Dan arrived at the apartment on that historic Sunday. The El trains did not roar too frequently on their abbreviated schedule. The street smiled outside, with wind and sun warming away the traces of the night's sleet. There was

cannel coal spurting and cracking on the living-room hearth ...
bright water colors of Sharon's own weird composition had an
aura all their own. It seemed like a piece of the Left Bank, a
bright happy chunk of the Village, set down on New York's
upper East Side.

As Dan drank his coffee, as he heard Blondie's wisecracks,
Dan watched Ellie Dunbar and thrilled to the wonder of her
physical persuasion.

Little things, the homely things, the framed snapshots of relatives and friends set up on twin dressing tables in the bright bedroom ... Dan saw these when he went gravely to wash his hands,
to rid himself of the detestable B-10 jacket. Here was domesticity
such as he craved. He was ready to embrace it all, ready to gour-
mandize on home-cooked bacon and popovers, and wishing
desperately that he might have furnished the raw materials —
that he might have paid the rent and bought the pleasant
draperies that hung about rickety windows.

He thought that she exhibited disappointment when she
learned that he was a mere truck driver, delivering a daily
tabloid through the upper East Side streets.

"But . . ." She hesitated. "Was that what you did before the
war?"

"No. I was just out of high school. I was working in the
clerical department of a chemical company and going to NYU
nights, starting to take a few classes there."

"What were you taking, Dan?"

"Oh, journalism, modern English, psychology. I went into
the Air Force in the spring of '41."

Sharon said that it was her job to do the dishes and Ellie said,
"Don't be a fool" — she'd do them herself. Sharon had taken
her to lunch the day before; Ellie had to show her appreciation
somehow. When Sharon still insisted, Blondie picked her up
in his arms and carried her struggling to the living-room sofa.

Dan joined Ellie in the narrow kitchen. He closed the door after considerable difficulty — there was a coffee table in the way, and a corner of the rag rug, too. Eleanor stood regarding Dan with an assured question in her eyes; she was not smiling.

"Why did you do that?"

"So we could be alone."

He went to her as she stood motionless beside the little sink. He put his arms around her and looked closely into her face. He thought that he could have kissed her then; she did not turn her face away. No, he had better wait.

She said, "You're a fast worker, Dan. At least you're trying to be. How long have you been here?"

"Almost two hours."

"And already you start pawing."

"I wanted to about five seconds after I came in."

An El train roared beyond the window, and Dan hated the train and longed for it to be gone — it took so long in its passing; he had to wait and wait; it seemed an hour. "Look," he said at last, in the comparative silence, "what are you doing this afternoon?"

"I've got a date."

"Break it."

"Dan, I don't go around breaking dates."

"Is it important?"

"It could be. I don't know yet."

"Forget it. Break the date."

"But —"

"Break it," he said, and at last there was a gleam of agreement in her face. Not long after they had finished with the dishes Ellie went into the bedroom and closed the door, and Dan could hear her soft voice talking on the telephone.

All right, she had said, three o'clock. He went home, leaving Blondie trying to take money from Sharon at gin rummy. How wonderful! — Ellie's apartment was only about six blocks from Dan's own room.

When he had returned to the Sunday-morning gloom of his north room, Dan stood looking at himself in the wide mirror over his old dresser. He gazed past a bower of neckties draped over the mirror post and saw himself, serious and shabby and smeared. He swore; he took off the old jacket and hurled it through the open door of his closet. He would really fix himself up for that afternoon date. All Ellie wanted to do was to take a walk in the park; she usually did that, she said, if the weather was good on Sundays. Either she or Sharon was constantly walking the neighbor's dog. Myron, the McAndrews' dog, should be walked again in the park on this miraculous Sunday; Eleanor Dunbar and Daniel Mallow would escort him.

As he lingered in front of the dresser he thought of those leather-framed photographs on Ellie's dressing table: a sad-faced woman in a silver oval — that would be the dead mother; a vague face, lumpy and distorted from an enlarged snapshot in the opposite frame — the long-dead father, of course. And Blondie, jaunty with wings and ribbons. That was all: there wasn't any guy there — not at the moment, at least. On Dan's own dresser there was a snapshot of a girl laughing coquettishly. She was Bernice Van Dieman, the girl from Providence.

Why he had kept that little picture on his dresser he didn't exactly know. It was a relic of the past; that was all. He would keep it no longer. The full illusion of Ellie's existence, of her merely being, of her merely walking about and using her voice and her eyes and her energy in the world — this overwhelmed him completely now, and he crushed Vandy's pathetic remains in his hand and dropped them into the wastebasket.

*Two-three Precinct. The address: Two-One-Two East One-Hundred-and-Tenth Street — in the basement — a Signal*

*Thirty-two. . . . Twenty-third Precinct. The address: Two-Twelve East One-Hundred-Tenth Street—in the basement—a Signal Thirty-two. Time: Four-Eleven a. m. WPEF Six-Four.*

The green car shot east. "Did you get the address?" cried Shetland, who had it branded white-hot on his brain.

"Two-One-Two East One-Hundred-and-Tenth."

"Right!" Joe could not talk now. He had to watch out for Park Avenue, going through this red light as they were going. Shetland pulled the switches of the police blinker above the windshield; the red light was flashing; they could see it reflected dimly on the hood of the car, for that block was very dark. With his horn Joe blasted a path across Lexington.

"Don't I pull the siren?"

"Too close! On a Signal Thirty-two we don't use the siren close to the scene. Might frighten away the perpetrators." As always Shetland wanted his car to be the first car there and this looked like a break. He had made two excellent pinches that way last year, and for one he had received a Commendation.

No near traffic on Third Avenue. They whistled past parked vehicles beyond Third and swung into a vacant space on the left. Shetland wrenched out the keys and flung open the door, catching the thong of his stick from the door handle as the door turned. Mallow pounded to the pavement on the other side of the car and slammed his door with a crash.

Shetland's flashlight was already sweeping the numbers. At 212 a tall mulatto woman waited on the steps. She wore a dressing gown caught tightly around her and she was beckoning. They raced up the steps . . . in the combined glare of their beams they could see that her face was tense and frightened.

"What's the trouble, lady?"

"I don't know." She spoke in perfect English. "It's on the roof—a kind of moaning or groaning! One of the tenants came down and told me."

"The call said in the basement. . . ."

"I was so scared, officer — just so scared — I said basement — I meant roof! I called on the telephone — "

The patrolmen darted past her and went vaulting up the stairs. These stairways . . . and at Joe's age . . . Shetland was breathing heavily by the time they got to the darkened third floor. He could hear blood hammering in his temples — pounding hard all over his body — and Dan Mallow was crowding with the spring of youth.

Rookie or not, he would let Mallow lead. "Go ahead," he gasped. The boy shot past him.

They clattered up the last flight and through the hall to the rear, where a short stair led to a door closed on the roof. Despite the thunder of Mallow's feet, Shetland was straining his ears toward the upper regions, and he thought he could hear feet running up there, and other sounds — he didn't know what.

"Get your gun out," he told Dan between gulps of air. Mallow flung the roof door wide and the two patrolmen sprang out on the roof.

Maria Inez Hernandez was over in a corner by the front parapet; the flashlights found her. She had been lying, crushed flat against a shabby winter coat a moment before; now she was released and struggling to sit up. For all the strange sounds she made — for all her tears — for all the savagery that had ruled her, Maria Inez was only 13.

She and her mother had come from Puerto Rico only six months before; they shared a third-floor apartment with 11 other Puerto Ricans. Summer nights, when her own mother had gone to work and when the snores and argument and confusion of the crowded apartment were too much for her, the girl had learned to creep away to the roof and sit wondering at lights and the stars. Although the air was now chilly with fall, she persisted in coming. There was an old coat which someone had given her

mother soon after their arrival — she could take that. She could wrap herself in it and sometimes find warmth there. In this manner she had been lying, skinny and unguarded, when two roof-prowlers came upon her. Then ensued the moaning — the sounds which had alarmed the top-floor tenants and sent them to summon the woman superintendent.

Flashlights claimed Maria Inez Hernandez now. She could not be frightened anew; there was no more fright left in her; she could only slobber and stare. Her torn skirts were pulled up, there was blood on the coat. She had been abused viciously.

*"Dos hombres!"* was all she could say as Shetland went down on one knee beside her. *"Policía"* he said. "Where did they go?"

*"Dos hombres!"* she wailed, and finding strength in her voice

she used it . . . her wail was a needle sticking into the sky, thin and sharp and steely.

Shetland heard Mallow exclaim, "Here's a plank," and so there was one: a wide plank extending from parapet to parapet, bridging the ten-foot chasm to the next building. Shetland was with Dan in what seemed like a single step. Their lights went sweeping the roof of the building next door, and the building beyond that was high — at least six stories. No fugitives could swarm that height of shabby brick.

Shetland saw them first, or saw one — a bobbing yellowish shape trying to squat down at the back corner of the roof, trying to avoid the avenging lights.

"Hold it!" he trumpeted. If he ever wanted to make a pinch in his life — to make it firsthand and with his fists — he wanted to make it now, but he must hurry. There was a persistent squeak of brakes as car after car came to a halt in the street below; there was the growing hubbub of aroused neighbors from that building — the mounting stutter of policemen's shoes on the inside stairways. Already Mallow had tested the plank with his hand. It sagged, but it seemed strong enough — at least those other men had crossed on it.

"Take it easy." Shetland breathed the words somewhere, with voice or with heart, in warning to Dan. . . . Mallow was half-way across the plank — walking steadily but slowly, one step at a time, his flashlight in his left hand, his gun in his right.

Shetland put his hands on the end of the plank to restrain its palpitation and, as he heard Mallow's feet strike the pebbles on the opposite roof, he swung his own weight to the parapet and started over. From distance beyond, there rose a frantic pounding, a banging, a jerking, a crunching of metal. That would be the door to the stairway which led down from the roof of 214. Oftentimes roof doors were secured on the inside, bolted or chained, or sometimes with a night lock set. This had happened now fortuitously: the men were not able to get the door open.

The plank sagged and teetered. Shetland's weight was half again as much as Mallow's, or nearly that; with gratitude he felt the sole of his shoe grip against the roof bricks at the farther parapet edge. Behind him there was a call and scramble. More flashlights bloomed whitely on the roof they had just left. "Over here!" he yelled across his shoulder.

At the farther side of a grimy penthouse built above the stairway, one young man still struggled frantically with the door. The other faded toward a corner and Mallow was after him. Shetland nearly reached the penthouse when the door was jerked wide. In his jagged beam of light he could see the man he was after: dark pants, a brown jacket, black hair. The fellow had hauled the knob off the door, but the door came open when he did it. The fugitive fell back, staggering, and then dove toward the entrance, Shetland after him with outstretched hand. He seized the jacket. The fabric tore. Shetland gave the best twist he could give as material yielded, and into a maw of unexplored darkness the young man went rolling down the first flight of stairs. He lay disheveled as the light found him at the foot. He said nothing, but Shetland could hear the shuddering breath that he expelled and could see him turn his face away, trying to conceal himself with one raw bruised arm.

"Don't try to get away," Joe said, "or I'll shoot. Get up!" He was at the man's side. He jerked the fugitive to his feet and dragged him up the stairway, whining and swallowing. Mallow had the other man collared in the far corner of the roof, and he brought him forward. Mallow had also a knife slash across the shoulder and partly down the arm of his blouse; it hadn't slit the skin. The other youth was squat, husky. Both were white. One of them — the fugitive caught by Shetland — had a pair of thin rubber bathing sandals twisted in a wad in his pocket.

On the roof at 212 policemen found a section of broken steel grating; they put it across. Other patrolmen came crawling over, Sergeant Hanahan leading the way.

"You got them both, Joe?"

"Yeh," Shetland looked at Mallow where he stood, hot-faced, holding the nippered wrist of his prisoner. "Look at that coat of yours," said Shetland. "Remember what I told you about savers?" and he didn't give a damn whether the sergeant was standing there or not.

Maria Inez Hernandez identified the two rapists, and she was carried to the hospital while they were taken down to be booked.

"It's your first pinch, I guess," Joe said to Mallow.

"Yes."

"Want to go to court tomorrow? I'd be glad to go if you've got any reason not to. But . . ." Shetland hesitated.

"I'll take the pinch," Dan said. Joe was pleased. He wouldn't have minded going to court himself but he liked the way this boy reacted to things.

Sergeant Hanahan told Shetland to finish his tour with another rook who had been assigned to a fixed post; Dan was left alone with the detectives and with his prisoners, in the Brains division upstairs at the House. The prisoners turned out to be Joe Afria, 18 years old, and Louis Colosimo, aged 19. Afria admitted to several previous arrests, mainly misdemeanors: disorderly conduct, malicious destruction of property and the like. Under further questioning he admitted that he had been charged with attempted rape the year before. Colosimo turned out to be an escapee from the Elmira Reformatory, where he had been sentenced to a three-year term for breaking and entering.

Dan sat watching the detectives . . . he aided as much as he could in booking the prisoners. He watched while they were being fingerprinted. "Looks like a good pinch," said Detective Suarez, and Dan reddened a trifle. He took off his blouse and examined it. Two other detectives also surveyed the rent and prophesied that a uniform tailor could do a good job on it; most of the cut fortunately was right next to the seam.

Colosimo wept and ranted on his chair. He kept demanding a lawyer even at this stage of the game. "You'll get plenty of lawyers," they told him. "Shut up."

Dan watched . . . this was October of 1947. Last spring he had been driving a newspaper delivery truck; now he was on the cops . . . he fought to keep his attention on the activity before his eyes. He must learn, learn; he must know all. One alert portion of his intelligence was centered on the mechanical details; the rest of his thought could concern itself with the past and with his private personal present.

Ellie — he would be seeing her tomorrow possibly. If he didn't get held up too long in court, maybe he could meet her after work and buy her a drink. Certainly he would see her in the evening. His mind went back to their first date — the first day, the immortal Sunday, when she had broken her date with a vague and unpalatable character — a man named Roger, of all things.

It seemed so long ago . . . they had had their walk in the park, with Myron, the neighbor's dog, hauling hard on his leash.

Myron was a strange mixture of collie, Dalmatian and beagle. He looked like something out of a bad dream; but he was affectionate, he loved Ellie, he loved Sharon, he loved anyone who would take him out to walk. Walking Myron meant going at a pace approaching a lope, and always the leash was ramrod stiff.

Less than an hour after they had started on their famous stroll in the upper reaches of the park, Dan and Ellie and the dog met Patrolman Izzie Ryan, Shield 2066, of the 22nd Precinct. Ryan was thick-necked, thick-bodied, with a seamed face mottled in pink and brown. He had gray stubble showing, for he had not shaved since the night before, and he had been on duty nearly eight hours that day. Flat curls of silver shone at his temples; his voice was moderate, his tone deep.

He had stepped from behind a rocky hillock and pointed his chunky finger, first at Dan, then at Ellie, spry and laughing and distant under the trees. "Come here a minute, mister. And her — ask her to come here, too." When they were both before him, shamefaced and guilty, Ryan delivered himself of his lecture: "We like our squirrels. We try to take care of them. They give a great deal of joy to children when they see them scampering. Wouldn't you feel bad now if the dog had caught one of the squirrels and torn the poor creature to bits?"

Pink of face beneath her make-up, Ellie tried to stammer out excuses. She could not do it as glibly as she had planned. . . . She had told Dan gaily, "Oh, Myron just goes crazy over squirrels. He needs to run a little — and that's so stupid — that law requiring us to keep dogs on leashes." Dan agreed. "Now, wait," said Ellie. "Wait until Myron sees a squirrel at a distance; then drop the leash and let him chase it."

"Maybe we'll get pinched."

"No, I've done it before, loads of times, and the police have never bothered me yet. They're never around — not even when you want them, I guess. Anyway that's what people say. Golly," she cried, laughing again, "I've got my little story all figured out! If a policeman tried to give me a ticket for that, I'd tell him that I couldn't help it — I was just relaxed for a moment and the dog jerked the leash out of my hand. Myron's too old and fat anyway; he goes fairly roaring after the squirrels; he couldn't possibly catch one."

The plump gray squirrel skipped at a distance, he sat up impishly in the cold wind. Myron's ears went up when he saw the fuzzy gray lump and he gave a snort of challenge. "Now *let go*," Ellie ordered, and the leash sped from Dan's fingers across the short cold grass. The dog went racing, his abbreviated legs a blur; the squirrel headed for the nearest clump of trees. The creature tore his way up the bark; he sat on a limb above, scolding volubly while Myron danced on earth and air beneath him. That was when the officer made his appearance.

"But it was an accident," Ellie explained. "It — he just jerked the leash out of his hand."

"He did nothing of the sort, young woman." A grin stole over the policeman's face. "It so happened that I was standing behind that boulder over there, looking about before I started back to the House, and I happened to hear what you said. It's a very ingenious story, but it won't do. Now, please go and secure your dog before he eats up one of my pet squirrels."

Ellie stamped away to capture Myron, trying to keep her nose in the air. Her old muskrat coat blew tight against her body — it wrapped her like the fur of an animal, sleek and endearing, and Dan watched her go with yearning in his glance, no matter how many tickets he was about to be presented with.

"O. K.," he said, "are you going to write out a summons?"

Ryan shined a button on the breast of his overcoat. "Who said I was going to give you a summons? I have given you a warning. I have told you the why and the wherefore of things. You look like a very nice young couple; I should hate to have to give you a summons." There was a power, a calm dignity in the old face; Dan looked at him with appreciation.

"You've got a very pretty little wife," said Ryan.

"I wish to hell I did have her. I mean for a wife. We just met this morning. We're on our first date."

"You're a GI, no doubt?"

"I was with the Ninth Air Force."

"The hell you say! My own son was in the 15th. Shot down over Austria — a prisoner of war, but back in this city at last and working at a good job, I'm glad to say." The old officer thrust out his hairy hand. "I'm glad to meet you."

"My name's Mallow."

"Ryan's my name — Isidore Ryan, if you must have the whole

truth, and the boys call me Izzie." He laughed comfortably. "I'm what is known as an anomaly, young man — that anomaly of vaudeville jokers — an Irish Jew. My mother's name was Reba Feingold, and my father's name was Patrick Ryan, and I've got 37 years in the Department. I've been a cop through all my manhood. I haven't made a fortune and they'll never put me in *Who's Who,* but let me ask you this: where else could I have had a front-row seat — a reserved seat, if you please — at the greatest show on earth ... the strange and terrible and wonderful things that happen to human beings?"

"You've seen a lot."

"I've seen everything," said the patrolman. "I wish I were the age of my boy, so I could start all over again. He says he wants to make money. Well, good enough; he's smart as tacks. He's in a bond house now, and someday he'll probably be an investment broker; but he'll never see what I've seen."

Ellie was waiting by the dry drinking fountain. Myron stood up on his hind legs, vainly seeking the water he knew flowed there in warmer seasons.

"Good-bye," said Ryan. "It's been a pleasure to talk to you and it will be a pleasure if I don't have to give you a ticket. So remember to keep that dog tight on the leash when you're anywhere near me. Ah, well," and he sighed, "I won't be here much longer. I retire on December 31st."

He insisted on shaking hands with them both. He went stanchly away over a hill to the south, walking slowly and not turning back but looking ahead and about him as he moved.

Dan said, "He's swell."

Ellie estimated him with her quiet gaze. "You mean because he didn't give us a summons?"

"Oh, he talked a lot while we were walking over here, catching up with you. He's had quite a life."

Ellie gave a little snort.

Dan said, almost explosively this time, "An old guy like that really gets me! There was something wonderful about him. You know what he said?" He tried to quote it; the words still boomed in his ears: *A front-row seat, a reserved seat . . . the greatest show on earth . . . the strange and terrible and wonderful things that happen.*

Ellie Dunbar declared flatly, "I can't buy that."

"Why not?"

"It's pathetic, that's all. He spent his years wandering around on tired feet, chasing children off the grass, telling taxi drivers to move on, upbraiding motorists. Yes, and his wife was an idiot, too, if she put up with it. If Patrolman Ryan had devoted that much enthusiasm to something sensible, his family could have had some advantages. Probably they live in some gloomy walk-up it takes him an hour and a half to reach on the subway when he goes off duty." She shook her head. "A cop. Gad!"

In the beginning, the value of being a cop had merely been a point of disagreement between them. Later, when Dan decided to take police training and gym classes at Delavan's under the GI Bill, their disagreement flared into an open quarrel. Ellie was sarcastic about his ambition, and when Blondie, whose job as a detective folded suddenly, decided to go along to Delavan's, too, she angrily accused Dan of having talked him into it.

"Imagine anyone wanting to be a cop!" Ellie had said bitterly, and from then on she had less time to see him alone.

Throughout the entire course of studies at the Institute, Dan was motivated by a determination to show Eleanor Dunbar that he could be just as stubborn as she, and struggled to prepare himself for the examination three months away. With Blondie he studied in the classrooms near Union Square and worked amid the throb and sweat of the gymnasium. They accelerated, they toiled, Blondie cheated in examinations ingeniously.

When they got on the List, Dan was 14th in the first hundred; Blondie was in the fourth hundred. It didn't matter: they were on, and they celebrated.

With four cocktails inside Dan and six inside Blondie, they made a noisy visit to the girls' apartment and found only Sharon; Ellie was at a party; she wouldn't be home until later. "You tell her," they crowed. "We're on the List! We got into the Academy! We're going to be sworn in!"

They went their way, carousing while Dan picked up the checks. This was a thrill that had not come since they got their wings in Texas so long before. Sometime after 11, fuzzy but still jovial, they wandered into Joe King's. They joined uproariously in *rathskeller* songs, they bought drinks for people at near-by tables. They could not tell the world why they were celebrating . . . it was a secret . . . they had their reasons, they roared aloud.

## CHAPTER 5

B LONDIE DUNBAR went to work in the Two-three Precinct some time after Dan did, but he had a permanent assignment in a car before his friend achieved such distinction. Theoretically there was a strong flavor of seniority about these appointments. The men with tenure in the patrol cars clung jealously to their tasks; they knew that Sergeant Breed could send them out to walk a post any time he chose. You got a Complaint against you in the wrong season, you fouled up your relationship at the House in one way or another, and you were no longer sitting down, you were no longer riding — you were hiking instead. The cars offered more variety, more action; they responded to all of the three important signals and to a thousand lesser instigations which, in many cases, might develop into something bigger than an ordinary Signal Thirty or Signal Thirty-two. In a car you were protected from inclement weather to a greater degree; you gained fame in the sector . . . shop-keepers were apt to respect you more than they respected the familiar man walking a post. You were of the shock troops; you skimmed fast. Troublemakers feared you; you were two, the man on post was one. You were an Elite Guard.

Blondie's assignment was a matter of luck, accelerated by enterprise and shrewdness. Among other things, he had slipped Sergeant Breed four choice seats for *Finian's Rainbow* — Blondie got them from a ticket broker whom he had spared the embar-rassment of being found in a hotel room with a lady not his wife. Blondie was nothing out of pocket, but his virtues were apparent to a tough and realistic cop like Sergeant Breed. Dunbar went into the Sector Four car the following month.

This assignment was attended by a good deal of gossip and profanity in back room and locker rooms. Joe Shetland especially felt a sharp-kindled antipathy. He had formed a high personal opinion of Dan Mallow already from their occasional tours to-gether. This was irrespective of his feeling of personal fondness for Dan . . . no, of course that could not be; Shetland knew better than that. No man but might be swayed by prejudice in such a matter. Nevertheless, it was obvious to one of Joe's experience that Blondie was a debonair freebooter who shrugged off any criticism of his new designation with an easy shoulder.

Bertenelli had been on sick report for ten days to begin with. He returned for a tour or two; he went sick again. During his absences Dan Mallow was alternated in assignment to Car 930 along with two other rooks and with several veteran patrolmen, none of whom Shetland regarded as the partner of his prefer-ence. Garney was too wheezy and too stupid — he understood the Spiks, but he wasn't quick enough on the uptake for the varied activity of life in a patrol car. Holdsworth drank too much on the job. Doone had a bad heart; everyone knew that. Kummer was of a sullen nature; and thus it went — Shetland wanted Mallow and nobody else.

Officially it was Captain Reardon who had the say about designations for duty on radio motor patrol, but Sergeant Breed had the captain's ear; his recommendations were tantamount to election. Shetland wasted no time in talking to Breed.

Bunch Bertenelli came back on duty for a short time, but only as a farewell gesture. While he and Shetland were breaking up a fight at 106th and Madison, Bunch was hit upon his tender jaw and again he went sick. It was nothing that would have bothered him in the old days, but retirement was certainly indicated now. Bertenelli took his final leave. Dan Mallow was assigned to Car 930 as recorder. The locker rooms buzzed again, but they were always buzzing.

Now that he was in a car of his own, Dan guarded it jealously. The title of Car 930 was vested in the City, but for eight hours out of the 24 the moss-green coupé belonged to Joseph Shetland and Daniel Mallow. They regarded with suspicion other crews who in turn also felt that 930 was theirs. Arguments befell at times. Who was responsible for that scrape along the right rear fender? Who had put a disfiguring dent above the left front bumper? Who had failed to detect that the brake bands were worn so flat that metal was squawking on metal? Inveterately other crews were responsible for these wickednesses — Joe and Dan were certain of that. They checked and double-checked each time they proceeded to the corner of 104th and Lex. . . . The rap went against the car's operator if anything was wrong; and Shetland was the operator of 930, Mallow was the recorder.

Tools and tire irons, an old milk crate in which they kept miscellaneous supplies in the trunk — once these were tumbled about in disgraceful fashion . . . a bundle of rags, chunks of carpeting . . . what was all that stuff doing there? Sergeant Breed wanted to know. Dan stood guiltily and heard Shetland up-braided. It wasn't Joe's fault; it was Mallow's. Somebody who drove the car on the Late Tour had committed this evil, and Dan promised Joe he would clean it out when they stopped at a garage. But he forgot; he got to arguing with the mechanic about a fight at the Garden. They drove off merrily with the trunk still uncleaned, and other crews ignored the mess later on and no inspection occurred. But the next morning . . .

"Car 930 O. K., sir."

"Get out. I want to take a look."

Breed went over the car thoroughly; he found dirt and dis-order, and Dan stood suffering while Breed condemned Joe. The next day Shetland got dumped. On the roll call he found Sour-puss Kummer's name substituted for his own; he was singled out on Post 40 up on Lex, but for one day only.

Joe only grinned at Dan's abject apologies. "Don't give it a thought. Breed pulls this every now and then. It's his idea of discipline. 'Improper care of Radio Motor Patrol.' " It worked, all right. Dan's eyes were those of an angry and inquisitive cat when he went over things from that time forth.

. . . Heater? Joe had acquired one by hook and by crook during the week before Dan was regularly assigned. It was secondhand but it worked like a charm. Eighteen dollars it cost. Joe picked it up at a garage over near Roosevelt Drive; he had done the garage man a favor or two in years past. Eight-een dollars—distributed among six patrolmen who rode reg-ularly in the car. Three dollars apiece, that came to. Joe put in his own three bucks; he collected promptly from three of the others. Galloway dodged . . . he was always in financial trouble, he shoved too much money to the bookies. He was an old-timer, but he declared the heater to be an extravagance. Galloway was damned if he was going to pay three bucks. Of course he didn't have the three bucks to pay.

Shetland didn't bother about getting any money from Bertenelli; Bunch was on the way out. When Dan's designation was made official, Joe collected from him instead.

"It's cheap at three dollars." Mallow pocketed the change from his five. "I never thought about a heater before. Why doesn't the City give them to us?"

"How old are you?"

"Twenty-five."

"But born yesterday. Why doesn't the City also give us bullet-proof windshields? They'd feel sort of good when we came barging up to a Signal Thirty, expecting a lot of lead to be tossing our way. Why doesn't the City give us spotlights? It would add about 300 percent to our efficiency on patrol, especially during Late Tours. But we don't get them."

Dan pondered about it. "You know, the public thinks . . . When I was a civilian, I always supposed these jobs were stepped up. I thought they had a lot of extra horses under the hoods, and fancy transmissions and all the rest."

Joe snorted. "We are living in a poverty-stricken community —a community that can't tear loose with any extra dimes to increase the value and power of its Police Department. That little matter of ammunition: how many guys are going to walk into a store and pay three bucks for a box of 50 cartridges? Even with a reduced rate for cops, you start blowing smoke rings down on the range and you're blowing about four cents a ring. It's O. K. by me; I love it. But what about these characters with three or four kids at home, and winter coats to accumulate? They're not going to buy an extra cartridge they don't need."

Dan considered this problem throughout some hours of their tour. A bright idea came to him, unaccountably, while they were waking a bottle-baby who seemed determined to freeze to death in a vacant lot at 109th and Park. Dan related his proposal when they were once more in the car. Why not write to the Commissioner and suggest this plan: the City should go into the ammunition business. The City should have its own cartridges, loaded by a regular cartridge company — maybe a reduced powder charge for range work — and they could reload the same shells, too, as was done in larger calibers. It wouldn't cost much that way . . . the City should require each patrolman to fire, say, 100 rounds per month. . . .

Joe listened idly, rapping his fingers against the wheel.

"Yeh, it's a wonderful idea. Who are you going to write to?"

"It was just an idea. I thought — maybe the Commissioner — "

"When you were overseas," said Joe, "and you saw something wrong — something eternally fouled up — how many letters did you write to the C. G. of the Air Force? Just how far do you think you would have got with him? Don't go skipping echelons, Patrolman Mallow. As for Breed: what do you think he would tell you to go and do?" Patrolman Mallow was humbled.

So they didn't have a free heater, so they didn't have a spotlight. So they had no bulletproof glass, no stepped-up engine, no inducement to practice marksmanship liberally; so they had to change spark plugs one at a time and clean them thus while they kept ready ears cocked toward the radio, even as they worked through the bounty of a friendly garage. So they had to drive clear up to the 28th, or over into the middle of Central Park to the 22nd, or maybe halfway up to the Bronx, to get their gas. So there wasn't any gas available in the Two-three Precinct. . . . They drove with eyes alert, they saw the pageant, they saw the strange and terrible and wonderful things. . . .

White, yellow, brown, russet-gray, polished jet . . . the faces moved, the crowds swelled in and out of bars on Madison and upper Fifth. Women wore their lemon and cerise gowns, the men skulked in greasy lumberjacks and spotted camel's-hair coats and ragged mackinaws. Cold weather was around them, and the Spiks hated it. They seemed to despise winter even worse

than the prison of their stinking abodes . . . winter squatted
close. The homicides were mostly indoors nowadays. Leapers
landed against ice when they cracked their bones in the courtyards . . . geyser steam came up from every cleared grating in
the roadways. Still the unkempt immigrants arrived. Day after
day those scabby buses growled to a halt in front of so-called
travel agencies. The nervous newcomers crept down bus steps,
lugging bundles they had knotted together in Puerto Rico on a
previous day. . . . *Americanos* pure and simple. They were of

the *Estados Unidos;* they were territorial citizens become on this instant New Yorkers. Next day the relief rolls would know their names: Hernandez, Rodriguez, Sanchez, all the rest. . . .

Persistently, airplanes taxied across frozen grass on Long Island flats; boats honked and hooted in the river; the dark hordes came. Still the home-going pants-presser was hauled into a doorway and bludgeoned over the head; still the narrow-faced, zoot-suited pimps ganged near a Lexington Avenue café and sold their wives to visiting merchant seamen, and cheated them in the selling. In the jungle that was the 23rd Precinct tigers walked lashing their tails . . . there were more tigers than the law allowed and not enough zoo-keepers to hole them up.

"This is just one big factory, Joe."

"What kind of factory?"

"Crime. You watch it being made day and night, and what chance do the children have? Remember — about an hour ago, when we had that truck smash there at 107th? While you were writing out the ticket I went over to listen to the box. A little kid came up to me; I guess maybe he was about six. Cute kid, too. I guess maybe they taught it to him in school, or somewhere . . . he kept grinning . . . he said, 'Hey, *policía*. You my friend, ain't you?' I said, 'Sure, I'm your friend. Hiya, Chico.'"

Joe said moodily, "A lot of them talk that way when they're little. Then you see them maybe when they're eight, nine, ten — that's when they start swiping stuff over at the market — grabbing and running. . . . Twelve or fifteen: they're the ones that start breaking in at 4 a.m."

"Like the two we got in the cellar under that hock shop on the Late Tour . . ."

"When they're 15, 16, 17, they start mugging. Then they start ze rape."

"But who's to blame? Who's at fault? Is it us? Is it *they*? Who is it? The landlords that rent out these filthy firetraps with rotten plumbing and rotten ceilings? A lot of the land-lords are Spiks themselves. . . ."

"Don't try to figure it. *Quién sabe?*"

The team of Shetland and Mallow became more and more dependent upon one another. Dan was checked out as a driver. He relieved Joe for long periods while they crawled the avenues. Then suddenly a signal would crackle on the radio and Car 930 would find itself with other cars jammed up on Roosevelt Drive beside the East River while people towed an ugly soaked bladder ashore . . . once that bladder had walked and lived on legs now swollen to the grotesquerie of telephone poles. . . .

No matter who was driving, the men had their alert system at every dangerous corner and underpass . . . the recorder's rubberneck scrutiny to the right as the car edged forward to the intersection, his sharp-bitten *"Clear!"* and then they were boring on once more. Their interdependence grew concurrently with personal trust and satisfaction in one another's presence. . . . It was not wise to argue while on a job. Some cops did that, but Shetland and Mallow felt that they must present a united front — that whatever disagreement about policy occurred should be debated in the sanctity of the car and not in an upstairs kitchen where a dozen frightened or angry people were listening.

Shetland had two more citations before the winter's end, to add to distinction already possessed; Dan had a green-white-blue bar on his uniform with a star blazing there. It seemed more important in this year than the DFC, the Air Medal, the Purple Heart lying in their leather boxes in a drawer at home. Peace and time had given him a new and demanding scale of values.

Dan learned the ways of fugitives as Joe had learned them long before: they fled either up or down, they fled either in or out. "In" was not as easy as might seem; there were too many courtyards behind those miserable buildings, too many fences broken down and open cellars gaping. Fugitives scooted aloft more willingly when the roofs were dry and windswept, when the sun had melted all accumulated ice and the cluttered gravelly areas were unglazed to the touch of running feet.

That was what happened on East 105th, just off Madison. In a little bodega the proprietor's daughter slipped through a rear door and ran to a telephone. Yes, she whimpered over the wire, four men . . . she could tell that her father didn't like their looks. They were loafing there, they were whispering to each other, she was certain that they plotted harm. It sounded like nothing at all, but the patrolman on switchboard duty gave it to Car 930 when Joe called in a moment later.

". . . Suspicious men. Probably nothing to it."

The green car slid alongside the curb in front of the shop two minutes later. When four young men rushed out at the rear, the patrolmen were fast after them. They fled out and then in and then up; the officers could hear wild feet scrambling ahead through the cold dimness of afternoon hallways. Dan went wrong for a moment on the top floor. He saw a ragged overcoat and other rags which someone had thrown out into the passage; he thought it was a man hiding there and lost precious moments learning how his eyes had falsified things. By this time Shetland was on the roof and all four of the runaways had jumped him. Dan made for the top stairs with plunging strides; smells of cooking were in his nostrils, the crying of a baby in his ears. Closed doors flicked past his gaze and on one of them he saw a garish holy picture stuck upon a door panel to bless the home: the Holy Mother and the Holy Child.

Above the child's crying there sounded the snarl and gasp of tussling on the roof. Dan went up like a rocket to join in it. He got there barely in time: one youth was on his back mooing with his broken jaw, one had a bloody nose but was still full of fight. Two of them twisted behind Shetland, pinioning his arms. They were trying to heave him across the few paces of dry tar and stone where there was no parapet, no little wall to guard the cliff at the building's rear. A proper trip and push, and anyone could be hurled over the edge.

They let loose when Dan appeared, and ran again. . . . One of them tossed a heavy object into a shaft as he loped away. They all halted, cowering, after Dan had fired one shot into the air. An observant neighbor in an opposite building had called for police when the men first resisted Shetland. This fortuitous alarm was turned into a Signal Thirty-two, Assist Patrolman, and partners appeared hastily on the roof to take grim stock of the damage done to the prisoners and to kid the life out of Shetland about his torn coat.

Obviously the shopkeeper and his daughter were correct in their assumption that the hoodlums had planned a holdup. Two of the youths were unarmed: one had a homemade blackjack in one pocket of his overcoat and a cap gun in the other; a few minutes later the bottom of the airshaft yielded a rusty and unlicensed Mauser. It was bent and dented by the fall, it was unloaded; just the same this was a good pinch and a lucky hour in Joe Shetland's life.

"They had me damn near to the edge."

"It's my fault. I saw that stuff in the hall and stopped —"

"I didn't even see it. I'm certainly glad you got up as fast as you did, sweetheart."

They trailed down through the building, following the parade of patrolmen and prisoners, and Dan did not smile when Joe Shetland glimpsed the holy picture on the fifth-floor door panel and lingered gravely to cross himself. Five stories down, and no parapet guarding the rear. . . .

# CHAPTER 6

Dan shared his personal life with Shetland; he shared the joy of Ellie. Initially he had feared that she would not approve of Joe, that she would find Shetland too ardently attempting a noisy humor which he didn't feel in his soul. But Ellie respected Shetland from the very start of their acquaintance; she perceived that he was rare and sound. Thus she was never resentful but hospitable instead, when Dan wished to include Joe for at least a few social hours during a Forty-eight.

Blondie, however, received the impact of Shetland's scorn. Joe had a difficult time checking his temper on many occasions, though he always succeeded. In January, Blondie made a killing at Tropical Park. (He played the horses often at long range. No one might estimate how much money he had dropped before he put $30 on a 15-to-1 shot and the horse came in.) For the moment, there was wealth in his wallet and he demanded dinner and an evening at the Café Grinzing. Ellie agreed to join the festivities. Blondie brought along his latest girl — a chattering, frizzly-haired baggage who checked hats at a famous fish-and-steak place in midtown. The partner of his patrols was there — a humorless and rawboned veteran named Leech, who came with his pregnant wife. Shetland was urged to bring "a friend." He came alone. He did not stay late, and brightened only when he conversed with Ellie under the cover of Viennese songs.

"I don't see how he ever made it," he said two days later.

"Who?"

"Your notorious brother-in-law-to-be — Patrolman Dunbar."

"How he made what?"

"Ever got through the Police Academy. Even how he got to the Academy in the first place . . ."

Dan smiled. "I told you how he got through Delavan's and got on the List and how mad Ellie was. I guess I never went on from there."

"Now's the time. Things are duller than dishwater on this tour. Enlighten me, sonny."

... Blondie had celebrated his appointment to the Academy by borrowing money from Ellie to tide him over until he could cash his first check. Blondie felt that $2400 per annum, padded by a $750 increased cost-of-living emolument, was a niggardly sum. Blondie relived, in cafeteria lunches with Dan and his fellow recruits, the glorious days of flight pay and overseas pay; he talked about how many thousand francs he had spent in a single night at the Bal Tabarin.

Nevertheless, for all his whimsical complaints, Patrolman Dunbar devoted himself to his tasks with zest. There had been few opportunities for cribbing at Delavan's, though he made the most of them. His record-breaking dash on the roof of Delavan's gymnasium could not be duplicated in the Academy but it could be talked about. The experience was related by Blondie with mirth, and received in the same attitude by those of his fellows who had not been present on Delavan's roof to learn how Blondie substituted his phony 20-pound weight for the prescribed 70-pounder. He became an impish if temporary tradition even among staid staff members at the Police Academy. He was the eternal winning youth who is passed along by the teacher, despite abysmal marks in solid geometry, because she cannot resist the way he smiles at her in class. To Dan Mallow this was a very old story; he had seen it happen in the war. Not that Blondie was by any means a coward — he wasn't. He was, when necessity required it, courageous to a fault. He was also prodigiously selfish and scheming and bound to get away with anything he could.

Blondie was convinced, or pretended to be convinced, that

in time Ellie would accept the fact of their joining the Department. Dan put Ellie out of his mind as much as possible. He dared not be haunted by the sense of loss, the misery of amputation, which would certainly overcome him if he yielded to it. He had a few private visions in which he appeared before Eleanor Dunbar, blue chevrons on his arm, having attained the most rapid advancement of any patrolman in the history of the Department. He was standing in the Mayor's office; the Mayor was pinning on his left breast the Department Medal of Honor, and Ellie stood entranced, yielding at last to Mallow's proficiency . . . the dreams faded. Dan would torment himself in this fashion only for an hour or two. On his way home he would walk the extra blocks which took him past the mystic apartment above that Third Avenue grocery. He would walk on the farther side of the street, watching keenly, pretending not to watch, and of course never seeing her at all. Once he did meet Sharon with Myron on leash. Sharon made considerable point of telling Dan that Ellie led a most active social existence. . . . Dan grinned and joked in response, he went home with rocks in his belly. He could not eat; he slept poorly, and made ludicrous mistakes in class the next day.

The Police Academy commencement exercises were to be held in a high school auditorium in lower east mid-town. The program would take place on a Saturday evening, and Blondie stopped by Dan's room that day.

"I suppose you've seen them," Dan said. "What's the chances they'll come?"

Blondie lay flat across Dan's bed, twirling his hat on his finger. "You know how Sis is. She's a regular clam sometimes."

Dan turned back to the mirror and went on with his shaving. "She won't come," he said, after he had wiped the lather from his lips. "On my account, naturally, there wouldn't have been a chance. But I thought — her kid brother, for whom she professes such regard — I thought she'd at least come to see you."

They waited that night amid wide semicircular rows of the school auditorium. It was quite an affair, with Mayor O'Dwyer and Commissioner Wallander participating. From where he sat (severe and stiff, awed by gold badges glaring on the breasts of high-ranking officers) Dan could observe throngs of friends and relatives and late arrivals being ushered into the balcony. There wouldn't be room enough for all — some were standing.

He saw a light green coat; his eyes bulged. That was Sharon; her spectacles shone. Ellie walked with her: Ellie in black and beige, so slim, so intricate and discomfiting. At least she had come to see Blondie in pride.

The Mayor gave his address. "There are men among you," he said, "who have previously served your country with distinction and honor. Some of you attained to high ranks in that service. But I must sound a warning to you now. You are all probationary patrolmen together. Whatever your war record, it's not going to help you when you walk into the Back Room for the first time." He had words of encouragement for the college graduates in the class, stronger encouragement perhaps for those of the men who did not possess college degrees. "The Commissioner and I had to compete with college graduates, too. I don't know what college he went to, but I never saw the inside of one," and the laughter rose warmly. . . . Genial phrases, couched in simple terms by a man who knew the job, a man who had walked a post long before in the midnight of Brooklyn. "A thousand men can do the right thing, the praiseworthy thing, but the one man who loses his temper brings a blot on the whole Department. No one is suggesting that you go out and allow yourselves to be beaten up and not use force to repel the attack, but that force must be only as much as is necessary. Rich and poor on the post, treat them all alike. Be kind, be big. You've got, in addition to the law behind you, a uniform, a gun and a stick. Be alert. When you encounter a criminal, take action. And remember — remember that you will be alone with God many times on post."

When it was over, Blondie pushed through the crowd into the balcony and returned to grab Dan's sleeve. "Listen, I just talked to the girls. They're going on home in a cab, to give you and me a chance to get out of our monkey suits. I'll meet you there."

"You mean — they're expecting us?"

"Didn't I just say so? We've got to have some kind of a celebration."

"Sure you haven't got it fouled up? You're sure that Ellie ... ?"

"I said *us*, didn't I? *Us* doesn't sound like *me*, does it?"

The strain between Dan and Ellie was apparent from the moment he entered the apartment. The place didn't sing as it had sung on the December morning of his first visit. Ellie moved with frosty graciousness, trying to be the perfect hostess. Wouldn't Dan like a drink? ... No. He had not drunk much at any time since coming back from the war. A few evenings with Blondie had constituted his only recent mild debaucheries; he hadn't tasted alcohol since the night when they toasted their appointment to the Academy.

Blondie sat arguing with Sharon, who was trying to lure him to a show. There would be a preview at midnight in one of the Times Square movie houses and Sharon begged him to take her there. After all, she had gone clear downtown to attend those dismal commencement exercises. This was the least Blondie could do for her. Dan suspected that Sharon was persistent merely because she wanted to leave him and Ellie alone. He wished dolefully that she would not take such pains.

Ellie was a stranger now, but a beautiful stranger. Dan ached in his need and desire for her. It was as if she had set out deliberately to make herself as inviting as she could. Her hair lay brushed into curves and films of gold; she wore a little black date dress with a wool top and satin skirt; she had new shoes with pretty straps and the slenderest heels. There was the antique gilt chain, which had belonged to her mother, weighting around her neck.

Dan slumped on the davenport and thought, "The hell with you. You're a snob. I can't help admiring you, but I can't help knowing by this time how important my work actually is — how increasingly important to me — and yet you scorn it. I don't care how gorgeous you are — I wouldn't touch you with a ten-foot pole!" (In the immediate echo of this diatribe he was ready to identify his own lie to himself — ready to attack and smother and plead with Ellie if she offered the slightest encouragement.)

"I'm busted. You ought to know that," Blondie brayed at Sharon. "I haven't got hardly enough to live on, to eat on, until I get my next check from the City. So I don't want to take you to that movie. Why? The answer is No Dough."

Sharon leaped up willingly. "I'll get my coat. I was just trying to pin you down." She hastened into the bedroom and reappeared with Blondie's hat and her own green coat. "Stupid — Aunt Sharon's always got dough, hasn't she? I'll even take you to Lindy's afterward." They went away amid their trivial bickerings, amid the false amusement the others displayed.

Dan and Ellie sat far apart; the air was peppery with discord. Ellie talked a little about her job . . . she wasn't too happy about the way things were going at the office; Mr. Hadley had hired a new assistant editor whom Ellie didn't like . . . oh, she didn't know. . . . Sharon had a good offer in Chicago — at least the suggestion of an opportunity that might develop soon. And an agent had said that he should be able to find work for her in Hollywood . . . they dubbed lots of those shots of girls' feet and legs in the movies. Ellie thought that she might like to change her base, too.

She had turned off the lamp near her chair; her face was in a shadow — even her eyes. Perhaps it was her retreat into comparative darkness that enabled Dan to speak so incisively.

"I can understand why you want to make a change, now."

There was an icy hush. . . . "Just what do you mean — *now*?"

He stood up and crushed his cigarette. "It would be embarrassing for you to have a brother on the cops, or even an old boy friend." Ellie caught her breath sharply. He continued: "I know I wasn't ever really much to you — not like Roger and some of these other characters you go out with." She tried to silence him indignantly, but the heaviness of his voice ruled. "I wasn't an important boy friend, but at least we did go around together for a while, a little bit, and you're ready to cut my throat, right this moment, because you think I persuaded Blondie to get on the cops. I didn't even suggest it to him, not even by inference; it was his own idea. To tell the honest truth, I didn't think he'd work hard enough to make the grade, but he managed. So he's on the cops and I'm on the cops. Oh, yes, you might be walking along the street — maybe we'd both get on a fire or something, one or the other of us — and there you'd be, walking along with some Harvard guy whose father had set him up in business. And maybe he'd ask, 'What on earth do you mean, speaking to that cop?' And you'd have to say, 'That *cop* happens to be my brother.' Or maybe, 'Oh, I used to go around with him a little bit, a year or so ago.' Sure, I can understand why you want to go away to Chicago or even California. Why don't you go to the North Pole? You know all about the temperature there! You" — he hunted for the word, and found it to his pained satisfaction — "you exude it."

She remained motionless in the big chair, her hair a mist, the persuasion of her eyes stifled by darkness. Dan stood sullenly by the front window, hands jammed into his pockets; he was aware that his jacket was caught up over the butt of his revolver, aware that the holster was exposed to Ellie's detestation, yet angrily he resolved not to pull his coat down.

Behind him, Eleanor inquired, "Are you finished with your outburst?"

He swung around. "It's true, isn't it?"

"It's really unnecessary for you to stay here with me merely because the others have gone out. Do you want to leave?"

His first impulse was to bellow, "I damn well do!" at the top of his young lungs; but anger, departing quickly, had left him deflated. "No," he said miserably, "I don't really want to go." He found a forlorn comfort in her continued silence. "I'm sorry I was so rude. I apologize. Would you like to go out and get a bite to eat? It's a nice night and it isn't too late yet. How about walking over to Madison for a hamburger?"

She went, but she was not as pliable as he; she could not snap quickly back from the attitude in which she was bent, her metal was too unyielding for that. Dan was overpowered by the dread of losing her forever, completely, because of this insistence on his own plan and ambition. A hope that she would change her mind had sustained him through recent months. She would not change; he was convinced at last.

Still he was seeking, seeking her, clinging to pitiful hope when she let fall a casual conversational laugh amid their strolling — taking pleasure in the mere fact that she exclaimed about a poodle they saw, or that she savored the chili sauce at Hamburg Heaven. But it was a fallacious encouragement; in less than 45 minutes from the time they left Third Avenue they were back in the vestibule again.

Ellie offered her hand. "I guess we're both rather tired. Probably we'd better say good night."

He muttered, "I know what you mean: we'd better say *good-bye*. I'll wait here until you're inside the apartment."

"Good night, Dan. Thanks — loads — for the hamburger."

Her stilted little shoes were twitching upward, step by step
. . . satin which adorned the moving limbs, it was gleaming up
and far away from him. The door would be opened and closed
in only a few seconds; he would hear that rasp of the key, the
opening door that would be, in fact, the portal of a cell block, a
place of bars and permanent restrictions such as he had seen
recently and so often. He would be jailed for keeps, but outside.

Dan spoke steadfastly, amazed at the clarity with which he
uttered his convictions. "You'd think it was a disgrace — my
wanting to go in the cops. You'd think it was a disgrace on
Blondie's part — the way you act, the attitude you've taken from
the start. Let me tell you something: I'm not ashamed, I'm
proud. That was one of the proudest moments of my life, tonight. I'm glad I'm a cop, understand? You ought to be glad
for your brother's sake, too. It's the only thing he's done to make
you proud of him since he flew his last mission."

The heels trembled and stopped. Ellie stood before the door,
her face turned down, groping in her handbag for the key.

"I hate to climb up on a soapbox," he said, "but I want to tell
you this: cops aren't slaves. We're not executioners, either.
Blondie and I are going to be helping people who can't help
themselves. You like to live in peace, don't you — to dwell in
safety? Our job is to keep that peace and that safety. Maybe you
weren't impressed by what Bill O'Dwyer said tonight but I was.
You heard him: he said that we'd be alone with God many
times. I'm not going to be ashamed of it, and if you had a brain
in your head you wouldn't try to make me ashamed. You'd be
proud, too." He could say no more; he was in awe of himself at
having said these things.

The yellow bulb in the hall made the key a quick jewel in
Eleanor's hand; the aperture of the lock was waiting to receive
it. Dan turned away. Above and behind him there was a trip-
ping, a flurry . . . he whirled. Ellie was coming down. She was

stumbling; it seemed for a moment that she would fall, that she would hurl her delicate body as a projectile toward him. Instinctively Dan lifted his arms as he ran up to her.

They were together, they were in the middle of the stairway. Her tears were explosive. She sobbed: "Blondie never told you — I thought maybe he had. He can't be trusted. Dan —"

"Oh, baby." He kissed her fiercely. Her body was breaking loose from its hardness, dissolving in his arms.

"Dan, I couldn't help it! It was drilled into me by my mother. That's the reason I made Blondie promise. I hated it; I hate it still. Dan, darling, do you love me?"

He was close to sobbing himself; he might have sobbed for all he knew. He managed to groan through the smother of their embrace: "I'm crazy about you. I want you, darling, I want you."

"Oh, Dan, it was in my blood. I couldn't help it. I hate the whole business. My father — our dad, Blondie's and mine — he was a cop. He died one night in a basement, shot to death by a man who wasn't fit to breathe the same air he breathed. . . . I couldn't help it, Dan. All I ever heard was — Oh, Mother Mary — *Don't ever marry a cop.* Night and day she drove that into me. You'll understand, won't you? You'll forgive me?"

"Baby," he said again.

## CHAPTER 7

THE RUN to 21 East 103rd came on a bright spring afternoon about 2:30. It was a Signal Thirty-two, Emergency Truck Responding, Proceed With Caution. They were some distance from 103rd when the call stuttered on the air, but they managed to be the third car arriving. Leech and Dunbar in the Sector Four car were there first; the sergeant was next on the scene. Joe and Dan ran up the outer steps through a crowd . . . odor of gas was apparent, even in the lower hall. White faces gazed from the dimness of doorways; they were mixed in this area — some buildings were American-white, some Puerto Rican.

Third floor, east side front. The front windows were already pulled open when Shetland and Mallow came charging in, with other cops only a stairway or two behind them.

Blondie greeted Dan. "Some deal. There isn't anybody here."

"Well, what's about the gas?" asked Joe Shetland, handkerchief in front of his face.

"Coffee boiled over."

Dan went into a little kitchen at the rear. He saw a high airshaft window which had not been opened yet; it would serve to accentuate the draft already blowing through. Dan climbed up on an old radiator and tugged the window open.

"That Mr. Miller," crowed the superintendent, "he was real careless! He ought to be fined or something."

"Who lives here?"

"I said Mr. Miller — that's his name. He just moved in. Believe me, I'll talk to him! I think you ought to arrest him, because he could have blown this whole place up. . . ."

"Sure he could," said the sergeant, "but it was obviously an accident. This happens every day here in town somewhere. Some character puts a pot of coffee over the gas flame, and then forgets and goes off and leaves it, and the coffee boils over and puts out the flame, and the gas keeps coming. Sure it's dangerous, but it was an accident. Just be glad it wasn't any worse."

The super went away, chattering and distressed because police were in his building.

"Sector Four: Leech, you and Dunbar stay on the job until all the gas is out of here. Be sure you close the windows. Be sure the door is locked. Get the super to lock it if necessary." Sergeant Breed nodded at Mallow and Shetland. "Avenue Car: clean out the hallways now. A lot of people came in here off the street."

He stalked away, shooing other patrolmen ahead of him.

Joe and Dan lingered in the apartment. A dark bedroom and a tiny bath lay beyond the double door opening off a scrawny living room; the kitchen lay in the rear. This was a cobbled-together kind of place, filled with the cheap appurtenances of a fly-by-night lodginghouse. A one-man flophouse, according to Blondie, who was searching for cigars and finding none.

"Hey, sweetheart," he told Dan, "you opened that high window in the kitchenette, and nobody told you to. You just crawl up on that radiator and close it again before you leave."

Joe looked intently at Blondie and seemed about to say something, then he shut his mouth tightly. "All right, lazy," said Dan. He returned to the kitchenette, crawled atop the radiator again and pulled the window tightly shut. He demanded with excessive politeness whether that was all that was required. He went to the sink and washed his hands, elbowing Blondie who was drinking a Coke he had found.

Blondie whispered, "Lookie! Does Mr. Miller like Scotch!" Five or six bottles of Scotch whisky of an expensive brand were grouped on a high shelf above Dan's head.

Dan said, "Not much else in the place. Probably the guy is an alky. That might explain why he went wandering off and left his coffee on the flame."

"He hasn't left a bottle open, has he?" muttered Blondie.

"Come on, stupid, get on the job," yelled Leech from the front room. "Let's close these windows and get rolling."

What occurred thereafter was discussed many times later, and by various people. A preliminary version was recounted by Leech to Dan Mallow under casual questioning; Blondie had his own version, of course. Up to a certain limit it jibed with Leech's. . . . Dan had his own ideas from the start, but it was not until afterward that Blondie admitted the historical truth of these theories.

. . . Windows were all closed.

"O. K." said Leech. "Sure the gas is off?"

Blondie took another peek into the kitchenette. His eyes went avariciously to the tall bottles in their printed paper wrappings — the Scotch on that high shelf which no one else except himself had noticed, to begin with. "Yeh, it's off. Let's go."

Leech went into the outer hallway. "Be sure you set that lock," he called over his shoulder.

"Roger." Blondie's fingers twisted the catch inside. Quietly he pushed up a little button: the beveled brass was caught and restrained. Blondie closed the door solidly.

They had to ring, ten minutes later, and were directed to an Aided Case at Mt. Sinai. They started south down Madison in the car. "Hold it," said Blondie at the 103rd Street corner.

Leech put his feet on the clutch and brake. "What you see?"

"I see nozzing," Blondie told him. "It's my conscience that's worrying me."

"What do you mean, your conscience?"

"That Signal Thirty-two up here past the corner. You remember — you told me to shut the door tightly?"

"Yeh —"

"Well, I have a strong suspicion that I didn't. I mean that I didn't click the lock. It worries me. You remember Breed specifically instructed us to lock that damn apartment. If the guy comes back and finds his door left unlocked by the cops, he'll register a kick. Now, what I suggest, *mi amigo,* is I hop off here and fix ze lock, and you go on around the corner to Mt. Sinai on that Aided Case. I'll catch up with you by the time you have the car parked and get down to Emergency."

Leech shook his head. "We're not supposed to separate that way."

"Whatever you say. We can drive around in front of there now. I'll run upstairs; it'll only take a minute."

Leech said, "I guess the Aided Case is a rough one. They told us to get right on it." He slid the lever into gear, then pulled it out again. "Hell, I won't meet the sergeant between here and Mt. Sinai. Go ahead — check that door — I'll see you in the emergency room." Blondie leaped out with a light heart.

There was a closed garbage can on the rear fire escape of the apartment building, and the door stood open from the hall — Blondie had observed this on the way down. He planned to enter the apartment, wrap the Scotch in newspapers, deposit his spoils in the garbage can and reclaim them immediately after he went off duty at four o'clock. There was a good $30 worth of the stuff or he didn't know Scotch, and all to be had for free.

Luck was with him: he met no one in the halls or on the stairs. There was a chance that the tenant had returned to his apartment in the meantime. Blondie knocked softly on the door panel and waited a moment; he knocked again. No response. He turned the knob and pushed the door open. He moved inside and closed the door quickly; no one was there. Blondie moved the button on the bolt block; the brass snapped into place.

There were old newspapers, a pile of them, accumulated on a soiled davenport. Dunbar had seen those papers when the cops were in the apartment before. He took several papers now and returned to the kitchen. The Scotch bottles were on the highest shelf. He moved a chair and stood upon it. This brought his eyes barely above the level of the treasure-laden shelf. He lifted off one bottle, then he stopped, staring through gloom under the greasy ceiling. Those bottles had been arranged like a little barricade to guard what lay beyond: a .45 automatic.

Blondie heard his own surprised gasp go out across the closed room beyond. There it was right in front of him: blued steel and grated brown grips. It was a Colt; he ought to know . . . he had had one in a holster hung above his cot during the war.

He lifted the pistol, pressed the button, withdrew the clip.

Loaded. Of course the guy might have a permit. If he did not, here was a Sullivan Law violation for sure. But just how the hell could Blondie hang that on the unknown Mr. Miller? Maybe the thing to do would be to take the Scotch, leave the pistol and forget all about it.

Blondie ran the clip back into the gun. Hell — maybe there was a shell in the chamber, too; but he could not linger forever. He returned the pistol to its identical position on the shelf. He nudged the bottles into place. He climbed down from the chair, shoved the chair back against the kitchen table and stood with his head cocked, looking at that high hoard and wondering. Far through the silence that seemed to wrap the place he heard someone ascending the outer stairway. Heavy footsteps approached the door and all in an instant there was the jingle of the key, a twitch of the lock. Mr. Miller had come home.

There was no fit place for concealment there in the kitchen. Blondie shot a quick glance behind him at the old refrigerator which jutted out several inches from the wall and past a broom closet in the corner. This was the nearest thing to a hiding place. Blondie stepped lightly backward two paces, three, until his shoulders were against the cupboard. It did not take long; it seemed to take very long. His right hand found his holster pressed the spring to release his gun.

Mr. Miller came almost directly into the kitchen, his whole attention given to the stove. Eventually it was learned that Miller had encountered the super on his way into the building and the super had told him about the coffee boiling over, the gas, the incursion of police. Miller was understandably nervous. He hesitated for a moment, bent forward, his high narrow shoulder blocking his face as he bent to look at the charred coffeepot, the confusion of coffee grounds and ashes. Still with his back turned to the corner where Blondie waited with revolver in hand, the tenant brought his gaze to the shelf above him. His

long arm reached aloft: one bottle was pushed aside by the groping fingers, then another. The hand found the .45 and brought it
down. Blondie realized that he should have acted before; he said
in a tight voice that seemed to roar through this sordid chamber:
"Police officer. Put that gun down."

Miller turned as if responding to an automatic summons.
Blondie could see only the black mouth of the pistol. . . . The
men fired almost simultaneously. No one would ever be able to
detect, police surgeons or anyone else, who got in the first shot.
The big bullet beat against Blondie in a sledge stroke; a little
distance to the right and he would have died in his tracks. . . .
The door of the broom closet held him up; he did not fall; and
brooms or mops, God knew what else, they clattered inside.

Mr. Miller had doubled forward, but he did not fall until

Blondie had fired twice more. Then Miller was on the floor, and a coffee can rolled across a low shelf beyond the stove. It was turning slowly and crazily with a hole in the side; either Blondie had missed with one shot and had hit that coffee can, or else his bullet had drilled all the way through, penetrating some soft portion of his enemy's body. The can teetered on the edge, it fell off and hit the floor and hit Miller's outflung shoe. Loose coffee burst out in a brown mound.

Blondie felt the great welt and numbness below his left arm, and a warmth oozing there. Maybe he should shoot the man again. No, the guy didn't move at all. He had fallen on his face with his chin pressed and turned against the linoleum. It was a long thin chin; yet the way Miller lay, he had pushed a roll of flesh out along the jawbone and it gave him a false double chin, and he looked queer with his eyes half-open, too. . . .

One thing: the Scotch. Blondie didn't want anybody to see that, right up there in plain sight. Already there were cries and scurryings in the hall outside . . . increasing exclamations and inquiry. Despite a growing dizziness Blondie mounted on the chair again; he had to step over Mr. Miller to do it. He put his gun away and reached down the bottles of Scotch, grabbing them by the necks, two at a time with his right hand . . . he didn't dare try to move his left arm much. There were only five bottles; he had thought there were six. . . . Here was a good place: under the sink — a little cupboard, containing only a washbasin and some filthy rags. He crowded the bottles together and closed the cupboard firmly.

He thought he was ten feet tall, with very small feet, as he stepped gingerly about the place and hunted for a phone. He could find no phone. Pacing as steadily as he could bring himself to pace, he went directly to the front door and got it open . . . excited faces: two women, a child, more people coming up the stairs. He saw the superintendent's fuzzy bald head again.

He rattled out the words: "Patrolman Dunbar. There has been a shooting here. Call the police." He sagged against the door frame and then pulled himself up again stanchly; he was worried about his side. Maybe he would bleed to death before he could make these crazy civilians behave and understand. "Call the police," he murmured again. "Just get the operator ... whoever's got a phone ... say, 'want a policeman.' Tell them to send ... ambulance," and he felt a blackening sickness. He tried to tell himself that it was only from the slam of the bullet, the fright and strain. He tried to tell himself that he was not dying, but the hall spun away from him and the faces also, and he heard the crash of his own falling as he went.

Dan and Joe Shetland returned to 21 East 103rd to find a dozen colleagues on the job and Blondie ensconced on the sofa in Apartment Nine — looking pale but delighted with himself, looking heroic and honest about the whole thing. Sharing his appearance as Exhibit A was the inert shape on the kitchenette floor, to be identified that very evening as the remains of one Henry Merkenspeyer, alias Henry Miller, a solitary bank robber wanted for one killing and several robberies. The next morning detectives investigating the apartment found a secret cache beneath the bathroom linoleum containing another pistol and a revolver, a quantity of ammunition and more than $7300 in currency.

An intern from Flower Hospital was engaged in giving first aid and diagnosing the extent of Blondie's injuries. Dunbar turned out to have a compound fracture of one rib with part of the rib being torn completely away by the bullet. Unless infection developed and as soon as the rib had healed, the intern prophesied that Blondie would be as good as new. He was taken to Mt. Sinai in a police car.

There was in Apartment Nine a believable atmosphere of

strain, since no one knew at the time that Merkenspeyer had a criminal record or was wanted elsewhere. Sergeant Breed had a loathing of trigger-happy cops; he did not leave off his persistent questioning until Captain Reardon arrived to be followed by people from downtown. Mallow and Shetland were outside, acting under Breed's orders to "clean up" the sidewalk in front of the building. At least a thousand people were blocking 103rd Street.

Belatedly, long after four o'clock, Dan and Joe changed their clothes in the locker room.

"What do you think?" asked Joe.

"I don't know what to think." A notion about the Scotch was already working in Dan's mind. He had been tormented by an ugly vision in which Blondie was surprised by an armed tenant while in the process of highjacking the liquor. Dan was fond of Blondie but generally suspicious of his motives. Murder, in a case like that? God, no — not Blondie. He would have blarneyed himself out of the situation somehow or other.

"What will they do now?" Dan asked.

"Oh, the usual routine. Apparently Blondie's not hurt too badly. They'll question him again tonight. They'll take his complete testimony and put their heads together. Has he had any Complaints?"

Dan shook his head. "Not that he didn't deserve a few from time to time," he added with honesty.

"Well, that'll enter into it. He's had some good pinches. How many Commendations — one or two?"

"One," said Dan. He added with grief, "And the usual gossip, the way I've had it, about how he got in a car so quick."

"Forget that old rub," said Shetland. "You know what Blondie ought to be praying right now, Dan? He ought to be praying to all the saints upstairs that this guy Miller has got a record as long as your arm."

## IN GENERAL ORDERS NO. 28. DEPARTMENTAL

## RECOGNITION. EXCEPTIONAL MERIT.

Detective Robert E. Dunbar, Shield No. 827, 8th Detective Division (was Patrolman, Shield No. 9576, attached to 23rd Precinct at time of occurrence). At about 3 p.m., April 16th, 1948, while on patrol duty in a building at 21 East 103rd Street, Manhattan, observed a man, apparently a tenant, entered the premises and produce a loaded pistol. Detective Dunbar accosted the man, who immediately opened fire. Although injured, the officer returned the fire and mortally wounded his assailant. Subsequent investigation revealed that the deceased man had a criminal record; also that he was a fugitive from justice, charged with murder and numerous other crimes.

Dan himself had escorted Ellie to Mt. Sinai that first night. They rode silently in the taxicab, sitting well apart. She had been almost vicious in the ferocity she turned on him when they met that evening. She said many bitter things; Dan sat weighted with futile sadness. She declared that if her only brother, her only relative in the world — if her dearly beloved little brother *died* — she hoped that Dan would not attend the funeral. She said it would hurt her too much to see him there, since she would most certainly hold him and his influence responsible for Blondie's death. Dan had replied "Funeral!" together with an oath, and had then been heartily ashamed of himself for speaking thus to Ellie. In his mind was a very clear picture of just what would be going on at the hospital that evening; the nurses would be making a bigger fuss over Blondie than they might have over Sergeant York. The little cuties whom Dunbar had already met in Emergency throughout his police routine would be hovering like a gang of Florence Nightingales.

Again he thought of the Scotch. Assorting the whole business, he was resignedly confident that Blondie had gone back to 21 East 103rd to lift that liquor, and for no other purpose. In line with Shetland's suggestion, Mallow was joining in supplication for the deceased Miller to have a record worse than Lucky Luciano's. It soon turned out that the prayers were not wasted; Merkenspeyer's name was spread widely amid the black type of metropolitan headlines. There were quarter-page photographs in the *Mirror* and *Record,* and a half-page picture from a similar angle in the *News:* Blondie, seeming calm and forthright (and adorable to women also) was propped up in bed at Mt. Sinai, enjoying a cigar furnished by a reporter.

Later, Dan's first private interview with Blondie was to the point. "So you're going to have Brains?" Dan demanded.

"There's a rumor to that effect."

"Forget about rumors. You know damn well you're going to be promoted to the Detective Division."

Blondie examined his nails; they shone — a student nurse had just given him a manicure in secret. "You know, that wouldn't be bad at all. Just think: a year ago you and I were still down at Delavan's. We didn't get appointed to the Academy until the middle of the summer."

Dan said, "Just one thing: how's about the Scotch on 103rd? When you and I were up there on that gas, it was on the top shelf. When I got back there after you had shot the guy I went to take a look. It wasn't there. Wha' hoppened?"

Blondie explained in low voice, "If you must know, he didn't have the gun on him. Where do you think it was? Behind the bottles. I was just trying to decide what to do about it when he came walking in. I moved back in the corner, and first thing he did was to come out there in the kitchen and pick up the gun. I stepped out and told him to put it down. He started to make war instead." He regarded Dan solemnly, almost pathetically. "Now what kind of a story would that make to tell Breed or Reardon?

Wha' hoppened, indeed? I gave him his lumps, didn't I — in the right place? I removed from circulation a character who had cost the law-enforcement agencies a lot of dough, and at least one life. Is that bad? Figure it out. There was just one thing: I didn't want to take a chance on anybody else seeing that Scotch and trying to estimate my motives, so I put it down under the sink before I went out to the neighbors. The detectives found it when they went over the joint. I wouldn't be at all surprised," Blondie added angelically, "but what some of those detectives inherited a little Scotch before they were through."

Dan arose and stretched. "Take it easy in bed. Me — I've got to go to work. I'm starting the Four-to-Twelve today."

Blondie asked, "When's the big deal coming off — you and Ellie?"

"Well, when Ellie first heard about your getting hurt, I thought it was curtains for me. But now that you are doing so well, she relented and we've decided on June, if we can make it for a vacation then. I'm clear at the bottom of the list on picks in the squad. The way things look I'd probably get October or November. Joe can have a pick for June; he keeps telling me to take his."

"Take it," said Blondie. "I would."

"You sure as hell would."

"It doesn't make any difference to Joe. He's not going to get married. Baby," said Blondie, "I'm going to buy you kids a beautiful wedding present — I don't know just what. I'm going to be rich, even officially. Just think of that extra 1200 bucks. Whenever you get tired of roasted English sparrows you kids can come and eat pheasant with Uncle Blondie."

Dan looked back at him. "You're too slick, chick," he said.

Dan's and Ellie's engagement did not run smoothly. There was the matter of an apartment on 97th Street, for instance. One of Mr. Hadley's writers dropped in at the office to talk with his publisher; the man had taken a temporary job which entailed travel. He mentioned casually that he planned to sublease his small apartment, and Ellie spoke her interest immediately. The writer, affable and fatherly, let her take a look at his home. When she saw Dan that night her voice was a flute, her eyes were flowers.

. . . The darlingest place you ever saw . . . of course it's in a rather old building but he's had it for years. He has it all remodeled into a kind of studio . . . balcony with an antique grille, and a stairway coming down . . . dropped living room, wood-burning fireplace . . .

"Wait a minute, wait a minute. How much — for all this splendor?"

She told him, and he whistled. "That's not much more than what you girls have been paying right here."

"Darling, mention no more El trains! And the park's less than a block away. We could take walks. . . ."

"Whereabouts is it — here in the 60's?"

"You couldn't guess! That's the biggest surprise of all: believe it or not, you could actually *walk to work* if you wanted to."

"Walk to work? You mean — ?"

She charged each word with ecstatic drama: "Daniel-in-the-Lions'-Den, listen to me. It's on — 97th — just east — of Fifth!"

He thought, "Sector Four." He tried to light a cigarette; it was a job, his hand was actually shaking. Poor kid . . . and she had been so excited, so full of anticipated pleasure. . . .

"Hon, we can't."

"Why, what do you mean? You said yourself it's only a little bit more than — "

"That isn't it. The location."

She bridled. "There's nothing whatsoever wrong with that location. I said 97th, I didn't say 107th. And less than a block off

Fifth Avenue. It's clear up above all that slummy, bummy, gummy area where — "

"Baby, it's too bad, but we can't. It's in the 23rd Precinct."

Ellie turned slowly away and sat down on the foot of the couch.

"It's mean," Dan told her. "I don't blame you for feeling bad. It sounded wonderful. But they've got an unwritten rule in the cops, and nobody's going to break it for me. Baby, they don't like to have a patrolman living within the boundaries of the precinct to which he is assigned."

Her gaze found his, her eyes were hard as glass.

"Ellie," he pleaded, "try and understand the situation. The moment we took that apartment, my address would be changed on the records. Then, when my name came up on the next promotion list, the chances are I'd be tossed over into the 28th or 25th. Maybe I'd find myself in the middle of Central Park like old Izzie Ryan, guarding the squirrels. . . . No, it isn't a rule graven on stone or anything like that. But it's policy."

She whispered with dry lips, "Of all the wretched, worthless, unjustified policies I ever . . ."

"Honey, you're wrong. Just take a look at what might happen if they didn't try to follow that custom. A patrolman might be called upon to take disciplinary action against the grocer around the corner — the guy to whom he owed a big bill. He might have to bring some pressure to bear on his own landlord. That's the way it would go. Familiarity breeds contempt. He wouldn't be an officer of the law to his immediate neighbors and friends in the vicinity; he'd be just good old Joe Doakes. Things would be a mess, especially where minor infractions were concerned."

When Ellie did reply at last, it was to change the subject, after one pained flare of resentment: "You've made it very plain to me, *officer!* At least nobody will kick us out of *here*. Sharon leaves for Chicago about May 15th. At least we can live *here by the El* if we don't find any place else. Now, where are you going to take me for dinner, if you please? I'm tired. I don't want to cook." Oh, he managed to coax her into affection again, but for all that the roundness of the evening was punctured.

Joe Shetland solved the honeymoon problem. Ed Gurney, his brother-in-law, owned a cabin far up in the Adirondacks. The nearest town was called Bettsville, but it was just a little place. Yeh, it was swell; Joe had been there; his niece and nephew loved it, they didn't talk about anything else, hardly, except that cabin in the woods . . . deep forest all around, and there was a lake and a rowboat. Sure, it was all equipped. Ed Gurney had piped in on a near-by electric line when he built the shack, so they had an automatic pump and a little bathroom and everything. The point was this: Joe's brother-in-law couldn't get away from the city until at least August first, and Mildred had no wish to stay alone in that isolated place with just the children, so —

Well, yes, they did rent it sometimes. As a matter of fact, there was to be a tenant there in June, but if Dan and Ellie wanted to wait until early July, the vacation picks could be switched around that way. Joe had talked to Patrolman Capek that morning and Capek was all for it. He had a pick in July and would much prefer to go in June. So Capek could take Joe's June pick and Mallow could take Capek's; that was the way they'd work it.

(What Joe did not relate was that Ed Gurney, miser that he was, had howled long and loud. He had a tenant for July all lined up — but nothing was signed. Shetland wrote out a check for the period of Dan's prospective tenancy at a higher rate than Gurney usually received, and Gurney was satisfied.)

No, Ed wouldn't think of charging them anything. "You know, after all, he's my brother-in-law; he knows you and I ride together." Joe swallowed over the lie. "He's a pretty good guy. Hope you two can get together sometime. Chances are he

couldn't have found a tenant for that period anyway. You know
— away up in the woods and everything . . ."

Thus they had a place to stay, and Blondie added to their
good fortune by offering them his newly acquired car —a shiny
blue secondhand convertible made possible by his increased pay
as a detective.

Ellie and Dan were married in a bright July noontime. They
sped home from the church with their immediate attendants
. . . the little apartment roared for a time with a jollity that
muted even the grumble of the trains. Blondie had his car
ready, parked nearby in a restricted zone, with all the neighborhood cops warned away from it; there were other cars in the
party, and taxicabs handy. Thus they made a triumphal parade
up past the House on East 104th just as the platoon turned out
for the Four-to-Twelve. For a moment there was considerable
unorthodox raillery and whistling in the street; even Sergeant
Breed parted his mighty jowls in a grin, and Captain Reardon
blew a kiss to the bride.

## CHAPTER 8

A T THE traffic circle below Pleasantville the newlyweds swung
north on the Taconic Parkway. Traffic was thinner and
moving faster than on the reaches of lower parkways; Dan no
longer had to damn drivers who straddled the lanes and blocked
him from his course. Ellie had complained earlier about the few
glasses of unaccustomed champagne fuzzing her ears and un-
settling her stomach; now she complained no longer. Occasionally when there was no tangle of slower cars to be passed, when
the parkway was empty and widely curving amid oak-studded
hills, Dan would drive with one hand on the wheel . . . his right
hand came down to lie upon Ellie's knees.

"Darling," she said many times, and put her forehead against his arm, and then realized that he needed his arm for driving.

He said, after an hour, "About this Hessian Inn."

"Yes?"

"Well, I was thinking. It doesn't seem quite right."

The girl sat up and regarded him more intently. "What doesn't seem quite right, lover?"

"I mean appropriate."

"But why not?" Her voice faltered . . . oh, surely there must be nothing to mar this mellow episode; yet Dan was frowning. She could see those stern triangles forming between his brows as he inclined his head. "Surely there's nothing inappropriate about it, darling. After all, we *are* on our honeymoon, aren't we?"

"Yes, but we haven't seen the place. I talked to a couple of the boys. Capek used to live up in Peekskill and he knew the place, and he said it's swell. Really a plush joint, but still we don't know what kind of a room we've got or anything. The walls may be thin. Somebody might be throwing a party next door. Maybe we would be right over the parking lot with a lot of traffic all the time. I just don't like the idea of the Hessian Inn, somehow."

"But where else could we go?"

"Well, here's what I thought, if it's O.K. with you. Somehow . . . to spend our first married night in a kind of roadhouse like that . . . oh, I don't know."

Mutually and in silence they considered this problem. At length she lifted her head and bent forward, whispering, "Dan, you'd like to drive on right through, wouldn't you?"

He grinned appreciatively. "That was kind of the deal I had in mind. It's an awful thing to put up to a bride, all of a sudden, just after she's hitched. How's about it? Do you want to . . . wait?"

In reply she slid her arms around him, very nearly causing the wreck of Blondie's car. "I think it would be wonderful! We could drive all night."

"Well, if we get sleepy we can pull up and maybe sleep a while in the car. And then in the morning, there we'd be. Our own little place. I mean — ours for two weeks."

They proceeded through this evening of sublime mystery, incredulous yet contented. The Hudson was a wild satin wonder as they crossed it, the country dusk a marvel never penetrated before; traffic lights turned into gems of polished intensity. Magic food was provided for the Mallows; they could eat little of it. They ordered extravagantly, they wasted good steaks, they drove again. They had their halts and conferences at intersections with a map spread wide and Dan's flashlight boring upon it.

Ellie slept . . . she was amazed when she awakened to find it was daylight and Dan pointed pridefully to the point they had attained. Ellie told her husband that he was the cleverest man alive, and in that moment he believed it. A sign: *Bettsville,* and they drove slowly past white houses, looking for the side route that turned off. Here it was — and a bridge out just beyond. They sniffed the scent of their wilderness honeymoon coming to meet them as berry vines thickened on either side. Three miles to the turn. Here were Simmons' store and post office, as carefully described by Shetland. Mr. Simmons was leather-faced, white-haired, with a cragged forehead. He spoke slowly, he smiled tolerantly upon them as Dan identified himself and took the cabin keys.

They went around the peculiar store, purchasing happily. Ellie owned a list, carefully made out; she and Dan had prepared it the previous week when he had his Forty-eight; and of course she had left it in the drawer of her dressing table at home on Third Avenue! Their eyes were bigger than their stomachs, most certainly. It seemed that they had enough food for the whole Seventh Squad when they got through, and even then they must have forgotten many essentials. They lugged cartons out to the car; Mr. Simmons briefed them on details about the cottage: the electric pump was tricky, and he explained how they must start the flywheel by hand . . . this little flat key was for the padlock of the pump house and tool shed where were kept the axe and other tools they might need. "It's pretty plain," he said, "but a real nice little shack. Quiet, too. No neighbors closer'n here." He stood with morning sun golden on his cottony hair — gaunt and rustic and honest, waving them on their course.

"Oh, darling!"

"What?"

"It's just happiness. Oh, Dan, I'm so happy I'd like to cry. I'd like to lie down on the floor and wave my heels in the air and shriek."

He laughed, and reddened as he grew bold. He said that he mightn't care about the shrieking, but he certainly would like to see her lying down on the floor and kicking her heels in the air. . . . Now, darling, be*have*. . . .

The vines, the tufts of soft pine and cedar, bending elderberry branches brushing the car, the electric wire sagging stoutly ahead. They crawled in second gear, then in low. Darkest shade, then the glimmer of lake water stealing among the trees, and here was the cabin, amazingly small and solidly built. Dan worked at the stubborn rusting lock; it opened with a reluctant squeak. The door swung wide . . . dark interior, and a fat field mouse scuttling to the fireplace. They were arrived in their first home, their wonder cabin, the core of dreams and confidence and clear young passion.

All day they thrilled, they worked and trotted. They were children in a happier legend than any recited by the brothers

Grimm. The cabin boasted two wall bunks, and a double bed, very ugly and old-fashioned — an intricate iron bedstead white-painted with dented brass knobs at the corners. When Ellie wanted to know, "Well, where will we sleep?" Dan asked if she were kidding.

"I know, darling. But we could have all that extra space. We could take down this big bed and put it in the woodshed and —"

"Look, Mrs. Mallow —"

"Oh, that sounded so strange! Say it again."

"Look, Mrs. Mallow. Would you rather have the space, or would you rather sleep with me?" She came to kiss him in reply. They kissed for a long time.

. . . They were ravenous again. While Ellie was storing away the groceries, Dan managed to acquaint himself with the whims of the kerosene stove. They cooked bacon and eggs and coffee, they made toast; they carried their food down and sat on the dock.

"Look at me."

"That's not hard to do."

"Look at *us*. I'm a city girl and you're a city man. Darling, I've simply got to save this suit. I should have put on slacks the first instant I stepped out of the car."

"No, you don't! Not unless we start climbing a mountain or something. You know I don't like you in slacks."

"All right, silly. I've got a little sun-back dress you haven't seen and I got it at Bloomingdale's veree cheap. It was a model dress, and marked down; it had a spot on it, and I cleaned the spot; and I saw the identical thing in Bergdorf Goodman's window; so aren't I economical by nature?"

"What color is it?"

"Oh, yellow and plaid and everything. I'm going right up and put it on." She fled away toward the cabin.

Dan lay back on the rickety wooden dock, replete, but still feeling the unreality of the occasion. Birds whistled and cried far down the shore . . . one of them sounded a little like a traffic whistle . . . he looked at his wrist watch. Nearly ten o'clock now. People on the Day Tour would have left the school crossings long before. Oh, the hell with that; school was out for the year; this was vacation. Dan closed his eyes and lay listening to his own breathing, the tenderness of lake sounds and slight motion of the water . . . these stole up to him and robbed him of tenseness.

"Dan, Dan!" Ellie was calling.

"What's the matter?"

"Sweetheart, something's wrong with the pump. The water won't run at *all*. It was just a trickle and now it's stopped. . . ."

Dan carried their soiled plates to the cabin. He admired Ellie's yellow gown with its plaid pockets and sash; then, since it was warmer, he took off his shirt and trousers and put on a pair of faded Levis he used to wear when he was truck-driving. He went to the pump house behind the cabin and worked for a solid hour and a half before he found what was wrong and made the necessary repairs. When he returned to the main room of the cabin Ellie had their luncheon ready. Dan thought that he had smelled deliciousness but was fearful of only imagining it . . . creamed salmon on toast, cheese, tomato and lettuce salad, plenty of milk. They finished off with a little box of chocolate cookies though Dan had most of the cookies. Ellie offered snide remarks about his waistline, insisting that he had put on weight steadily ever since he left the Academy, and especially since he started riding instead of walking a patrol post.

"What did you say? I'm getting *fat*? You little devil, I'll beat you black-and-blue."

She ran away, she fled around the table, he could have caught her easily then, but it was more fun for him to chase, more fun for her to flee. . . . Oh concentration of childishness and play! Now Ellie was running out of the cabin door and Dan was pursuing, making all sorts of threats. She screamed his name again and again in mock terror, scrambling awkwardly when she came to the boulders. She slipped and fell at last.

"You wouldn't have caught me," she breathed when he was bending to pick her up. "You wouldn't have caught me, you big bully, if I hadn't had these new shoes!" He gathered her up; she began to kick and struggle again; he spanked her lightly, but her outcry would have done justice to a murderous flogging.

In the afternoon they slept for a time, after so many miles, so many labors. Later, they put on bathing suits and ventured to the margin of the lake, but one touch of icy water was all they needed — they went in only to their knees.

Dan said thoughtfully, "We could go skin swimming with perfect safety."

"If it were night I might consider it but — oh, heavens, it's *freezing*. Let's get out of here. . . ."

Night now, or almost night on this easterly slope; the birds were diminishing their cries; the lake roosted anciently motionless and mysterious, suspended on the tips of dark reflected forests.

"I'd be frightened to be up here alone, Danny Boy. Honestly I would. It's so far away from everything."

"Sure is." Ah, wilderness and barbarians and predatory menace he knew so well, but here they were of another style. He glanced at his watch and wondered, as he had wondered earlier, how things were going on the Four-to-Twelve.

Night, thin and pungent outside; the stars glared hard and cool. After dinner flames roared in the fireplace.

"Now listen, Mrs. Mallow, I'm going to do the dishes."

"No, you're not. Don't start that so early in the game or you'll acquire a reputation for being henpecked."

"I am going to do the dishes," said Dan firmly. "My motives are purely selfish. I want to give you plenty of time."

"Time for what?"

"Time to fix yourself up."

"Oho, so that's what's on your mind!"

"Listen," he told her, "I've heard all my life about honeymoons and trousseaus, and brides putting on a lot of voluptuous negligees and fancy lace and gold slippers and God knows what...."

"Danny Boy, you're going to be disappointed."

"I bet I'm not. What makes you think so?"

"Because," she cooed, "I have no gold slippers. Not even one. They cost too damn much. Oh, pardon me, Mr. Mallow!"

"*Patrolman* Mallow to you, and watch your language. I don't want to have to lock you up."

Dan set out the liquor. He'd selected this supply from their wedding presents; several of the cops had given them liquor, in each case making pointed suggestions to Dan about its proper application and demanding that they, the donors, be toasted when the stuff was consumed.

Brandy, he thought. Ellie would consider that the proper thing. He felt his face warming even while he opened the old bottle and drew out the fragile corroded cork. This was an affectation . . . still, it was his honeymoon — Ellie's and his. She would enjoy brandy. It offered an elegance to things, if indeed more elegance could be added to the wonders already apparent.

Dan's bride came to him: his wife, his mistress, his idol, his boss, his playmate and his pet. She forced open the moisture-swollen door of the little bathroom and stood against the distant light, wearing a sheer black negligee; there were only fire-flickers in the main room. Then she had turned the light off . . . she approached, smiling tremulously, embarrassed at participating so deliberately in a revel, yet drawn by appetite, sustained and molded by her pride.

"Oh, *boy!*"

"I broke over," she whispered. "I knew you were crazy about fripperies . . . it seemed a foolish thing for a bride to buy. . . . Danny, isn't it wicked?"

"Ellie —" His voice was hoarse — "You're the most beautiful thing I ever saw in my life. I don't deserve this." His gaze and heart took in. Oh the wealth and wave and glinting of her hair! Oh the intentional challenge of her eyes, the figure apparent beneath the sheerest net!

A burst of light came against his eyes. *Outside,* his awareness told him . . . *for heaven's sake, what's that outside?* In the near wheeling of head lamps he saw Ellie's face gone pale, her eyes grown glassy as she turned toward the window.

"Dan. Somebody's out there. That spotlight —"

"Some so-and-so." He was prepared for murder in this moment. "If somebody thinks they're pulling a gag they're going to be sorry!"

By the time he got the door open, the electric spotlight had been turned off but headlights of the intruder's car were staring still.

"Who the hell's out there?" His fists were ready and stony. "Who is it?"

"New York State Police. Trooper Clark."

"What do you want?"

The trooper became a bulk with shape, a menace pale-hatted . . . the flashlight was so close and angry in its whiteness that Dan could see chilly little insects drifting in the beam.

"Are you Patrolman Mallow, New York Police Department, Shield . . ." The flash swung away suddenly and concentrated upon a scrap of paper in Trooper Clark's hand. "Shield 6483?"

"Yeh."

"Sorry I had to disturb you, Mallow. They called in at our station about an hour ago and sent me over here. They gave your address in care of Simmons' store."

"That's right. What — ?"

"Afraid I've got bad news for you. You're ordered to report back at your command in New York City immediately."

"Why?"

"Did you see today's papers?" asked Clark.

"I don't know from nothing; haven't seen a paper in two days. Got married yesterday and drove all night to get here. We were —" already he was putting it into the past tense — "we were on our honeymoon."

"That's tough," the trooper muttered sympathetically. "Must be the strike. I heard on the radio that they all go off the job tomorrow morning at 7 a.m."

A strike had been brewing earlier in the week but Dan had paid small heed. At the moment he couldn't recall just who . . . tugboats . . . elevator operators . . . commercial truck drivers? Oh, yes, *he* had been a commercial truck driver. Now, in a detestable role, he would be called upon to protect the God-given right of union members to strike, as well as to protect the people they were striking against. In this instant he despised organized labor with the most vicious loathing of which he was capable; he wanted to forget that he had ever had a license and a union card in his clothes. . . . Public enemies . . . he ought to mash the nose of the first picket he observed parading, and whose right to picket he was sworn to sustain.

Dan walked into the cabin and closed the door. He went over to the bathroom door and halted with his knuckles near the panel. "Ellie." No answer; he opened the door. She wasn't in the bathroom. He turned. She was lying on the bed, face down, her head buried in her arms. Shadows had not revealed her . . . in that jet negligee she had seemed only a shadow herself.

He stood by the bed. "Ellie."

She stirred.

"Don't act like it was my fault. Baby, do you think I really want to go?"

"Then why go?" Her voice was muffled with her face hidden in the blankets; he could barely hear the little moan she made.

"I've got to go. You know that. We'll have to go back. It's just one of those things."

"Of course, darling." Ellie said evenly. She sat up and brushed the back of her hand across her mouth . . . she wasn't looking at him, she was looking at the fire. "I guess it will always be one of those things, won't it?"

"Ellie, quit it. It doesn't do any good."

"Oh, I'm talking out of turn, Patrolman Mallow. Probably I'll always talk out of turn."

"Are you sorry you married me?"

She groaned. "Don't be an idiot. Just let me suffer awhile. Let me suffer out loud. That ought to be a woman's privilege, oughtn't it? — a wife's privilege, a cop's wife's privilege?"

In the car Ellie would not talk; Dan tried to make conversation. Only in another hour, when they had reached the wide flat strand of main highway and slowed down for the turn, did Ellie fire her last angry missiles.

"That vile Captain Reardon. He gave you permission. . . . Joe Shetland gave up his vacation, and Captain Reardon authorized it. Didn't he, Dan? Didn't he?"

He said, "I told you before; I'll say it again — *and for God's sake, let it be the last time:* the only time a New York cop is off duty, beyond the call of duty, is when he's gone sick. And I'm not sick . . . just sick at heart. You married me. Now there isn't anything you can do about it."

She could not reply, but time and her affection did the trick. Before the night was gone, before they were well out of the impassive mountains, her hand had struggled over to touch his upon the wheel. When they stopped to take a nap they dozed together; Dan's arms were binding Ellie, hers were securing him.

They reached New York City late in the afternoon, some 50 hours from the time they were married. Dan went on the Day Tour at 8 a.m. the following day. They spent their honeymoon on Third Avenue with El trains rumbling.

## CHAPTER 9

ON A muggy autumn evening at 10:14 o'clock Mallow and Shetland pulled up beside the box near the old Carnegie Mansion on 91st Street, and Mallow stood at the phone.

"Got a good one for you," said the voice at the other end. "It just came in. This is Sergeant Chatlos—"

"Yes, sir."

"The address: 1202 Park Avenue. Apartment 3-D. The name is Lazare." The sergeant spelled it carefully. "Got that? An attempted burglary—could be an actual burglary. She was a little hysterical."

Dan went back to the car and read the address to Shetland.

"One-two-oh-two," repeated Shetland. "Hey, that's plush: the corner of 94th. It's no Spik outfit."

"Sounds like a good address." The sergeant said it was a babe who rang in."

Shetland turned north on Fifth Avenue and they whistled toward 96th. The building was old, as better apartment houses went in that area, but the canopy at the entrance shone crisp and new. They walked over oriental rugs on their way to the elevator. Miss Edna Lazare was awaiting them apprehensively in Apartment 3-D.

She had the door open and when she heard the elevator she opened the door wider. She was a statuesque blonde wearing a black cocktail dress. She looked like dough. The whole place did, though Dan saw Shetland give the tenant a swift double take on the way in.

"Miss Lazare, you called the police station?"

"Someone broke into my apartment."

"Anything missing?"

"Almost all my jewelry is gone. Everything of any value, except what I was wearing tonight." Her voice was deep and throaty. There seemed to be a little twitch to the vowels sometimes as she spoke. Her brown eyes examined the two patrolmen quietly and appraisingly as she gave them information. She put out a half-smoked cigarette as she talked and lighted a fresh one immediately.

She lived there alone. Her apartment had never been entered before by burglars nor had she heard of any robberies, actual or attempted, in the building. She hadn't been at home since midafternoon. She had gone out for cocktails and dinner with some friends. She was tired, her friends were going on to a night club so she asked that they drop her at her building. She came upstairs — it was only about 15 minutes ago — and it was just like this, just the way it was now: drawers pulled out and things strewn around.

"Have you got any idea how they got in?"

"Yes, I think — the back door — I think they — what do you call it? — jimmied it or something."

She put her red-nailed fingers against her mouth and chewed lightly at her nails when she wasn't talking. All the while her expressionless brown eyes watched the officers unwaveringly.

After checking the bedroom, they hurried out at the rear: Mallow went down, Shetland went up. The service stairway was gray-painted, clean, empty, forlorn. Dan found that the rear doors on the ground floor and in the basement were locked and bolted from within. He made a swift tour of corridors adjacent to the storage chambers and found nothing; he went up and joined Shetland on the roof.

Joe's flashlight circled about. "Nobody here. There are these two buildings adjacent . . . they could have crawled across. It's quite a drop one way and quite a climb the other but any active person could do it." He dusted his hands against his pants. "I was over there myself a minute ago."

"See anything?"

"*Nada*. The stairway next door is locked from the inside. What do you think about the babe?"

"I saw you looking her over when we came in."

"I don't know . . . it was that name that got me. Sounds like a phony. Dan, can you detect a Spik when you see one — even a pretty one?"

Dan thought about it as they went down the service stairway. "Could be," he muttered. "She is swarthy. Seems well-fixed."

"Well-stacked, too, Dan. Probably kept."

"Shouldn't wonder."

They re-entered the kitchen of 3-D where Edna Lazare was waiting. She exhibited once more the little marks of prying and leverage on the door and its casing; it looked indeed as if someone had managed to force the lock by shoving a thin piece of metal into the crack and wedging the bolt aside.

"Can you remember whether you had this other bolt turned — the safety bolt — before you went out today?"

The young woman shook her head. "It's got a regular night lock; I always leave it on. Sometimes I've forgotten to turn the safety bolt, I guess. If you'll just come in the bedroom again, I'll show you where they got my little jewel case and opened it."

"Not us, lady. This is a case for the detectives. Will you please show me where your telephone is?"

Joe called and gave his report. The call was transferred to the 23rd Squad of the Detective Division, and an immediate investigation was promised. While Joe was in the act of concluding this conversation, Miss Lazare gave a sudden sob and buried her face in her hands. She had seemed to be in perfect command of herself before, but now she sat on the pale modernistic couch and sobbed dryly for a time.

Dan sat down near her and petted her arm a little . . . he was trying to soothe and reassure . . . such kindness seemed indicated. He wished that Joe would quit winking at him from across the room; he was afraid he might laugh. Somehow the situation didn't seem very tragic. It was difficult to feel sympathy for a floozie like this, even though her gauds were stolen.

Dan started for the door. "I'll get down on the radio," he said. "You stay here, Joe, until the Brains come."

He sat in the car and listened to the humming of the radio and the occasional call which stuttered. Soon a pair of headlights deviated from the stream burning past in southbound traffic of Park Avenue, and a dark sedan edged into a parking space some cars behind him. Dan heard the opening and closing of the sedan doors; two young men moved across the wide sidewalk toward the lighted canopy. That snap-brimmed hat of dove-colored felt, the easy challenging swing of the arms: Blondie . . . apparently he had been on night duty in the Brains Division upstairs at the House, and was detailed to this job.

"Hey, stupid," Dan called to his brother-in-law.

The detectives came over to the car. "What have you got here?"

"A sireen. She says her jewels were stolen."

"3-D?"

"That's it."

"I bet she's an old bag," said Blondie, "or you'd be up there yourself, and Joe would be down here on the box."

Blondie waved farewell to Dan; the detectives went past the canopy and disappeared into the building. Dan watched Blondie go, not with malice but with an unruly annoyance squirming inside him. He didn't know why it was but it seemed a lot of these characters got awfully smart the moment they wore civilian clothes. . . . Detective Third-Grade. O.K. Twelve hundred bucks a year Blondie was earning over and above Dan's salary, and in the opinion of the Department and the public alike this stipend was well deserved. Dan didn't begrudge Blondie his increased income. There was one good thing about it: even with all the nerve in the world, Blondie couldn't come around trying to borrow money from him or Ellie any more, when his pay checks were of such proportions.

Presently the door was blocked by Joe's big shape; he lounged over to the car.

"Want to drive for awhile?"

"Sure." Dan slid under the wheel.

Shetland had a cigar balanced between his fingers. "Where's the sergeant?"

"Just went past. He didn't even stop; he knew we were on this job."

"Which way did he go?"

"South on Park. Down through One and Two."

"Then go over to Madison and let's work north. He's probably been up there, and I want to enjoy this smoke. Look at this —*La Primadora*. A great big long one—big as a telegraph pole. Must have cost maybe four bits."

"Where did you get it?"

"From the babe."

"I thought she lived alone. So she smokes cigars?"

"Well," Shetland said cautiously, "I guess she has them for guests—guests and police. She offered the box: Jarrick took one, I took one—"

"And Blondie took two."

"Wrong. He took one when she offered the box; she left it on the table and Blondie put two more in his pocket, the cute little thief!"

Dan did not reply. He felt that Blondie was riding for a fall, but he'd had notions like that before and Blondie always came up smiling.

Blondie and Jarrick examined the apartment and they questioned Miss Edna Lazare. She gave them the same expressionless stare of her unblinking eyes. Once again a hunch was working in Blondie's mind. He really didn't have anything much to go on; after all, there were a lot of burglaries in Manhattan daily. There was nothing unusual in a woman's reporting a theft of this nature. Women like Edna Lazare always had a lot of baubles on hand—bracelets, watches, rings, pins and what-not— at least until they got broke and had to sell them. Miss Lazare declared that she was insured to the amount of $6175 with the Trans-Union Fidelity Company and showed her policy to the detectives. Her gems were listed. She was wearing a moderately expensive aquamarine brooch and an aqua ring; everything else of insured value, she contended, had been stolen. A cursory glance at the list showed Blondie that something like five thousand dollars' worth of jewelry was missing or declared to be missing. This was November; the insurance policy had only a month or two to run. It added up to something—Blondie didn't know what.

Marks on the kitchen door: there were creases in the wood, paint had been rubbed off adjacent to the lock. The men looked at the floor: there were a few scraps of flaked-off paint on the heavy linoleum.

"Did you see anything left around, Miss Lazare? Any tools, or anything lying around the kitchen?"

The girl shook her head. "No." Blondie puffed on his excellent cigar and filed this remark away for future reference.

Lingerie scattered about . . . dresser drawers pulled open, the little gold-stamped leather-covered jewel case carefully forced open but otherwise undamaged — Blondie wondered about that. Why hadn't they just carried off case and all? Blondie kept making additions to the evidence and to his suspicions. He took advantage of an opportunity, while Jarrick trailed behind Miss Lazare into the living room, and examined the girl's handbag. She had less than $3 in currency. Well-kept women of her variety (if indeed she was kept) would ordinarily travel through life with a comfortable backlog of loose change.

She had said she was a model . . . that was what they always said. But it was a good joint: the furniture looked expensive, there was a nice automatic phonograph in the living room and big stacks of popular records . . . lots of dance music, a few top-notch soloists, rumbas and sambas and all that stuff.

"I was just noticing your records. Are you a dancer, too?"

"I used to dance," said the throaty voice. Blank eyes lingered in his gaze before they turned away.

He made another excuse and left Jarrick with the woman in the living room. Blondie went back to the kitchen and made a great to-do about examining the rear door again. While rattling the knob, he looked about. A drawer in a built-in cabinet stood open about an inch. He thought: "What would she do — hide it somewhere or throw it away?" No, she would hide the instrument if she had used it. Silently he pulled open the drawer, working noiselessly, and saw a miscellaneous mass of bottle openers, knives, spoons, other utensils, all heaped upon a box with divided compartments. He pulled the drawer open to its limit and was rewarded: behind the box lay a space next to the rearmost board. . . . Blondie slid his fingers quickly around the tool: a screwdriver of the kind you might pick up in any dime store; it was new and little used. Still rattling the knob, he held the screwdriver quickly to the light. Gray paint? Yes . . . some of it still clung to the metal shaft. Blondie applied the screwdriver to grooves and abrasions of the doorjamb . . . it fitted, easy as silk.

Silently he restored the implement to its place and pushed the door shut. He went back into the living room, but took care to leave his initialed handkerchief behind him.

Blondie told Miss Lazare there was nothing else for her to do now except to notify insurance people in the morning. Yes, he admitted, it looked pretty bad. Trouble was — crooks disposed of things like that out of town. It was difficult to trace jewelry of the four- or five-hundred-dollars-apiece variety, and most of her stuff was like that.

The detectives said good-bye; they went out and rang for the elevator.

Blondie slapped his pocket. "Hell. Left my million-dollar handkerchief back there in that kitchen. Just a minute."

He rang Miss Lazare's bell again. The door was opened so hastily that he thought she must have been there all the time, listening to their departure. He followed her through the apartment as she went to retrieve the handkerchief. "Certainly sorry to bother you again but it was a real good one. My sister gave it to me for my birthday." He laughed. "I like nice things."

"So do I." Her look played with his and then fell away.

"Miss Lazare, I may come back tomorrow and make a further examination of the premises."

"What time, please?"

"In the afternoon. I'll make it by four if I can. No need to bother you; if you're not home I'll have the man let me in with a passkey. Would that be all right with you?"

She looked at him. "Is that customary, Mr. . . . . ?"

"Dunbar," he told her again. "Detective Dunbar. Sure — it's

routine. Sometimes you can make a better check by daylight."

"Oh, yes," she said, "that would be all right. I think I'll be home — at least from two o'clock on."

"Fine. You know how it is in this job; just depends on how busy I am, and what else comes up. Good night."

"Good night." This time, when the outer door was closed, he heard her feet tapping away through the hall.

Blondie went off duty promptly at eight a.m. He went to his little one-room apartment in the East 50's and slept serenely for some hours. This was a Wednesday. He was off duty until he had to go on precinct patrol the next day.

Two o'clock, she had said. He shaved and showered hastily. He put on his favorite tan suit and walked into the building at 1202 Park Avenue at exactly 1:27 p.m. He should have made it even earlier, but he was somewhat reassured when the doorman said Miss Lazare was not at home. Blondie displayed his shield; no other persuasion was required — the door of apartment 3-D swung open a few minutes later, and Blondie closed it against any intrusion except that of the tenant.

He tossed his hat on a coffee table. After a moment's thought he went into the bathroom. No luck — just as he had feared, they had pressure toilets in all these large buildings — not the old-fashioned reservoir of water at the back. He had thought of a toilet reservoir, perhaps because he had been successful in locating a missing .32 caliber revolver in that fashion a few weeks before. . . . The bed? No. Upholstery? Somehow he couldn't see Miss Lazare ripping up any of those expensive cushions.

Blondie returned to the living room and prowled about, halting when he observed that the rug was rumpled beneath one corner of the automatic phonograph. There was little dust here. He got down on his knees and looked carefully. The phonograph cabinet, heavy, of good mahogany, had been shoved back and forth two or three times since the last dusting of that room. Blondie pulled it out again and got down on his knees.

It was all so simple that he had to laugh. She had put the jewelry in a rubber bath cap and tied the whole thing securely with a red ribbon, and the little hoard was dangling and spinning, a fat and guilty pendulum, up above the mechanism in the lower rear portion of the machine. . . . Blondie supposed that people like this babe thought they were cute and original.

Boy. Was she a dish!

He sat down on the davenport and opened the rubber wad at his leisure. She had been meticulous in the information she gave. Here they were: topaz ring set with rubies and diamonds; amethyst brooch; aquamarine bracelet; emerald pin; the clips . . . everything. Blondie bound the ribbon tight again and put the object in his pocket. He helped himself to a fresh cigar and turned on the radio softly; he was still fiddling with the dials when Miss Lazare arrived. He could hear her approaching the door rapidly. Apparently they had told her downstairs that the police were in the apartment again.

She looked very smart and well-shaped. "Well. You're certainly making yourself at home, aren't you?" An edge whetted in her voice.

Blondie said, "Let's dance," and nodded toward the radio-phonograph. He thought she caught her breath; he couldn't be sure. He stood offering his arms. Maybe she was a little pale, but at last she came into his arms, and so they danced . . . she felt soft and sleek, she smelled good . . . Blondie felt within himself a mingling of recklessness and duplicity.

The music stopped. The announcer's flavored voice began its ritual, and Edna Lazare fell away from Blondie's grasp. "Listen, you." She laughed nervously. "You're a funny kind of cop."

"Why so?"

"Oh, worming your way into my apartment like this, and wanting to dance and everything. Maybe I ought to report you."

Blondie said softly, "I don't think you will. Come here. I'll
show you something."

He led her out to the kitchen and showed her the screwdriver.
She was mute.

"Ever see this before?"

"Yes, it's my screwdriver. I got it a while back. I was fooling
with some fixtures in the bathroom."

"It was used to make those marks on the door."

"How do you know?"

"See—it just fits. A little paint on here, too, girlie."

Her voice was brittle. "So what? I suppose the burglars—"
She hesitated, her face was paper-white; she had fallen into this
trap so easily. . . .

"Give me your hand," he said, and when she didn't move he
took her fingers in his own clasp and slid them into the side
pocket of his coat. For a moment he could feel the fingers there,
exploring the knobby wad the jewelry made inside the cap . . .
then she realized what she was touching.

Edna Lazare jerked her hand free and turned away from him.
She walked into the living room and sat down stiffly in a chair.
She turned her face down. Her hand was clenched.

She groaned. "So now I suppose you'll arrest me."

"What was the matter, honey? Broke?"

"Yes." She began to sob. "I didn't know what else to do,"
and she blubbered for a time, and her make-up was spoiled. It
hurt her appearance for the moment . . . but she was still a witch
and then some. . . .

Oh, she had been having trouble. Domestic trouble. Her
Friend—well, they had quarreled. Here she was, stuck with
that apartment.

"You planning on making up with your—Friend?"

"I don't know. We met a couple of times and talked but—
here I was . . . gee, I couldn't afford to keep this place on my

own I tried to get some work — oh, honest to God, Mr. Dunbar, I just couldn't sleep nights!" She sobbed again.

It wasn't really a *crime,* was it? Everybody knew the insurance companies had lots of money . . . they wouldn't get hurt very much . . . they could afford it . . . honest, she had never done anything like this before in all her life . . . she wasn't a crook . . . she guessed she was just weak . . . it was such a temptation. . . . I thought I could get that money and it would kind of tide me over." She mourned at Blondie in pathetic dissolution. "What are you going to do with me?"

He said, "Get on the phone."

"To call — ?"

"Right. The Detective Division, over at the House, first. I'll give you the number: Lehigh 4-8634. Tell them you found the jewelry. It was in a trash can in the kitchen; the burglars must have dropped it on the way out. Tell the detectives it was all a mistake and to forget it. Then call the insurance company — the place you called this morning — and tell them the same thing."

Edna made the calls; she talked casually and well. There was some agitation in her voice, but over the telephone that might not be discerned. She hung up the receiver after the second call and pushed the phone away.

"You're a lucky girl."

"What do you mean?"

"Oh, I'm an easygoing kind of guy. Everybody makes mistakes, don't they?"

She shook her head. "Gee, I sure made one."

Blondie said, "I'm off duty until tomorrow. How's about us having a little drink?"

The heavy eyes came to his again and for the first time there was a bright filigree in their deepness.

"You good-looking bull," she whispered, "you just took the words right out of my mouth."

Blondie pursued a sordid romance with Edna Lazare through the winter and into the spring. He passed from the stage of the provocative and dangerous detective with a hidden whiplash coiled to that of a bland conqueror whose caresses were appreciated by his lady with increasing fervor.

Edna could tell lies with the aplomb of her lover, but not so successfully. Soon Blondie came to own a considerable store of facts concerning her, although it did not interest him particularly. Her name was really Elena LaCruz; she had been born in New York before the Puerto Rican influx reached ominous proportions. One thing she would never make clear to Blondie: that was the identity of her anonymous supporter. From little things that were told, and from other evidence that came his way, Blondie realized that the man was middle-aged, if not elderly, and that periodically he quarreled with Edna, striving from some compulsion to break off the relationship.

It was during a period of nonsupport that the girl in desperation had framed the jewel robbery to collect her insurance. But soon after Blondie's connivance the Friend signed a new peace treaty with Edna Lazare. Then it was necessary for the two deceivers to play a cautious game. This gave a spice of danger and concentrated iniquity to a condition already illicit. It was fun; Blondie enjoyed it. Doubtless the flavor of uncertainty protracted his liaison with Edna past any normal term.

She provided him with a rear-door key, and customarily he entered the building through a service door on 94th Street. Thus attendants out in front never saw Blondie. Edna cautioned him repeatedly; he shrugged, but obliged her. He must never enter the apartment — even by this devious means — until he had ample assurance from her that the coast was clear.

Not too long after the original encounter with Miss Lazare, Blondie grew loquacious to Dan Mallow one evening when their free time coincided and while Ellie attended a bridal shower.

Dan was treated to lurid passages in the Dunbar-Lazare saga.

"So that's the babe who had the jewels stolen, at 1202 Park?"

"You saw her. Want to admit that I've got a pretty neat deal?"

"I supposed you have, if that's the kind of deal you want. What about the jewelry? Did you ever get a line on it?"

"It was scrubbed the next day. She found the stuff. Apparently she frightened them when she unlocked the front door — they dropped it into a trash can on the way out — "

"Sez you," said Dan.

Blondie rolled up his eyes and looked long-suffering. "You're a hell of a buddy, buddy! You don't believe a thing I tell you."

"With considerable reason," said Dan. "O.K., here comes the check — and this is one time I'm not going to pick it up."

Dan knew about that rear-door key, and the injunction whereby Detective Dunbar was forbidden to enter the castle of his partner until properly cleared. But he could not forsee the perversity which might assail Blondie one hot evening. He could not see the stealthy trip to the third floor, the key twisting quietly in the rear door, the waiting, the creeping inside, the exploration, the repeated self-assurance that the Friend was out on Long Island where he had been for the entire week-end. Dan might not reckon specifically the hour of Blondie's short-lived luxury in the air-cooled apartment, with the hum and bumble of the city comfortably disregarded outside — the cold highball, the luxurious puff of an indolent pipe — and then the alertness as the front door opened, and the shock to find that the person who came was not Edna Lazare but the Friend himself, also seeking her.

"Hey, *chiquita,*" Blondie called in welcome. He put down his pipe and swung his feet to the floor, and then stood rooted, realizing that the tread which quickened along the hall was that of a man, heavy and threatening.

The Friend came in. He was broad-shouldered, full-bellied,

thick-necked and curly gray. He was 50 or thereabouts, and his eyes bulged honestly as he took a deep breath. "Who the hell are you?"

"Who the hell," Blondie repeated with as little politeness, "are you?"

"What are you doing in Miss Lazare's apartment?"

"I'm waiting to see her on business."

"Looks like a hell of a business to me! I guess I'll call the police."

Blondie asked evenly, "Are you sure you want to do that?"

The big man gulped and swallowed; his rage was cooking. "Get out!"

Well, well, it was too bad. Even Blondie realized, for all his atrocious self-assurance, that this comfortable idyl was terminated effectually. After all, he couldn't afford to pay the rent, and the Friend could. Nevertheless he had his personal dignity to maintain: he didn't like to be ordered around by a meaty-faced sententious old sinner who ought to have been home with his own fat wife. Blondie put on his coat leisurely. "I must say that you're not very hospitable."

The man rushed upon him and called him a name; he should have done neither. He should have remembered that he was corpulent and 50. Above all he should never have tried to seize a muscular young man of Blondie's training by the throat or shoulders. Dunbar acted automatically and in hasty resentment at the attack, but certainly he had no intention of working a ruin upon his assailant. It was like slow motion; the man outweighed him 50 or 60 pounds, and was as tall as he, but he moved like a cow. Blondie thrust his arms inside the other's grasp; he gave him a judo cut — the sideswipe of his hand — and kicked smartly against his shin in the same instant. The man went down; he fell heavily and cracked the corner of the coffee table with his temple as he went. He rolled and twitched,

he groaned; blood began dribbling from his mouth and nostrils.

There was only one thing to do: get out of there fast. Blondie went. He had closed the rear door, he had scampered down the untenanted staircase, he was out into the solid dark hotness of 94th Street in less than 70 seconds from the time the Friend tumbled. Blondie took a deep breath, and strolled through shadows toward Madison Avenue, smoothing and buttoning his coat as he went. He was safe in a bar at Madison and 93rd long before the first calling of frightened neighbors reached the ears of the police.

No, Dan Mallow knew nothing of these details. He could only feel, as he had felt in November, that Blondie was headed for perdition. Dan never dreamed that he would share it.

## CHAPTER 10

FIVE DAYS after the Mallows celebrated their first wedding anniversary, Dan and Joe were on the Four-to-Twelve Tour. It was desperately hot, with a threat of storm lingering beyond the Hudson yet refusing to burst loose over Manhattan. Policemen simmered in their cars; they fought people away from the fire hydrants; tempers of the public were short on this afternoon and evening, and the police temper suffered as well. By 10 p.m. Shetland and Mallow were near exhaustion . . . usually the last two hours were the longest portion of any tour.

They attended an Aided Case at Flower Hospital, then rang the House at 10:25 p.m.

*Twelve-Oh-Two Park Avenue. Apartment Three-D. A disturbance.* They were making the turn at 96th and Madison before the import of this address burst through the humidity.

"Twelve-Oh-Two Park?"

Shetland crawled past the red light at 96th and Park and swung south. "We had that last fall. Remember? There was that girl—I thought she might be a Spik—had her jewels stolen."

"Three-D. Was that the same apartment?"

"Sounds familiar."

They drew into the vacant space in front of the building's canopy just north of 94th. The doorman came to meet them. "How long does it take to get a cop around here, anyhow?"

"Take it easy, Johnny. What's the matter?"

"I called at least 20 minutes ago! The neighbors heard all that noise, and we knocked on the door. . . . They said it sounded like a fight—"

The doorman rode up to the third floor with the police. Some women were hovering in the hall. The woman from 3-E, next door, insisted that she had heard men's voices in argument, then the sound of a struggle, then silence.

"How long ago?"

"Nearly half an hour. I called downstairs. I guess they didn't believe me," and she glared accusingly at the doorman.

Shetland whispered to Dan, "Remember this place now, don't you?"

Dan was suffering guilty considerations, all of them about Blondie and what his brother-in-law had told him in the spring. They had not discussed Miss Lazare to any extent since. "Yes. The babe with the stolen jewels."

Joe inquired of employes: "What's the name of the tenant?"

"Lazare. Miss Lazare."

The neighbors sniffed with gleeful innuendo. "She lives there all alone, that Miss Lazare. *All alone.*"

"Have you got a passkey?" Joe asked the doorman.

"There's one downstairs."

"Go get it."

The doorman strode nervously away, then on impulse he turned and beckoned. Shetland went to him. The doorman said in a low voice, "I think that man's in there. Miss Lazare — she went out this afternoon and didn't come back. But — "

"What man are you talking about?"

"We fellows on the job just call him Mr. Brown. He comes every once in awhile. He came up here awhile ago on the elevator. . . ."

"Get the key," repeated Shetland.

The key was brought, they entered the apartment. Down the short hallway they could see a light burning in the living room, and they told the employes and sight-seeing tenants to wait at the threshold. They proceeded to the living room and found Mr. Henry Benelian lying unconscious, just as he had fallen.

The patrolmen's involuntary exclamations and their hasty activity as they reached the door of the living room brought the others thronging. Tenants, doorman, elevator man — they babbled excitedly until the officers cleared them out. Quickly they searched the apartment; no one else was hiding there. The back door had the night lock set although the bolt was not turned.

Henry Benelian: so the cards in his wallet proclaimed him to be, and he belonged to the American Legion, he belonged to the

National Rug and Carpet Association, he belonged to a lot of lodges, and he had over $350 in currency, and was tailored by Brooks Brothers. He lay severely injured — unconscious. He had been struck upon the side of the head by a blunt instrument; maybe he had a fractured skull. Not much of a fight . . . only that coffee table upset, and the things upon it, and Mr. Benelian's hat crushed under his shoulder on the floor.

In an ash tray on another table under the lamp, lay a good Dunhill pipe half full of ashes and tobacco, still slightly warm to the touch. While Shetland's back was turned Dan dumped the ashes and slid the pipe into his pocket. It was bad enough to have it, not only in his pocket, but on his conscience. No need to saddle Joe with *that* knowledge.

Telephone calls . . . Canal Six-Two-Thousand: that was the number you called to get an ambulance. And Lehigh Four-Oh-Five-Three: that was the number Dan called to inform the lieutenant of what they had found at this address and to summon detectives to the job. The Brains came before the ambulance arrived . . . repeatedly Dan and Joe went out to clean up the halls. Detectives Lew Jarrick and Al Moreno took this squeal; their commander, red-haired Lieutenant Innes, accompanied them.

The pipe felt heavy in Dan's pocket. He wondered that others could not see the bulge in his uniform; he wondered why they did not fall upon him with cries and place him on suspension and under arrest because of the evidence he was concealing.

Miss Lazare arrived almost simultaneously with the Reception Hospital ambulance. She didn't burst into tears; she did turn pallid; she stared, and nibbled at her nails. . . . Mr. Benelian. He was her Friend. No, she hadn't been home since early afternoon. An old girl chum had come to town and called her. Edna joined the girl at a movie and later had dinner with her at the Hotel Astor. The police could check on that, she mumbled.

"How did he get in here?"

"Well . . . he had a key." A key on Mr. Benelian's ring fitted the front door, so that much was true.

Shetland and Mallow took their leave; they toured briefly up Madison and back on Fifth. They broke up one crap game and jarred into wakefulness a bottle-baby who was sprawled beside a bench next to the park. Then it was midnight; they returned to the House, and in the locker room Dan had to await an opportunity to transfer the telltale pipe to his civilian clothes. It was the same pipe. He and Ellie had given it to Blondie on his birthday; they had picked it out together at the Dunhill shop down on Fifth. He couldn't mistake that one: all that carving on the bowl, and even the new stem — hand-cut, as Detective Dunbar had pointed out to his brother-in-law the week before.

Dan turned down an invitation for a cold beer, and he didn't head for the subway. He kept walking, up Duffy's Hill and south on Lex. In the end he walked all the way home: straight down Lexington Avenue and finally over to Third. He touched the pipe in the side pocket of his sport coat and drew his fingers away. This was nothing to fondle — it was a burden of shame and confusion. So what would happen now?

Blondie had been there. Circumstantially, he must have been the man who brawled with Mr. Benelian and knocked him unconscious. Dan couldn't imagine Blondie wielding a blunt instrument against an old fatty like the injured man. Probably the fellow had hit his head when he fell, or something like that. It was all too apparent . . . the Friend . . . Miss Lazare admitted that Benelian had a key. One hell of a mess.

If Benelian should die — and certainly he was hurt severely — there would be a homicide rap out of this for someone. Dan didn't know what to do, he didn't know what to do, he didn't know what to do. If he told Joe, he would be merely hauling Joe into it, too. Joe would be faced with the same gruesome decision confronting Dan Mallow now: whether to talk or keep his mouth shut. It would become a cowardly sharing of official, legal and moral responsibility without actually shifting any of it. The guy might die. Even if he didn't die ...

Why hadn't he just let that pipe lie there in the ash tray — let somebody else find it, and try to identify the owner? But almost simultaneously with his seeing the pipe tilted in that ashtray, he had seen Ellie's face.

Not in imagery but in disconsolate fact Dan stood looking at her face again. He had crept silently up the stairway. Ellie was pregnant now and she tired easily, especially after a hot day. Dan had taken off his shoes before he moved into the bedroom and saw her lying there pearled with the sweat of sleep, but with countenance serene.

Ellie loved her brother with an embattled ardor which appeared blind to others. Dan felt that it was not blindness ... she knew, she knew what Blondie was like. But what might she say and do, how might she feel, if Dan became the instrument of Blondie's destruction, whatever the justice?

Dan undressed in the living room so that he would not disturb his wife. He turned off the light and sat naked, slumped in a chair, bare legs stretched out across the floor. At last he went to sleep in that position.

Dan was at the House before three the next afternoon, which was a Tuesday. He imagined that people in the Ninety-five Room stared from their den and conjectured on why he was wandering there in unseasonable eagerness.

Upstairs waited the Detective Division. Couldn't he just step inside for a minute? Couldn't he call to some of those shirt-sleeved men and see them look up from desks where they were bending? Couldn't he just say, "By the way, I was on that job at 1202 Park last night. What about the guy? Did he die? Did you get a line on the perpetrator?" Never that. They might start wondering why Mallow was so damn interested.

Dan climbed in affliction to the top of the stair. He heard voices in the front room, he saw the door of the hall washroom swinging and Detective Jarrick stepped out. . . .

"Hi," Dan said weakly.

"Hello, Mallow."

Dan spoke from a clammy throat. "You ought to be home asleep."

Jarrick stretched his hairy arms and yawned. "Oh, I had to come on for an hour or so. They made a pinch this morning on an old case I'd worked on."

Dan asked, as easily as he could, "What about the one last night? Did the guy—" he got the word out—"die?"

"Oh, that one over on Park. No. They took him to Reception, then they got hold of his family, and the family had him moved over to Doctors' Hospital. Moreno just called up a while ago: he's still unconscious, still on the critical list."

Dan tried to make his steps casual as he moved toward the rear door. "What about the girlie?"

"We checked: that was a straight story about her having dinner down at the Astor. The guy, though—what's his name? Benelian—he was keeping her, or so the manager of the building thought. The girl claimed Benelian hadn't been there in three weeks or something like that. She claims she didn't have any other friends, but probably that's a lot of bunk." Jarrick whistled. "Did you get a good look at her? I wouldn't mind something like that myself." He went into the Squad Room.

Everybody grumbled about the heat. Bouncy Carroll stood next to Dan's locker and said that he wished he was riding in a nice cool car on this Four-to-Twelve, and not walking in the sun. . . . Nice cool car: that was one for the book. The Four-to-Twelve was the worst tour of all in this heat. More pumps were

turned on during those hours, there were so many little jobs to
do. Once in a while you got a break on the Late Tour in summer: maybe you had a run over near the river, and you got to
take an illicit spin down Roosevelt Drive with wing glasses
turned to shoot the air against your face.... Nice cool car — yeh.
You stuck to the seat; the cover on the upholstery was pressed
into knots and wrinkles to rub through your sodden clothing.

They squabbled, they joked, they went down and stood for-
mation.

As they paraded across in front of the desk, the man at the
switchboard yelled, "Shetland!" and waved a slip of paper. Joe
went to get the slip. After they were told to take their posts outside, he showed the paper to Dan. "Payroll job."

"Whereabouts?"

"It's not a regular. Sixteen-Oh-Five Madison: real estate office.
He just called in; he's got a lot of cash, and wants to make a
drop at the National City branch on 86th." They got their car;
they did a routine turn past the House and went over to Madison.
A shirt-sleeved youth waited on the step at 1605, and he beckoned
out a swarthy man in a Palm Beach suit. Dan got out; Mr.
Ortiz climbed to sanctuary on the seat between him and Joe.

Bad people in the neighborhood, said Mr. Ortiz. It was dangerous ... he had all this money ... a fellow paid him in cash — over $2600 — he didn't want to leave that in his office safe. Crooks were apt to break in. . . . The officers sat moody and bored, conducting their share of the conversation in monosyllables. At 86th Street, Shetland turned east and halted in traffic opposite the National City Bank, waiting for a break in the line of buses, trucks and cars — waiting for a chance to make a U.

"We ought to have come over on 84th to Lex; then we'd be on the right side of the street."

"Correct. I was just asleep at the switch."

"Hold it, Joe; too much traffic. I'll walk him over."

This wasn't the best policy in the world but it seemed the only thing to do. Shetland sat, already parboiled and dreamy. He didn't know quite what he'd do on his Forty-eight ... maybe take his niece and nephew to the beach. He didn't care much for crowded summer beaches but the children loved to go. Their mother said that Joe spoiled them — he ruined their digestions with hot dogs and frozen custards and too many Cokes. Shetland smiled within the solemn set of his jaw. He was imagining Frieda in her pink beach outfit ... she was surely a cute kid. The beach outfit had a little floppy pink hat — a kind of bonnet — and she looked like those pictures of *The Sunbonnet Babies* in an ancient book to which Joe and Mildred had become heirs when they were children.

Mallow walked back alone. He opened the door on the right-hand side and fanned himself with his cap.

"Where is ze man, Señor Mallow?"

"He didn't want to go back to his office. He was going over to the subway and go downtown."

A youngish, dark-haired woman trotted from the sidewalk, calling shrilly, "Policemen!" and waving an envelope in her hand. She ran between parked cars, and the driver of one was backing up; the woman skipped out of the way with a cry as Dan sprang toward her; bumpers clanged together.

"You'd better look out, lady. You oughtn't to walk between parked cars like that."

"Please. I got a paper; I want you to serve it."

Dan said, "We don't serve papers. What have you got — a summons?" He opened the envelope and examined the document. It was all right: she was haling somebody into Court.

"We don't serve papers like this. You serve it yourself. We go along with you in order to keep the peace," and he grinned at Joe above the woman's shoulder.

"Keep the peace!" she echoed. "I'll say! It's my landlord. He's an old guy but he's mean. I'm afraid to go up there alone."

"Wait a minute," called Joe. "Maybe it's down in the 19th."

The woman pointed. "Just around the corner. Over there, north of 86th."

"That's us — that's the 23rd."

Joe called, "Get in the car, Dan. I'll take it."

"You're too old and tired; you weigh too much. Which floor is it on, lady?" He sighed. "Fourth? O.K. Let's go."

Shetland told him, "I won't pull around there on Lex; I'll stay here where the street is wider."

Dan shepherded the woman toward the corner and held her back until the light changed; then they crossed to the north side and vanished up Lexington.

Joe took off his cap and wiped the sweat glued against his bony scalp; he wished for a fan. He let his eyes move over vehicle tops to the building across the way. Apathetically he saw the RKO theater marquee, and watched the drift of customers past the ticket office. Cars passed, they blocked the way, the street opened up again . . . heat watered Joe's vision and distorted things. Nearly 4:30; the sun glared hard. Up in the northern sectors people would be gushing the hydrants no matter how they suffered for lack of water in ensuing dry seasons.

A building exit next door between the movie and the bank ...
a young man came out. He was bareheaded, he wore a tan suit,
he wore black sunglasses and carried a brief case. He turned his
head quickly from left to right, left again, and then set his pace
toward Lex. Idly Joe watched this brisk young man ... the
light was changing, the fellow went across Lexington and
mingled in the crowd waiting to board a westbound bus. Joe
saw the blank dark disks of the spectacles turn again, the sun
caught them and made them shine; the man had gone aboard
the bus, the light was changing back to red. The bus stood there.

Voice ... a woman squealing. Joe turned his head.

At the rear entrance of the building next to the movie a
little knot of people gathered. There teetered a woman in a
white blouse and black skirt, her hair disarranged; even as he
looked Joe saw a man reach forward with a handkerchief to dab
at the woman's face. Shetland turned the handle of the door and
stepped to the street. Traffic went past, the light changed to green
at Lexington. Roar and vapor from faulty exhausts rose in the
burning air. Joe observed the woman (traffic had passed him by
and he could see her once again): a long strip of adhesive tape
dangled loosely from her wrist; she waved her arms and yelled.
She saw the radio car across the street, or someone told her it was
there; she broke out of the growing crowd and lunged toward
the curb, the adhesive still dangling.

That building and that doorway; the young man, he'd come
out ... dark spectacles ... and carrying a brief case and walking
fast. Well, hell — it mightn't be ...

Joe couldn't take a chance. The bus was bumping past the
intersection, coming on, and he was in its path. He had his
whistle out so quickly ... how he got it out that quick he didn't
know. He was there in the middle of traffic, he heard brakes
squealing right and left, but Shetland had eyes only for the

bus: the big flat-fronted bus, larger and larger it grew. He heard his whistle note go up, he had his hand on high. The driver turned his head, and Joe could see him straining, wondering, bearing down on the brakes. The bus jolted to a halt.

Joe ran around the front; he struck his fist against the door. Squeal and hiss . . . the doors flung open. Joe put his left hand on polished metal inside the door while his right hand sought the revolver holster at his hip. The notion assailed him that he might be doing a foolish thing; that was a busy building, lots of people came in or out. Just because a young man in a tan suit, carrying a brief case, had walked away with alert briskness and boarded a bus . . . If there had been a stick-up there was no assurance that the young man had committed the crime. Shetland was always loath to produce his weapon at close quarters in a crowd of people. But still he'd better give this guy a toss. At least he'd better see what was in that brief case and —

He was thinking these things all in a second as his shoes struck the steps, as he swung in past the driver and saw those rows of sweaty faces gazing at him and saw the twin dark disks of the young man's spectacles well toward the rear, and saw how white the fellow's expressionless countenance appeared.

Joe moved down the aisle. "Hold it, Johnny," he flung at the driver. He shouldered past a plump Italian woman, and her flowered dress was damp with perspiration; he could smell it.

He was hit, and hit too hard. Was it two blows, or three? It was like running against the ends of sharpened stakes; they hurt; they took his breath away . . . simultaneously the blows had jammed against his body, striking belly and chest. Joe saw the young man standing up, he saw the gun: the man had fired it . . . automatic . . . he was waving it, hoping to shoot again, but the bus was one vast screaming mass of people getting up and trying to get out, and trying to knock Joe Shetland down, and Shetland was alone with God on post.

He had his own gun out of the holster. His arm was a long arm, the gun was far away from him, far away from his shoulder; still he couldn't shoot, for there were all those people. He blundered on, his left hand sank against one of the metal handholds at the corner of a seat, he clutched, unclutched, he found another handhold, his feet were balancing him ahead. Round discs, the sunglassed face: it stared above a seat top toward the rear. By this time Shetland was as far as the rear door, more than halfway back, and he clutched a polished shaft of chrome. Still beyond — three seats beyond — the pale face, the bare head, the crew-cut hair, the spectacles so circular and blank and black. The man had made a fortress of his seat, or he was trying to. He fired once again.

. . . Outside, get outside . . . he'll kill someone if he keeps shooting at me here. . . .

First step down, all right; Shetland's feet found pavement down below, his knees were jelly, limp; he stiffened them.

Joe had his left hand on a window ledge — oh, boy — and it seemed to him that he was holding up that bus . . . he thought the bus was falling now. It tipped halfway, the street tipped, too, but Joe was using every bit of strength he had ever possessed to keep everything upright. Another window open . . . scatter glass against his face . . . another shot. How many had the fellow fired now? Joe counted: must be four or five. . . .

His left hand on the open window frame was straining. He hoisted, wriggled, panted, found the space beyond his eyes. His right hand now, he had his gun, he put it in the window frame.

He saw the face. It turned away and was climbing now. Oh, tall young man in your tan suit, climbing over that far seat . . . wait, now, wait. He's nearly at the top; now shoot, now squeeze, and feel the gun jump up, and bring the front sight down and squeeze again once more, and watch the tan suit whirling far away, and whirling to a stop.

*Hey, Dan.* He hoped to say it; couldn't say it; but he heard the voice of Dan, yelling: *Let me through here.* . . .

It was difficult to assort the facts. Shetland was dead when lifted from the street. The man in the bus had been killed by Joe's bullets, one of which had gone through his arm and into the chest cavity, the other through the base of the brain.

As finally compiled for official and public uses, the story began with the appearance of a man named Murphy who had once worked as an office boy for the Empire State Finance Corporation and who walked into that office, carrying a brief case and wearing sunglasses. He spoke to an elderly bookkeeper who remembered him; he chatted with this man until all customers were out of the office. Then he closed the door, produced a gun and compelled the manager to bind his employes with adhesive tape. Murphy himself tied up the manager. He looted the open safe, a cashbox and drawers, and walked out of the building leaving the loan-office door closed behind him. A secretary, Miss Sylvia Rosenblatt, had been struggling quietly with her bonds; she managed to free herself a moment after the young man's departure. She ran to the street, crying for help. She fell down as she rushed out of the office and hurt her cheek: that was why a man daubed at her with his handkerchief.

Apparently Murphy realized he was trapped the instant Shetland stopped the bus, and chose to begin shooting before he was challenged. Dan Mallow, far around the corner on Lexington and four stories aloft, heard the gunfire; he came as fast as he could. By the time he reached the scene Shetland had killed the thug and collapsed.

Thus facts were gleaned — were separated, washed, dried and put together neatly. Confusion became heroism: a disordered mix-up would be reduced to neat agate type in General Orders, with the posthumous award of the Department Medal of Honor.

"Darling, it's four o'clock. Please lie down."

"Ellie, I can't. Seems like I've just got to sit here. I don't know whether I told you: I went all the way through the whole deal — made out the card — everything. Did I tell you about Sergeant Breed?"

Her voice was slender through darkness, laving him with tears. "No. What about Sergeant Breed?"

"Well, he stood there and looked at Joe, and they were talking about an ambulance — Hell's bells, he was dead by that time. Then Breed said, 'He's not going to ride in a damn ambulance — not his last ride, not Shetland.'" Dan's voice broke. "You know what Breed did? Phoned for a wagon — you know —

patrol wagon. He told me to go along. That's the way we went down to the morgue. I mean — " He swallowed, then began anew: "That's how Shetland went down to the morgue. In a wagon."

She knew that something was expected of her; she kissed his forehead.

"Honey," he said, "would you mind getting me a drink? What have we got?"

He heard the sound of the switch in the kitchenette. Ellie's voice came back to him. "We've still got some rum, and here's a weentsie little bit of Cointreau. We had that on the honeymoon. Remember, darling?"

"Get some rum, please." But when he tried to drink it he gagged and coughed.

"Darling, won't you please take off your clothes and lie down?"

"No. I don't want to go to bed."

"Danny, let me say something. Will you, please?"

He mumbled a response.

"Try to remember how it was in the war. I know you had other friends — one of them was killed right beside you. It's a *thing,* Dan. It comes to everybody."

"That isn't the point. If I hadn't — " He trembled, then went on: "I told you about the summons. That woman — she was a German lady, her name was Schultz. If I hadn't gone up with her while she handed that paper to her landlord, well — instead of letting Joe go, the way he was willing to. He volunteered to do it. The way he wanted to . . ."

There was a long silence; then Ellie spoke with calmness and dignity. "I'll always love you for that, Dan. You were being kind. Joe is — was — in his middle 40's. He was big and heavy, it was a hot day, you tried to save him the stairs."

"Yeh. I tried to save him the stairs. I got him killed." He

broke down and cried savagely for the first time, and her arms were around him. "Ellie . . ."

"Darling, you did it before — I've even heard you joke about it. You said you had two roommates shot out from under you. You could take it, then. You and Blondie both."

He stiffened, he turned dry as old tobacco in her grasp, he turned as hard as lead pipe.

"But, Dan, what — ? I'm merely trying to — "

"Yeh. Blondie! All right." He fairly roared it; he could hear the echo of his voice go banging across the caverned width of the avenue. "Blondie! I'm going to tell you the whole thing. Baby, I'm going crazy; I've got to talk. It isn't just Joe — I mean — Joe's being killed in the line of duty — " He asked, after a pause: "Remember your dear little brother's birthday?"

"Yes."

"What did we give him?"

"A pipe. We got it down at — "

"Go look. It's in my top drawer, behind all those handkerchiefs."

She cried, "Dan, I don't know what you mean!"

He poured out the story, he told it hatefully. He had reserved most of the oaths merited by the man who slew his friend; he anointed Blondie with them now.

"You see the situation I'm in. I was thinking of you, I guess, thinking of the fact that Blondie was your brother. I just stuck the damn pipe in my jacket. I didn't want Joe to see. He never knew about it. And now that guy — what is his name? — it's Armenian — some kind of a rug guy — Benelian. He's in the hospital; and if he dies — do you realize that would be a homicide rap? Against Blondie. If I tell — "

Dan walked into the kitchenette, he drew water from the tap. The stuff was lukewarm. He opened the refrigerator door and tried to take out the bottle they kept there. It slipped from his hand and smashed upon the floor in a slather and splash of water and glass particles. He stepped out of it gingerly and turned and drank the lukewarm flow from the tap. He left the light on and came back into the front room.

He could see Ellie: pale shape, motionless in her thin night-gown; he could see the slight swell of her protruding abdomen, the child of his she was carrying.

"I guess — sometimes in the past," he said, "you've thought that I was pretty tough about Blondie — hard on him, I mean. Oh, yes — he's spoiled to the hilt. Women have spoiled him; folks have let him get by with stuff. Well, here I am now, holding the bag for him. I had a hard time trying to get to sleep last night. I guess maybe I didn't sleep much; but I didn't feel the way I feel now. I keep thinking of Joe. He got killed this after-noon, doing his job. I don't know just what happened on that bus. But he went along, hanging onto windows while he bled to death inside and out, until he could get that guy and not hurt a lot of other people while he was doing it."

He cried, "Ellie, he was a good cop. I rode with him from the start, almost. He — he wasn't any saint; he liked to have a drink, liked to tell a story. He didn't go blabbing around about every Regulation. He smoked in the car!" Dan laughed dryly. "Just like anybody else. But he did his job. And then I try to stack him up against a guy named Blondie — and what's on the other side? Blondie's been playing around with this babe for months; and then somehow or other he's up in that apartment and gets in a row with her boy friend and conks him on the head and gets the hell out of there. I'm the goon who comes in; I'm the weak sister who picks up the pipe. Ellie, believe me, I don't mind so much about *me*. I keep thinking about *Joe*. Do you understand what I mean?"

She broke in before he had finished, before the sound had left his lips. She came to him, her head turned against his chest.

"Dan. There's one thing you'll have to do. Turn Blondie in."

"Ellie, I—"

"You were on that job; you and Joe went in and found a man badly injured. If you had discovered the perpetrator at the scene, you would have arrested him, wouldn't you?"

He groaned, "I just can't see myself walking into Reardon's office. I tried to—I tried to make myself *see* myself doing it. But I thought you'd hate me."

"I'll never hate you, whatever happens. You're good, Dan. I love you. I have a wonderful feeling whenever I think that I'm going to have your baby."

There were other things . . . he told her about them now. His dry voice murmured on and on . . . little cheating things, the conniving things, the shooting of Merkenspeyer, the whisky. . . .

"Dan, why didn't you tell me all this before?"

He tried to make laughter; there was only a wretched squeal in his throat. "Ellie, what would you have said to me then? You know how you are about Blondie."

She sighed. "I was an awful fool. I've gone on for years—babying Blondie, picking up after him, giving him money, spoiling him. Somehow it's all so clear now. It's as if I were standing over there across the room, looking at myself, wondering why or how I did it."

They said nothing for a time . . . gently she called his name. "There's a way. Tell Blondie he's got to turn himself in. Go to him. Find him—wherever he is. Tell him he's got to do it."

"Suppose he says no?"

"If he won't go to his commanding officer, then you take him in yourself."

He went down and stalked through shadows. Blondie lived on East 58th, in an old building over near Sutton Place, and

Dan moved east on 62nd Street. In the vestibule of Dunbar's building he reached for his flashlight. Of course he had no flashlight; he snapped his lighter in the vestibule, found Blondie's bell and rang three times. He tried to reckon Blondie's schedule in his mind . . . five-day chart: only one or two nights out of five was Blondie apt to be in the Squad Room. Hell — he was probably out wolfing. Again the blind, accusing rage. . . .

Dan Mallow was turning away when the automatic door switch began to throb. He climbed two flights to the corridor which gave on Blondie's quarters.

Blondie held the door open to see who was coming. He was naked. He had been sleeping raw, quite appropriately in this heat, and when he recognized Dan he came out into the corridor, nude as he was.

"Dan!"

"Hi."

Blondie squeezed his hand. Still holding Dan's hand, he led him into the hallway of his small apartment and closed the door. He put his left hand on Dan's right shoulder and patted him. He could brim with sympathy when it did not inconvenience him. "I'm sorry. I stopped over at your place about seven o'clock, as soon as I heard about it. Did Ellie tell you I was there?"

"Yes."

"I didn't know just what would happen — I thought probably you wouldn't finish out the tour. . . ."

Dan pushed past his brother-in-law down the narrow re-modeled hallway. He said over his shoulder, "I went all the way through on the thing. Downtown with — with the body. I'd just as soon not talk about it." He halted abruptly, and turned. "Sorry. I forgot to ask: are you entertaining company?"

Blondie shook his head. "Not at the moment. I had to get a little sleep. I go on day duty at eight. How about a drink?"

"No."

Dan tossed his hat to a chair. In the yellow glow of the bed lamp he saw something where the hat struck. He picked up two long wisps — pale chiffon stockings — and there were frilly garters to go with them, and one of the garters fell to the floor when Dan lifted the hose.

"Who were you entertaining? Dick Tracy?"

Blondie grinned contentedly. "Just an old friend — somebody I hadn't seen in a long time."

Dan stood with his hands in his pockets and looked at Dunbar squarely. "What about the babe at 1202 Park?" He stood watching Blondie's discomfiture and found cruel joy in the sight.

Blondie said lightly, "That's ancient history now."

"So you go on day duty tomorrow — I mean today — Wednesday. That means you were on precinct patrol day before yesterday, Monday. So that means you were off Monday evening."

Blondie asked, "So what?"

Dan sat down on the disordered bed . . . he thought he would collapse, he would fall backward on those same tossed sheets where Blondie had been romping. "I didn't come over here to have you commiserate about Joe, and I didn't come to talk about babes or about your five-day chart. Remember Askins?"

There was a silence long enough for Blondie to journey back across the Atlantic and across the plains of northwest France — long enough for him to take a position once more on the embankment of that road that led through Courmeilles to Genicourt.

"Of course I remember Askins. Who are you trying to kid? We roomed together from the time we left England."

"Remember the day he cracked up?"

The naked Blondie looked down at Dan. "Listen. What's all this business about Askins and the war and everything? What's that got to do with anything?"

"I was just wondering whether you remembered how it felt to lose your best friend."

Blondie whispered, "Not so nice."

"Probably you felt the way I feel now. You've been all stamped on and chewed and mixed around. You've been torn up inside and outside, and a lot of things come to the surface, maybe, that weren't on the surface before. You feel like you've got to hit somebody. You know you've got to hit somebody, and you don't know just who to hit."

Now his gaze rose to meet Blondie's. "Most people don't, that is. Well, I do. I'm going to hit you."

Blondie went away and found a cigar on the table. He bit off the end, played with the cigar, blew out the smoke. Somewhere among a muddle of clothes and pillows he found a yellow beach robe. He put this on and sat down on the other end of the bed and looked quizzically at Dan. "Go ahead — sock."

"There's no use pretending you don't know about that job at 1202 Park. I mean about Edna Lazare. I mean about her boy friend: Mr. Benelian. Don't try to give me a lot of bull."

Dunbar blew out a vast cloud of smoke. He rolled up his eyes and looked pained.

Dan said, "It must have been talked all around the Squad Room."

"I was off yesterday. I don't know what they talked about up there."

"Oh, yes, you do. Your bump of curiosity is too high, and your conscience was too guilty. Probably you went over to the House and hung around. You took a busman's holiday — no doubt of that."

Blondie sighed. "All right, if you must; I did find out about it. Benelian's still on the critical list."

"Suppose he gets off the critical list by dying? Wouldn't that be a homicide rap for somebody?"

"I suppose so."

"For you."

Blondie leaped up with an air of threat, the coarse robe fell away from his muscular legs. "What are you trying to pull? Are you trying to be Great God Almighty? I know you feel terrible about Joe. But what are you trying to pull on me?"

Boats, the late night boats, the early morning boats, they grunted on the river so near; thin traffic gushed on the bridge, and there came a truck or a bus, making the old building tremble.

"Sit down, Blondie. If you want a busted jaw on that pretty face of yours, you just try to start something. Do you know what you did? You left your pipe in Edna's apartment after you clobbered the guy. You left him lying there and you beat it. Joe and I were on the Four-to-Twelve; we got that job. When we went in I found your pipe in an ash tray. Still warm. It was the one Ellie and I gave you for your birthday."

Blondie's face was pale under its summer tan. "O. K. But it's circumstantial."

"Circumstantial. But true."

"Well, you ought to know better than to ask me any questions. If the guy recovers, everything's in the clear."

Dan shook his head. "We won't wait for that, sweetheart."

He found himself on his feet. He was standing before Blondie and his fists were clenched. "I was screwy, I guess . . . I was thinking of Ellie. You've polished all the apples you're going to polish in the 23rd Precinct or on the 23rd Squad. I found myself holding the bag for you on Monday night, but no more. Either you go to Innes and tell him, or I go into Reardon's office and put that pipe in front of him. You make your own choice."

Blondie lay back on the bed and closed his eyes. Looking down at the smooth handsome face, Dan felt a pity that transcended any emotion of comradely relationship, any affection he had ever possessed for the man before. This was a collapse, a surrender unpleasant to witness. It was as if Blondie had run gamely ahead of the wolves of misfortune, the grimmer beasts of justice, for a long time ... now the avenging animals surrounded him and he could hear the snapping of their jaws.

Again the illusion of Shetland occupied Dan's mind. When again he heard his own voice it sounded like the snarl of the same demons besetting Blondie Dunbar. "How about it? You decide. You decide quick."

Blondie did not move. "Dan, I didn't think you'd do this to me."

"Neither did I. ... You had it coming."

"I'll go to Innes."

"When?"

"He usually comes in about ten or eleven a.m. Sometimes earlier if we're busy."

"I'm not taking any chances on your backing out. I'm going to the House, too."

"No need of that."

"I don't trust you. You might get cold feet; I wouldn't blame you much. If you do — then I walk into Captain Reardon's office."

Blondie sat up and put his cigar in an ash tray. He went into the kitchenette and snapped the light chain. Dan heard him opening the refrigerator door, he heard the clink of bottles. Blondie called, "Want a drink? I do."

"I'll take one now. Blondie, what actually happened up there at Edna's on Monday?"

Blondie told him while he poured out the liquor and mixed the drinks. "I didn't have time to make up my mind about anything. He tried to grab me. For all I knew he wanted to kill me. So I gave him the business."

Dan said, "I guess where you made your mistake — your last

big mistake, I mean — was in getting out of there fast. You should have stayed right by that telephone and called the House."

Blondie smiled weakly. "Where I made my mistake was in having you on the Four-to-Twelve that night." The glass shook in his hand. "I guess this means the end of me in the Department."

"You ought to have thought about that before."

"I told you it all went too fast. I didn't think about anything except scramming. If I'd had a brain cell working I wouldn't have left that pipe."

"If I'd had a brain cell working I wouldn't have picked it up, either. Well . . ."

The hot night was paling to blue beyond the window, the tall glass was icy and misty in Dan's hand. There was a clamminess about the rigid feel of it, and Dan wondered whether Shetland was clammy in the morgue, and knew that he was.

"Cheers."

"Cheers," muttered Blondie, and they drank.

That morning they went together to the House and Blondie walked upstairs to his doom. Things were quiet, the attendant was sweeping, a lost child was brought in by Patrolman Hoenicke. She was a honey, a pretty little coffee-colored girl wearing a white sun suit, and she sat on the high desk and attempted to give Lieutenant Abbott a bite of the ice-cream cone which Hoenicke had bought for her. Dan stood before the board in the Back Room and tried to read the notices. Once his anger had been solidified into purpose and had been expended as a just but terrible weapon against Blondie, he felt weak and overcome by petty worries. It had seemed to Mallow, in the first agony following Joe Shetland's death, that he should never be alarmed or even confused by inconsequential matters again. Compared with the assassination of his partner, this dilemma of Blondie's was trivial.

Yet (because of relationships past and present) Dan found himself agonizing along with the culprit upstairs. If Benelian was worse, most certainly if he died, Blondie would be up to his neck in trouble of a most unfragrant kind. But if Benelian survived comfortably and could not identify his assailant or chose not to press any charges, things might be a little easier for ex-Detective Dunbar. *Ex* he would most certainly be.

Dan tried to stir his stiff feet from the floor. He had heard Reardon come in, he had heard his quick voice greeting Patrolman Dubowick and Kelly in the office. The captain would be there now, and available.

Dan rehearsed what he must say. "Sir, I've got some days coming. Four days on that Bureau of Operations Order 236 . . ."

"Yes, The taxi strike last spring."

"And a couple more. I'm due to start the Late Tour tomorrow midnight. Would it be possible for me to take those days now, right after my Forty-eight?"

"Go ahead and take them."

There would be a solemnity in the place. There was sympathy — for him, for one another, for the whole Department — in the breasts beneath the soggy blue shirts. No one would refuse Dan the right to take those days . . . now, when he needed them most. There was no civic emergency.

His feet moved at last — not to the captain's office but to the stairway. He went up to the second floor. He could see all the way in through the Squad Room from the hall. The door to Innes's private office was shut and there were no arresting officers lounging about: at least the lieutenant was not interrogating a prisoner. He was interrogating Blondie and no one else.

Dan's head swelled and ached as he turned away. He thought of that other Dunbar, dead so long ago in the line of duty. In some ways Blondie really had the makings of a good cop. Yes, in many ways . . . too bad. Now that Dan Mallow knew his brother-in-law was trapped in a befitting purgatory, he could go downstairs again — not with a light heart, but at least with the grim unholy satisfaction that whatever justice ensued would be visited by the proper agency in the proper way, and not through his own emotional crusade and jurisdiction.

That night Dan and Ellie bought a copy of *Cue* and searched through the movie lists for a good comedy. They found a W. C. Fields revival in progress on the West Side; they went over there after dinner. Dan had heard nothing from Blondie since morning. When he and Ellie returned from the movie, however, there was a note shoved under the door.

*Dear Dan:*

*Maybe you didn't think I would be a lucky person again, as you said I always was before. But, believe it or not, I have been luckier than you forecast.*

*First, Lt. Innes checked with Benelian's doctor and the guy was removed from the critical list this morning; he is coming along fine. They think he'll be out by the end of the week.*

*Anyway, toots, I'm still a cop. They flopped me. They sent a Forty-nine downtown for the revocation of my appointment to the Detective Division. I will be reassigned, in uniform, but to some other precinct.*

*Dan, I suppose you think I will hate you with undying hatred, but such is not the case. I guess any decent person, under the same circumstances, would have been compelled to put the pressure on me. I cherish absolutely no grudge. All I really feel sorry about now, because I am so glad I was not kicked out of the Department, is about Joe Shetland. He was one swell cop.*

*Give Ellie a kiss for me.*

*As ever,*
*Blondie*

This note was written on some queer pink stationery which Blondie must have purchased at a corner drug store for the purpose. Beside his signature was a rough drawing of a little round-faced something-or-other trying to look like an angel. It had wings and wore a halo with rays shooting out.

The services were held on Saturday from a Catholic church in Greenwich Village where Shetland had, for a period in his youth, donned a cassock as an altar boy. It was an Inspector's funeral. Dan was a pallbearer, so were Leech and Capek; the other five bearers were all men who had worked with Shetland, who had known him well and would wish him comfort now on the strange Tour he was riding. The Mass, the Colors, the Departmental flag . . . faces Dan Mallow had seen before, and one face in particular: Mayor O'Dwyer's. The Mayor stood at attention as the cortege went by; he stood with hat held opposite his left shoulder. *You will be alone with God many times on post. . . .*

Then, with Ellie, Dan walked in a bleak block they did not know; they walked in a neighborhood and a world they did not know. They walked toward an existence in the cops which Dan did not know and would have to learn all over again. They walked away from Shetland's funeral.

"Ellie."

"What, dear?"

"How would you like to go out with me and get blind?"

She squeezed his hand. "I'd love to get blind with you, but Joseph Shetland Mallow might not like it."

"No. I suppose he wouldn't. Would J. S. like a malted milk?"

"J. S. Mallow adores malted milks. They sit very well on his funny tummy."

"*Bueno.* We have ze malted milk." Not then but later a strange idea occurred to him. Funny: he had never even considered such a possibility before. "Ellie. Suppose it's not J. S. Suppose it's a girl."

She chuckled over her soda-fountain glass. "You stupe. Joseph*ine,* of course."

Planning for Dan's days off, they thought of a car, they thought of woods and quiet places. Rather timorously Ellie suggested asking Blondie for his roadster but Dan merely grunted. Finally on Wednesday he borrowed George Capek's car; it was an old crate but it held together . . . they wandered Long Island. They walked beside the shore, holding hands, letting the peace of time and water move in behind them. They visited friends; Dan could drink, and he could laugh again, and he could hear B-26's in his sleep . . . He would hear those engines, and see little Christmas trees of flak bursts ahead and on both sides . . . *I don't want to fly a tour over Berlin or the Ruhr. Flak always makes me lose my lunch* . . . he was awake again, listening to the sea and the night birds, remembering other friends long lost in Infinity.

A wide wild precinct Shetland was roving now . . . no, never roving. *Fixed Post.* Dan whispered it to himself, and then he turned over and found his wife's hand, and fell asleep holding her hand with a peculiar quietness that approached contentment.

## CHAPTER 11

H E RETURNED to duty on the Day Tour, turning out with the platoon at eight a.m. the following Friday. The night he walked among those lockers . . . "My name's Dan Mallow. Are you Shetland? I guess I'm riding with you tonight." This morning he stopped at the Ninety-five Room on the way up; he stopped in the Back Room to look at the flimsy roll call fastened with thumbtacks against the board.

Car 322. Operator: Mallow. Recorder: Foynes.

Who the hell was Foynes? Dan remembered the first time he had looked at a flimsy like that to see the XXXXX and to see his own name. Those X's concealed the activity of Bertenelli and made Dan a partner of Joe Shetland, and made him a part of Shetland whenever he would patrol the Precinct in the future, whenever he would put his hand into his pocket and feel his shield. . . . Dan put on his shoes. There wasn't any place to sit in that locker room; you dressed standing in front of your door, you dressed leaning against the lockers. Quickly Mallow drew his trousers on, he pulled them up over his shoes. He stood naked to the waist, fresh sweat already bursting on his neck and shoulders, and he saw a rookie walking toward him between the narrow rows.

"Hi. Are you Patrolman Mallow?"

"Yeh."

"I'm Tom Foynes."

"Hiya."

"They had it on the roll call. I saw the sergeant downstairs. He told me to ride with you today."

"I guess I saw you," he said to Foynes, "last week. I guess I saw you when we turned out for the Four-to-Twelve. Be right with you." He put on his tie. "You been in a car before?"

"No. Just on post."

They pried out a grating at 105 East 106th Street. A cat was in there, crying. She was upside down, mixed with coal and rocks. The police pried out the grating and rescued her. A crowd gathered, and someone who tried to pet the kitty got scratched.

It was growing hotter. The hydrant next to the Daughters of Israel Home at 107th and Fifth Avenue was a roaring torrent. Foynes turned it off. . . . A Negro girl sat beside the fire-station driveway on 114th east of Madison; firemen were grouped around her. This wasn't a run; it might have been if Car 322 had not come past just then. The girl was sliced down her forehead, across the hollow of her eye, through her left cheek and into the chin; she was bleeding badly. They got a tarpaulin out of the firehouse and put it on the seat of the car before they took her to Flower ... they saw the girl again before noon, crossing Fifth Avenue, with bandages slabbed on her face. "Hey, listen, honey: who cut you?" She grinned lopsidedly with the right side of her face. She had not talked before, she would never talk now. "Just a friend of mine cut me." Foynes exclaimed in his youth and greenness: "She's got a fine bunch of friends!" Dan said, "They all have ... there goes that pump at 107th again."

Naughty boys on 116th were shooting an air rifle at the window of a store across the street in the 23rd. Foynes spotted the imps on a roof, and thus they carried the war into foreign territory of the 25th. They managed to seize both boys and rifle on the roof; they brought them down for delivery to patrolmen of a 25th Precinct car who had halted beside their machine. "We make to you the little present," Dan told the cops. "You can take them to the electric chair; and for heaven's sake try to teach your people not to bust windows over in God's country!"

Down Madison ... they saw the pump at 107th and Fifth spewing merrily again. They turned it off; it was the fourth time they had done so.

A fight in the market on East 114th. Some of the bottle-babies who did odd jobs there had fallen out with one another, and three of them were tangled by the time eager children scurried over to Madison and beckoned the radio car to the scene. Dan and Tom quelled the disturbance; they sent the bottle babies packing; Foynes was bitten slightly on a finger while separating the combatants, and Dan insisted that he stop at Mt. Sinai. "You don't know what you're apt to run into up here. You don't want to go around barking like a dog, do you?" Foynes looked grave while the nurse attended him.

They went back to work. A man ran out of an apartment building at 22 East 89th Street, yelling Fire; they put the blaze out, they poured water on a davenport cushion in a third-floor apartment. Someone had already pulled the alarm; the trucks came anyway. . . . At two o'clock the sun was a high hard blaze, the pumps gushed everywhere. They turned off the one beside the Daughters of Israel again; they hunted grimly for the offenders. No, no — none of the neighbors knew anything about it; they had seen no one, no one . . .

Suddenly Mallow and Foynes saw a blue-shirted patrolman scrambling over the Central Park wall opposite. He raced across the avenue, stepped through remains of a rusty fence bordering the vacant spaces at the southeast corner and began to kick about in the dirt. Dan looked his astonishment while Foynes twisted the hydrant nut. The dashing patrolman was Blondie. He was slightly off post since he had emerged thus miraculously from the green forest of the 22nd Precinct, but he had good ideas. Blondie squatted down, grubbed in the dust and straightened triumphantly. He had retrieved a wrench from the hollow where it was hidden under debris.

Dan Mallow went to meet him. "Hi, Sparrow Cop. How's the squirrels?"

Blondie brandished the wrench. "What's the matter with you guys over here? Water all over Fifth Avenue! How come I have to do your work for you? I got sick of seeing this pump going all the time, so I kept watching. Pretty soon I saw that one kid — see, there he is — over there in front of Flower, in the blue skirt — that little one about ten years old? You'd better spank him. I saw him come over here in the dirt, dig around, get this wrench, turn on the pump and then put the wrench back."

Dan said, "Blondie, I take it all back about the squirrels. I give you ze Commendation." He pretended to pin a medal on Dunbar's chest.

"Thanks, Commissioner. Who you got riding with you? Who's this character?"

"Meet my partner. Tom Foynes — Blondie Dunbar."

"Hiya."

"Hiya."

They took the contraband wrench along in the car with them. Blondie said in traditional parlance, "Look out you don't get mugged," and disappeared into the park.

"Time?" asked Dan.

Foynes looked at his watch. "Like they used to say in the Service: 1500 and 54 hours."

"Only about six minutes to go. Let's move over east here and work down close to the House."

They reached Park Avenue; trains roared heatedly overhead. "Boy," said Foynes, "this is going to be wonderful. A shower . . ."

"Where will you get a shower?"

"At home. See — I live down near Gramercy." He looked at his watch again. "Got a few minutes more, and it's four o'clock. Then we proceed to the House?"

"Right."

"So we go in at four o'clock, and in ten minutes more I bet I've got these filthy garments off of me, and I bet I've got on a nice dry cool shirt and some nice clean pants, and I'm running for the subway. Maybe by 4:40 at the latest, I am standing under that shower in my mother's bathtub. Boy, oh boy, oh boy —"

"Hold it!"

The box was sputtering; Dan stopped the car and they bent close. *Two-Three Precinct. The address: Three-One-Five East One Hundredth Street. In the basement. A Signal Thirty-Two. Proceed Quietly . . . Twenty-third Precinct. The address —*

They raced for 106th; Dan pushed the siren button. Foynes

was tense: this was his first run of any consequence. He cried, "Are we supposed to use the siren on a Signal Thirty-two?"

"Long as we're not too close! That's six blocks down and away over past Second Avenue! Watch it—"

Foynes leaned forward as the car swung toward the underpass. "Clear!" he barked. Dan stepped on the gas; they sped east with siren whining.

*MacKinlay Kantor*

"IF I can't be with the people I like best all the time, I'll take those I can get," MacKinlay Kantor admits. "I like people and I've got to have them around me." This unaffected enthusiasm for the human race, which irradiates his writing, also makes Mr. Kantor the best party insurance a hostess could wish for. When he comes into a room the whole atmosphere is suddenly more stimulating, just because he is there.

"Mack" Kantor was born in Webster City, Iowa, in 1904, and began to help with the family budget by delivering papers when he was eight. He was seldom without a job from then on. When he was 18, he broke his leg in an automobile accident. It was badly set and he suffered chronic osteo-myelitis — with constant pain — for 20 years. The depression of the '30's hit hard. He was married to pretty Irene Layne, an artist, with a four-year-old daughter and another child on the way when his main source of income, a detective magazine, changed its spots to a news magazine and no longer needed his crime stories. For the five months before the Kantors' son was born, the family income was exactly $30.20.

*Long Remember,* his first important and successful novel, was published in 1934 and established him as a top-flight writer. Since then he has been writing steadily — a total of 22 books, including *Arouse and Beware* and *The Voice of Bugle Ann.* His *Glory for Me* (1945) was the original story of the Academy Award-winning movie, "The Best Years of Our Lives."

Mr. Kantor's fund of information on the Civil War is prodigious, the product of his intense research for *Long Remember.* His knowledge of police methods is now equally encyclopedic, thanks to the 15 months he spent in and out of patrol cars and station houses while writing *Signal Thirty-Two.*

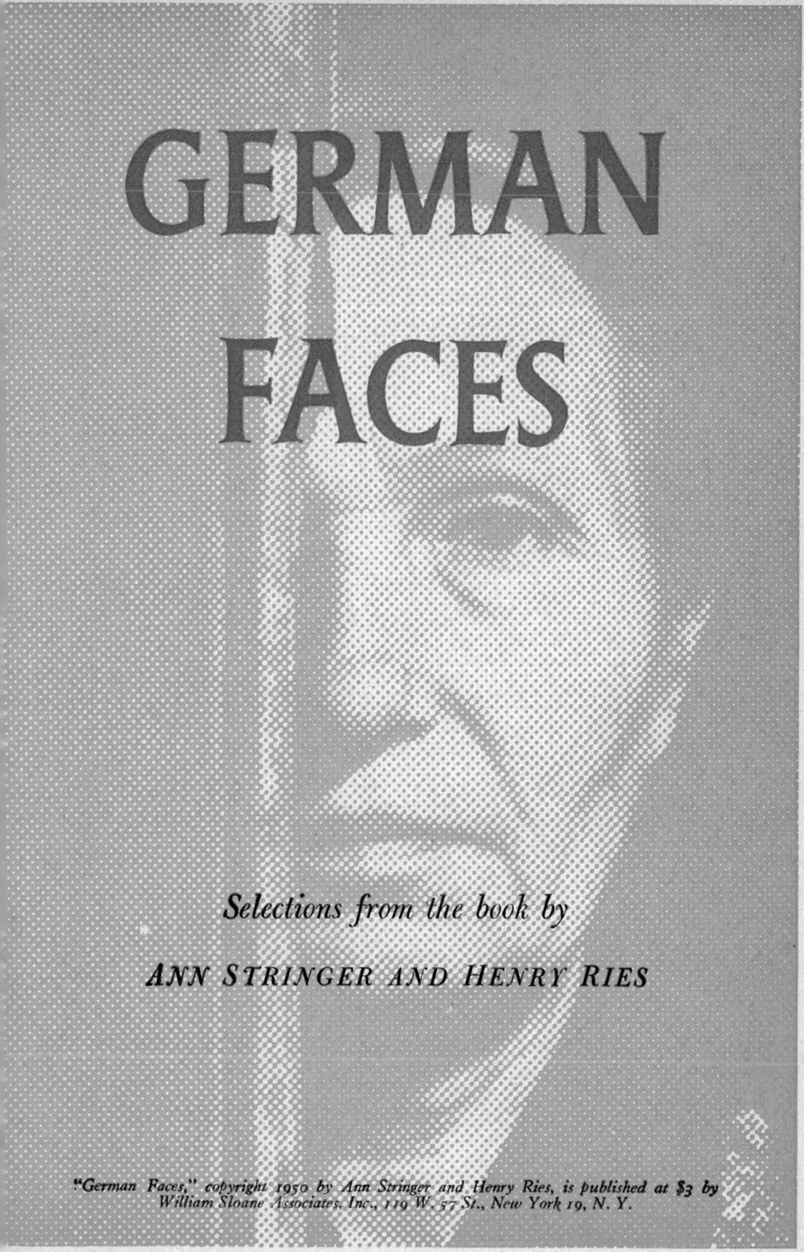

# GERMAN FACES

*Selections from the book by*

*ANN STRINGER AND HENRY RIES*

*"German Faces," copyright 1950 by Ann Stringer and Henry Ries, is published at $3 by William Sloane Associates, Inc., 119 W. 57 St., New York 19, N. Y.*

*J*N THIS book of photographic interviews the authors introduce a brilliant technique of visual presentation that carries remarkable impact. Opposite each portrait is a page of text largely in the subject's own words, so faithfully recorded that the reader almost feels he is present at the interview. Here you meet the typical "little people" of Germany today—Emil, the miner; Otto, the railroad engineer; Gretl, the good-time girl; Joseph, the fiercely independent Bavarian farmer; Karl, the one-legged salesman, tough and unyielding as the nails he peddles. *German Faces* dramatizes a world problem in unforgettable human terms.

"A surgically precise and true dissection of the postwar German soul." — Hal Lehrman in
*The Saturday Review of Literature*

# PREFACE

THE PURPOSE of this book is to present graphically and succinctly the Germans and Germany of today. All interviews were conducted in German, the native language of one of the authors. Therefore, there was no possibility of misunderstanding a *double-entendre,* an inflection or a colloquialism. Each quote is presented in context as it occurred in the conversation, of which complete stenographic notes were made. The background facts of all the subjects are a matter of record in authoritative files.

All photographs were taken after the interviews, when the subject had relaxed sufficiently to avoid posing. None of the faces was retouched.

Germany is the focal point of the East-West split, the arena in which the clash of the titans is being waged. We believe that the weight of this peculiarly tragic land of extremes, as a deterrent or as a contributor to world peace or world war, is nearly as great as that of the U.S.A. or the U.S.S.R.

"We are the straining, burdened nation of the middle between the heights and the depths. We were bad and good, but seldom mediocre. Even death courted us in a special way. German eyes have seen the riders of the Apocalypse."

It is through these eyes that we have reported and written about Germany. These are the eyes that look at you from the pages of this book.

                                        Ann Stringer and Henry Ries

# OTTO GUETTEL

The Anhalter Bahnhof, the Grand Central Station of Berlin, is a ruin of its former grandeur. The steel roof is gone, the glass shattered, the walls sieved with bullet holes. The Anhalter Bahnhof is a hollow ghost, smelling of death. On the cracked steps the baggageman sits, dreaming. Otto was born the year the Anhalter Bahnhof was opened—1880.

"This station and me, we're old friends. She's almost my home. We've seen it all, the good and the bad. But the worst came during the last days of the fighting, when the Russkies already were at the Reichstag. That was when our lunatic SS men did their last noble deed here. Four thousand people, mostly invalids and women and children who had run here for shelter, were killed that day by their own madmen. Those fine elite guards dynamited the subway under the station, and what wasn't crushed to death drowned in the waters of the Spree River which gushed through. If they escaped that, the black men shot them."

Otto took a long drag on his cigarette. "It's a dead station, mister, filled with death. The only life we've had here since the war was the sound of your planes flying the airlift. And didn't that make me and this station feel useless? We couldn't even bring in the goods for our people. It all had to come through the skies."

Otto lighted another straggling, homemade cigarette, leaned back elbow-first on the sharp step and went back to his silence.

# MARTHA WOLFERT

She sat beside a window, the empty lunch box and the empty wicker baskets forming a hopeless barricade around her.

"Twice a week I come all the way to Berlin with my three baskets full of field flowers. For an old woman, that's not easy, believe me. But in the Russian Zone where I live, nobody has money for flowers. They are worried about where to get the next meal. They can't think of flowers.

"Sometimes I wonder if it's worth the three-hour train ride. If I sell all my flowers, I can make about 25 marks. I have to pay 14 marks and 60 pfennigs for the round trip, and I give the baggageman 80 pfennigs for helping me with my baskets. A whole day picking the flowers, another day traveling and selling, all for nine marks, 60 pfennigs. It's very little."

Germany's wars have taken nearly everything from Martha Wolfert. At 62, there's not much left. "My husband was barely 30 when he died fighting for the Kaiser, leaving me with three young sons. Then came Hitler's war. My oldest was 29 when he fell in France. Ernst was buried at sea just a week after his 27th birthday. And Karl—I don't know, maybe he's dead, too. Or maybe he's still alive in Russia. Whenever I see released prisoners arriving here, I ask them about Karl. I always ask, and I always get the same answer."

# VERA ROEHLER

It was nearly empty in the big hall. Only the one train, and a few scattered groups, waiting. Frau Vera Roehler, a refugee, didn't mind talking. Slowly she began to tell of the past few years and of her flight from East Prussia.

"We were a convoy—women and children and the old—all fleeing westward. It was a bitter winter, snow so deep the wagon wheels sank under and stuck. We thought that as long as our own armies were behind us we were safe.

"But the German retreat passed us, and there was nothing between us and the Russians. And then they came. . . . I can't tell you about it, and anyway you wouldn't believe me. For me, it was 24 times. How I counted, I don't know, but I remember that—24. There was one who was very young and he was a little shy. But all the others did it, so he did, too. I like to think that he is the father of little Petra here.

"She was born in September '45, in a refugee camp near Berlin. I hadn't wanted her. My husband was killed at Dnepropetrovsk, and Klaus with his sickness was more than I could care for. But once she was here, breathing and crying, I loved her. And the boy loves her, too."

It was time for Vera and the children to look for seats on the train for Meissen.

# GRETL LANGE

"Hello, stranger, what can I do for you? Didn't think you'd find a good-looking blonde like me here, did you? Among all these PWs, black marketeers and old women."

She took the cigarette slowly, making it plain that she was accustomed to American brands. "I'm getting plenty sick of this long trip every week-end in a stinking train, crowded with yokels who gape at you if you light a Chesterfield or eat a bar of chocolate."

Gretl lives in Weimar and comes to Berlin every week-end to see her American boy friend. He has been trying to find her a room near his barracks so she can stay in Berlin permanently. "He's afraid he may get in trouble with his commanding officer. But I know it can be done easy enough."

She took off her hat and fluffed out her burnt blond hair. "I'm going to move to Berlin, one way or the other. There's nothing for a girl like me in the Russian Zone. Did you ever try having fun with a Russian? Well, I have, and it's not much fun, either. All the Russians have is vodka and more vodka. Their PX doesn't even have nylons, but in the Western sectors you can get anything you want."

She pulled another Chesterfield from her own full pack. "By the way, are you going to be around here long? Maybe we could have a real long talk next week-end. We could have a lot of fun together, don't you think?"

# KARL VOLTER

"I know what you're thinking and why you want to take my picture. A cripple, a poor cripple with a crutch on each arm. Well, you're wrong, mister, just as wrong as the rest of them. They pity me, just like you do, but I can outsmart them all. It's not two legs you need these days. It's brains."

Karl buys nails in the Western sectors of Berlin and sells them in the Russian Zone. "They grumble about my prices, but what can they do? Everybody needs nails. And I've got them.

"Sort of degrading for an ex-officer, limping around from door to door, begging a '*Guten Morgen*' and peddling out of a suitcase to a bunch of stupid peasants, isn't it? I thought so, too, at first, but I got over that. It's all part of the game. And I won't be knocking on their doors much longer. They'll come knocking on mine. In a year or so I'll be able to set up my own shop. I'm smarter than the whole miserable lot of them.

"One thing I've learned during these years: Be sorry for nobody! No sympathy! I'm strictly out for myself, and I hate all the rest of them. You understand? I hate the whole bunch!"

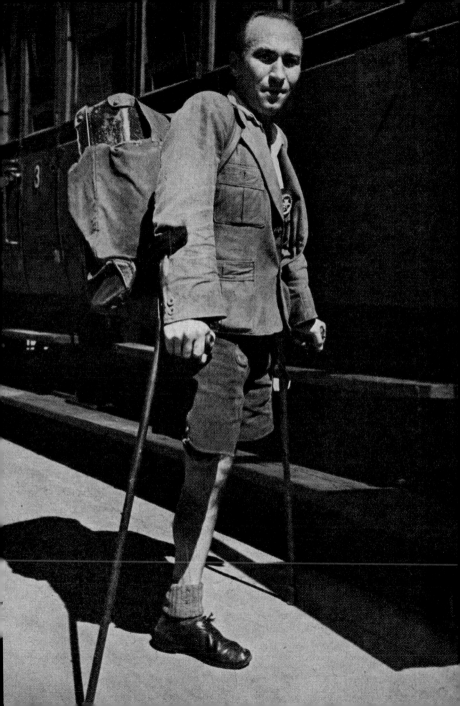

# RICHARD LEMPKE

Still wearing his old *Wehrmacht* topcoat and cap, he boarded the train and settled himself slowly. He spoke slowly, too, as if time meant nothing. He told of his six years in Russian prison camps. It was a familiar story, life in the Ukrainian mines, the cold, the lice, the hunger.

"Six years on dry bread and *kasha* and sometimes a herring. Life out there is cheap, and many of us didn't make it. But I held on some way. I had to get back to Gerda and the boy.

"When the water in my legs crept up to my thighs, they sent me home to Silesia. But the Poles have it now, and nobody there could give me any information. I thought they might be with my sister in Erfurt, so I went down there. Nothing. Then I tried my uncle in Hanover. He thought they might be with my wife's girl friend in Berlin.

"So I came to Berlin. But the Evacuee Service here knows nothing. The Red Cross, the Refugee Organization, the same. Always nothing."

Richard leaned back and patiently folded his hands. He had no home, no job and no plans. Only the gnawing will to find his family.

"Do you think she's still alive? I probably wouldn't recognize the boy. He must be seven now. But Gerda's a wonderful girl, and she's waiting for me somewhere, I know. If I only knew where."

# HEINZ HELMUTH

"The Hitler Youth? Sure, I was in the Hitler Youth, and what did we do that was such a crime? Hikes and a healthy outdoor life, and sports and good songs. Are those things so bad? We had our own leaders, young men who understood youth, and they taught us many things. Myself, I was leader of a platoon. . . ."

Heinz stopped and for a moment seemed almost sad, but only for a moment. "And now that's gone. That's why everything was so hard right after the war. It wasn't only the hunger and the ruins. It was mostly that we had nothing left to believe in. You had taken it all away.

"But the Russians permitted us to form a new youth organization of our own. And since I've been in the *Freie Deutsche Jugend* I've learned that I still belong. I've just finished a special course in leadership. That's why I came to Berlin, to attend the Karl Marx School, and now I'm going back to Saxony where I'm supposed to become head of the youth group in my home town.

"The *FDJ* has better organization than the *Hitler Jugend*. We have a new flag and new songs, and leaders who know what they are talking about. That's what German youth needs. Not your baseball and Coca-Cola and candy."

# FRIEDA BRUNNER

"And I tell you, this is the last time we spend money to see that doctor," a bitter voice shrieked. "He tells me you need 'fresh milk and fruit and white bread.' Do I have to bring you all the way to Berlin to hear that?"

Frau Frieda Brunner was talking to her son, Winfried, who sat silent and hunched. Frieda lives in Wittenberg. Her husband is still a prisoner of war in Russia. The boy has TB.

"This makes 11 times I've traveled with him to the hospital in Berlin. Again, today, the doctor took an X ray. And you know what he said? 'The boy needs good food.' As if I didn't know!

"But where will I get the fresh milk and butter? Not in our zone. You should see what the Russians leave us to eat. Bread that's mostly water and sour as wine. Instead of meat, we get white cheese made of blue milk, and sometimes some sugar—if we're lucky. That's all, and that doctor tells me 'the boy needs good food'!

"Believe me, sometimes it's too much. Sometimes I'd just as soon end it. But there is no end to it, and there's no way out. God has punished me. He's punished me with this sick child—and I don't know for what."

# HERMANN SENF

"Life in the Russian Zone isn't as bad as you Americans would like it to be. I know. I've been home more than a year now, and I've made out all right, even though I was in the SS!

"After I was captured at Stalingrad I joined Marshal von Paulus' 'Free Germany' corps and we all got good food and privileges. I thought it might be rough for me when I got back. But I've been through the mill and I'm all cleared."

Hermann is a foreman in the gigantic synthetic rubber factory at Leipzig. He had come to Berlin to attend a convention of foremen from Eastern Germany.

"I've got a good job now with a lot of responsibility. If I'd been in the Western zones, I'd probably still be picking up rubble. And that's another thing. . . .

"You Americans put up a big howl about the Russians 'stripping' their zone, but at least they left the plants here. With your dismantling, you even took away the means of production. No, sir, you can't talk to me about the Russians. Not after I've seen Dresden, my home town—all ruins from your raids. And you try to tell us the SS and the Russians are inhuman!"

# OTTO NUSCHKE

For 14 years a fireman, the past 20 years an engineer. "The war was terrible. I don't mean so much the bombing and death and all that. I mean us, me, the railroad! The way they handled our locomotives, I wish I hadn't lived to see. They killed them. First they chased them to Poland, then all the way to France. And then to Serbia and Russia, beating the engines to wrecks. They didn't give a damn. And bombing did the rest. If anybody thanked heaven when the whole mess was over, it was us railroad men.

"But now we're forgotten—or worse. See what they left for us? Burned-out, dilapidated stock. And single tracks. Can you understand what it feels like to run on a single track? You sit up here and tremble for fear you'll miss the right-of-way switch. And waiting for the oncoming train to pass, you tremble because you could start a forest fire. Why? Because they give us nothing but soft-coal briquettes. That's like feeding flour soup to a heavy worker three times a day!

"And what do we Germans do about it? Nothing. In the Russian Zone you'd think they'd forgotten they were Germans, the way they flock to join any Russian-backed organization."

Otto pointed to the slogan which had been splashed across his locomotive, the slogan of the Communist Party in Eastern Germany: "'Unity and Just Peace!' Their 'Unity' means slaves again. And their 'Just Peace' means a new war."

# A House in Essen

Deep in the smoke-filled valley of the Ruhr, a block from Essen's North Station, lies one of the busiest sections of this capital of the Krupp empire. Stretching from the railroad overpass, the Friedrich Ebert Platz grinds with heavy traffic. Opposite the skeleton of the Gertrudis Cathedral stood House No. 109. For a time it was the only house left standing in the entire block along Friedrich Ebert Strasse, and it listed badly toward the square, one wall splitting off from the other three. In its last days, when it was condemned, shorn of its plumbing and several rooms by the bombs, it was the home of five families, 18 people.

At 7:30 one morning, after a thunderstorm, House No. 109 collapsed.

First the wall, which since the bombings had been inching away from the rest of the house, crumbled, killing a passing miner on his way to the pits. Frantically the occupants stumbled down the quaking staircase and out into Friedrich Ebert Strasse. Huddled beneath the tower of the Gertrudis Cathedral, they saw the weary old house saggingly give way and fall into rubble. None of them was injured. All of them had lost homes before.

The following interviews were obtained from some of the occupants, during the time when 18 people still found shelter in the doomed structure.

# HANNELORE KURZ

Hannelore was 14 and was ill at ease, alone with a stranger. She had just brought home a handful of flowers, and she looked around the bare room for a place to put them. "No, Dad won't be home before late tonight. He's gone to Düsseldorf to look for a job. Since he was let off eight months ago, he's looked everywhere.

"Dad worked in a big factory where they make gas out of coal. He found that job when he came home from England, where he was a prisoner of war. We were so happy then; we were sure things would be better."

Shyly, Hannelore told of the years since her father's return. At first inflation made Herr Kurz's wages almost worthless. Then, with currency reform in the summer of 1948, money was valuable again. "You should have seen how Essen changed overnight. All of a sudden we could get shoes and clothes, pots and pans, food and everything. But then Dad lost his job. Last June they got orders to have the whole plant dismantled. I'll never forget the day Dad came home and told Mother. He said it would have been better if he'd stayed in England as a PW, and Mother cried."

Hannelore found an empty beer bottle and placed the flowers in it. "I don't understand it, sir. I thought the war was over and that all of the tearing down was finished. Can you explain it to me?"

# EMIL BAUER

Emil was old, but he wasn't beaten. He had a lot of quarrels with the way the world was going, especially on this day. "Leave me alone, can't you? The Coal Commission was in the mine all day asking questions, and here you come with your notebook."

Emil had just come home from the pits. He still wore his miner's cap. "If you want to know anything, why don't you talk to that Commission? They know all the answers. No matter what we in our Works Council tell them, they know a better answer.

"We ask for a living wage and more food. What do we get? Currency reform that cuts our salary to one tenth and on top of that you take away our extra rations. We tell you we want socialization of the mines and what happens? You Americans come along with your ideas of 'free enterprise' and the mines stay capitalist.

"I'm no politician, but I know what's good for the mines. Let them that worked the mines own 'em. We've hewed coal under the Kaiser, the Weimar Republic and Hitler. We've dug it out during two foreign occupations. And we'll keep digging it, if you'll just leave us be.

"No, sir. If you want to hear the answers you'd like to hear, you better go to your own boys. Go see the Commission. They'll tell you."

# USCHI SCHNEIDER

"No, thank you, I prefer my own. Besides, you might as well learn that not every *fräulein* falls for your American cigarettes."

Uschi was getting ready to go to the British Officers Club where she works behind the bar from 6 p.m. until closing time. "Sometimes you people make me laugh! It's always the same: a cigarette, a drink, and you think you've invested enough to proceed to bed. At the club, night after night, it's the same old line, and I must say I'm getting pretty darned bored."

Uschi had quickly learned her way through the Occupation. Like many other German girls, she had no boy friend when the war was over. The German youths were in prison camps and when they straggled home they had no cigarettes, no money.

"I finally met Johnny, though. He's nicer than the rest and I've been going with him for more than six months now. He's a captain, and we're going to get married as soon as he gets back from his furlough. Johnny said he had to go home first to tell his family in England. Maybe he just wanted a smooth way out.

"But what if he doesn't come back! I'm good-looking and there are plenty of others around now. I don't mean just the English and Americans, either. Times have changed. The German men are getting some of their spunk back at last."

# KARL FRITZ SCHNEIDER

Karl Fritz had been around. "The war wasn't so bad. Plenty of excitement and buddies you could trust. Not like it is today with everybody squealing on everybody else. Yeah, I was sure they'd tell you I was in the SS. Well, what of it? Right after the war, everybody thought it was a crime. But now, who gives a damn?

"I lived three months in the railroad-station bunker until my old lady and Sis found room for me here. But all the time I had my black-market business—cigarettes, food and dollars. Dollars was my main line. I was doing fine until currency reform came along and ruined the market. Mom is always yammering at me to get 'a good, steady job.' But not me. I'd go nuts standing behind a counter and smiling at fat old women who came in to buy a bag of potatoes.

"I like excitement. It might even be fun to start shooting again, huh?"

# WILHELM VOCKE

In the dark hole that was his room, Wilhelm Vocke sat whittling a hunk of dry bread and munching it slowly.

"What can I tell you, sir? I'm washed out, finished."

He was a Ruhr miner for seven years before the war, until his asthma forced him to seek work above ground. "When the war came, they took me. First into the Labor Front, and then in 1940 into the army. Two months of that and the medics gave me a discharge. Too old, too sick.

"There was plenty of work for a construction laborer, so I did that. Only, later, it was mostly destruction work, tearing down bombed houses, tearing down shaky walls, tearing down, tearing down. I was bombed out three times myself. Since '44, when I was bombed out the third time, I've lived and slept wherever I could find a bed. And it got harder and harder to find good stuff to drink, too. Now I go to the country begging, just plain begging. I got nothing to trade. No income, no insurance, no pension, no work, no schnapps."

# ANNA GAHMANN

"What do you want? I haven't got anything, and I don't want to buy anything either."

The door had almost closed again when Anna realized . . ."Oh, you're the American who's been talking to the other tenants. Please come in, sir. I knew you'd been in the house. You can't keep a secret here. No, sir. The riffraff who live in this rat's nest now don't know anything except to gossip and beg. Just a bunch of parasites, living off other people's charity, that's all they are. Why, none of them had written permission to move in. Me and my husband, Wilhelm, we have nothing to do with them."

Anna and Wilhelm have lived in House No. 109 longer than any of the other tenants. They moved in—with written permission—after the first bombing of Essen.

Anna resented the British occupation even more than she did her neighbors. "The British are purposely starving the Germans"; "They looted German gasoline"; and "They have no *Kultur*. We Germans have no use for them, I can tell you."

# MITTENWALD—PRIDE OF BAVARIA

The war hardly touched the picture-book mountain village of Mittenwald. In the late thirties the mountain-eering and skiing craze made it a flourishing resort center. In 1939 the once isolated village of less than 4000 swarmed with 50,000 tourists. The war merely brought new tourists—guests in uniform, who played and paid as heartily as those before them. And Mittenwald's seasonal prosperity lasted the year round.

After the war, long columns of refugees, expellees and displaced persons appeared. Nearly 4000 of them surged into Mittenwald, doubling its population. One out of every four persons in the Western zones today is a German expellee, a burden. In Mittenwald, the ratio is one out of every two persons. They occupy the rooms originally reserved for spending tourists. Mittenwalders, unaware of hardship during the booming war years, dislike having to face pinches now. They consider the expellees intruders and "unwholesome elements," and bitterly resent their presence.

# Mayor Johann Neuner

This tense, slight man officially presides over the mountain village. His fanatic eyes reflect the hatred, prejudice and selfishness which are Mittenwald. His qualifications for mayor were powerful: an old-time Mittenwald family name; nine years in the army as a career soldier who reached the rank of sergeant; an iron discipline; and the support of a well-intentioned but befuddled American captain.

"As mayor, it is my first duty to bring back prosperity to our people. Mittenwald is a resort town, and we need rooms for tourists—not for expellees and refugees. After all, they have an entirely different mentality and they could never be happy among our simple mountain folk."

Neuner's "simple mountain folk" fully agree with their mayor on the necessity of getting rid of the newcomers. In fact, they are eager to get rid of everything new, such as the open forums timidly introduced by the American Military Government.

"Naturally the forums went over big with the refugees and Communists. At first I ignored them, but later I called my own town meeting. Of course, only myself and my deputy mayor spoke, because we were the most qualified. The bleaters and Communists complained, for they had hoped to start a fight.

"We want no interference here from foreign elements. Actually, only one person opposes us. He is the former General Zimmer with his crowd of malcontents."

# Richard Zimmer

This is the man most hated and feared by the tight, bigoted Neuner clique.

Educated in Stuttgart as an architect, Zimmer entered the *Wehrmacht* Engineer Corps to escape Nazi politics when Hitler seized power. After his notable feat of constructing in seven hours, under fire, a 1500-foot bridge across the Dnieper, he was promoted to major general. Shortly afterward he was relieved of his post, however, for having dared tell his superiors that further defense was "a stupidity." Relegated to a minor post in Salzburg, he remained there until the last days of the war, then surrendered to the Americans in Mittenwald. Zimmer proved—even in those hotheaded days—that his record was clear.

"I then found work with a construction firm here. When a citizens' committee representing the trade unions and the expellees asked me to run for mayor, I entered politics for the first time. I was beaten, but I think we have made headway toward solving the problem of the expellees. We must absorb them, give them homes and a chance to work; not isolate them in a ghetto of misery for the poor."

Hated for his courage and his ideals, seriously ill, frozen out of his construction-firm job by Neuner and his supporters and prevented from finding another position because of his army rank, Zimmer's future is bleak.

# FRANZ KARNER

Husky, arrogant and 25, Franz is the drugstore cowboy of Mittenwald. He had early training in the Hitler Youth, volunteer service with a *Wehrmacht* mountain battalion, and one year as prisoner of war in Russia.

"War is war, and I saw enough of it to know. But that was a man's fight, live weapons and a real cause. My year in Russia? Well, we'll get even with them someday! But here in Mittenwald, what kind of a war is this? Since I came back in the summer of '46, I've seen more miserable creatures than I ever saw in prison camp. They leech themselves to us like ticks to cattle. If only they had the guts to fight it out, man to man.

"Sometimes I just wish one of them would have nerve enough to come to me. I'd show him who belongs here and who doesn't. Our deputy mayor, *Herr Doktor* Ferchl, has suggested opening the old army camp outside of town for the refugees. I think it is a very good idea, for then they would have their own place, and we could have ours again."

He had never heard of the German Youth Administration, sponsored by the Americans to help the new German generation get away from the Hitler ideology. Franz's life is full and interesting, though. Working on his father's farm, drinking beer with his buddies at the local *Bierstube* on Saturday nights, he waits impatiently for the departure of the refugees and the Americans.

# KARL KNOEBL

A staunch Bavarian priest, Knoebl is the protector of morals, morale and culture in Mittenwald. Born in Bavaria 57 years ago, he presides over a congregation of some 5000, including a large number of expellees.

"My main problem is to promote understanding between the locals and the newcomers. It is a hard task. There really isn't room for the expellees here and the overcrowding turns the villagers against them. Also, many of the newcomers are outside the church, and my parishioners naturally look at them with suspicion. I know that life is hard for those hapless people. If they could only go back to their homes."

Knoebl is more than the parish priest. He is an able politician and, although not a native of Mittenwald, he has ardently shouldered its burdens. In the tiny, over-crowded village, he and his housekeeper and an assistant were the only occupants of a large, four-story house until the trade unions forced him to take in an expellee family of three.

Knoebl's position in Mittenwald is an important one and he holds it with dignity. He has gained fame for "courageous, outspoken" statements from his pulpit against the occupation authorities:

"The so-called victorious nations who pass themselves off as liberators want only to crush us so that we cannot rise again. They talk about guilt and punishment, but I ask, 'What have we done?' "

# ANNA FUCHS

Knoebl's church was silent and deserted save for one person. Anna Fuchs knelt in a far pew, alone. She prayed for her oldest son, who is still a prisoner in Russia. And for the rest of her family, wandering through Germany.

Anna is a refugee. At the age of 67 she fled from the Rumanian province of Bucovina to escape the Russians. Her husband died during the flight, and Anna and her youngest son came to Mittenwald in March 1946.

"I'm afraid they don't like us here. Not that anyone ever said anything to me directly, but even in church I feel I'm not wanted. That's why I come only on weekdays when I can be alone."

With her son and four other refugees Anna occupies one and one half rooms, formerly rented at high prices to tourists. She has never asked any assistance from the Mittenwalders. Her son found work in an American Army camp, and pays the rent and buys their food. But there is little else—except the unadmitted bitterness and a fragile hope.

"Once I came here on a Sunday, the first Sunday after we reached Mittenwald. But I couldn't pray that day. I felt all these well-dressed people staring at my old sweater and nobody greeted me. It seemed that even the priest . . . but I must be wrong; he is a servant of God."

Anna crossed herself and returned to her prayers for her son in Russia and her scattered family.

# JOSEF KLEIN

A 35-year-old refugee with a long trail of concentration camps, slave labor and forced marches behind him, Klein was the first Jew to open his own store in Germany after the war.

Josef was born in Senta, Yugoslavia, and lived there until he was arrested in 1942 by the Nazis. He was in Dachau when the war reached its final phase. When the Americans approached, SS men herded the inmates south. They got as far as Mittenwald. Then the SS guards ran away. "Suddenly, after all those years, I was a free man. Dressed in my striped, pajama-type concentration camp uniform, there I was, free!"

Klein stayed in Mittenwald, married the Polish girl he had met during his slave-labor days and decided to go into business. "That was a job! The whole town was against me, an outsider and a Jew. They tried everything to discourage me. The mayor said, 'Why do we need a leather-goods store? We never had one before.' Finally I took my petition personally to Garmisch, the county seat, and six months later I opened my store.

"I can't complain; I've done well. But I know they don't like it that I own the biggest store in town. And now with anti-Semitism increasing again in Germany, I may sell out and try to go away. Maybe I'll be lucky and get to America."

# JOSEPH PINZL

"Times are good and times are bad, but we farmers know that he who works can always eat. I've always worked, and I've eaten pretty well even during these hard years. But let me tell you, 32 years ago when I came here, there was nothing—only that snow-draped Karwendl peak back there and the frozen, rocky ground here."

Farmer Pinzl prides himself on being a "self-made man." He has a fine family of four children, a good, prosperous farm, a large home and a thriving trucking business. He refused to join the Nazi Party and managed to get out of the *Wehrmacht* after 11 months of home service because of his wife's illness. When Mittenwald fell to the American Army, Pinzl helped them locate the hidden Reichsbank gold, and he has used the credit gained by this deed to cover up his numerous black-market dealings since. Although arrested several times, he has squeezed by with only one short jail term and explains his black-marketeering as "a service to Germany, since I put all my money into cattle and livestock which Germany needs."

Only two things exist for Pinzl—his family and his farm. For these he will do anything, and he will fight anyone who interferes—from the Nazis to the present American occupation authorities.

# GERMAN FACES

Defeated, but never inwardly accepting their defeat, guilty of horrendous crimes on a national scale, but never admitting their shame: these faces are Germany.

Five years ago they mirrored the fatigue of a people who had fought the world and lost everything. They were lined with the neurosis born of ruin, destruction and defeat. They were shadowed by the stigma of atrocities committed by many, condoned by most.

But the cataclysmic conflict between East and West overshadows their defeat and slowly assuages their guilt. As mutual distrust and fear spread between Washington and Moscow, each side helps revive the forces which slumbered in the recent enemy. Aware that an impoverished Germany would become as dangerous as a powerful Reich, the West extends economic assistance. Seeking to enlarge its territorial gains through the cold war, the Kremlin alternately flashes promises and instigates chaos. Both sides are rivals for German favors.

Never mediocre, always excelling in both good and evil, the arrogant and disciplined Germans demand the best that the two salesmen have to offer. Compared to the flagrant appeal of totalitarianism, democracy is colorless and weak. To a people who respect and admire only strength, who have never really known freedom, democracy is a difficult ware to peddle. The ideology of the Kremlin, which requires no burden of thought, is more in keeping with the German tradition of Bismarck-

Kaiser-Führer. If the Germans choose the East, it will be theirs only to serve, and serving they do very well. The little people who "have never done any harm" have always faithfully served their masters, whoever they happened to be.

Regardless of their diverse designs, the three protagonists have a common goal: one Germany. The West hopes for a united, dependent ally; the East demands a "united people's democratic" satellite; and Germany's ambitions are unity.

Ally or satellite?

The Germans have yet to make their decision.

*Ann Stringer*
*and*
*Henry Ries*

*German Faces* marks the debut of a new team, for it is the joint effort of a couple who met in the Russian Zone of Germany (both on newspaper assignments) in 1947 and were married two years later.

Henry Ries left his native Berlin in 1938, convinced that he could not face the future under Hitler's terror. He was then 21. Armed with $10, two cameras and a sketchy knowledge of English, he arrived in New York without friends or connections. His strenuous efforts to become an American citizen and to join the U. S. Army were rewarded in May 1943. After more than a year with the 20th Air Force in the CBI theater, he was transferred to Berlin on an intelligence assignment, in the course of which he translated Himmler's secret SS files.

After the war, Mr. Ries stayed in Berlin on the staff of the New York *Times*, traveling all over Germany, with excursions into the Russian Zone. In 1949 he moved to the *Times* Bureau in Paris, where he and his wife are now living.

Ann Stringer (Mrs. Henry Ries) was born and raised in Texas and entered the newspaper field early as a staff member of the Southern Methodist University paper. Shortly after graduation she married William J. Stringer, Jr. As United Press correspondents, they traveled widely in the United States, South America and Europe.

Mr. Stringer was killed in France on active duty in August 1944, and two months later his widow was sent to London as a war correspondent. She entered Germany in January 1945 with the Ninth U. S. Army, was on the scene when our forces seized the Remagen Bridge over the Rhine, and filed the first dispatches on the meeting of the American and Russian Armies at Torgau on the Elbe. Since the end of the war she has spent most of her time covering Germany for the UP and the Columbia Broadcasting System.

*Decorations by James Alexander*

# MISCHIEF

A condensation

of the book by

CHARLOTTE ARMSTRONG

CONSIDERING the spate of mysteries and "suspense melodramas" which are published each year, it is extremely rare when a book in this class causes literary critics to reach for their pet superlatives. Yet that is precisely the effect *Mischief* has had. Small wonder, for Miss Armstrong has put an icy finger on one of the most purely terrifying situations present-day life could provide—a little girl at the mercy of a malevolent baby-sitter.

"Charlotte Armstrong has outdone herself this time. . . . *Mischief* is packed with meaning and terror in each phrase." — New York *Times*

"Read this in broad daylight and follow up with a triple bromide."
—Avis De Voto in Boston *Globe*

"Impossible to forget." — Dorothy B. Hughes in Los Angeles *Daily News*

# CHAPTER 1

A MR. PETER O. JONES, the editor and publisher of the Brenner-ton *Star-Gazette,* was standing in a bathroom in a hotel in New York City, scrubbing his nails. Through the open door his wife, Ruth, saw him fix his image with his eye, heard him de-claim over the rush of running water, "Ladies and gentlemen . . ." She winked at Bunny.

Ruth in her long petticoat was sitting at the dressing table, gently powdering her thin bare shoulders. Her carefully red-dened lips kept smiling because she knew this long-drawn-out ritual, this polishing of every tooth and every toenail, was only to heighten the wonderful fun.

It was The Night. Ruth sighed, from a complexity of emo-tions.

What a formula, she thought, is a hotel room. Everything one needs. And every detail pursued with such heavy-handed com-fort, such gloomy good taste, it becomes a formula for luxury. The twin beds, severely clean, austerely spread. The lamp and the telephone between. Dresser, dressing table. Desk and desk chair (if the human unit needs to take his pen in hand). Bank of windows, on a court, with the big steam radiator across below them, metal-topped. Curtains in hotel-ecru. Draperies in hotel-brocade. Easy chair in hotel-maroon. The standing lamp. The standing ash tray, that hideous useful thing. The vast closet.

Over this basic formula they had spread the froth of their preparations. Her rose-colored evening dress swung with the hook of its hanger over the closet door. Peter's rummaged suit-case stood open on the luggage bench and his things were strewn on his bed. The dresser top was piled with stuff that at home would have been hidden in the drawers. Powder and ashes had spilled gloriously on the carpet. All the lights were blazing.

All the lights were blazing in Bunny's room, too, the adjoining room that was exactly like this one.

Peter turned the water off, reached for a towel, stood in the bathroom door in singlet and his dress trousers with his suspenders hanging down over his rump. Turning out his patent-leather toes, he bowed. "Ladies and gentlemen . . ." He began to pantomime, clowning for Bunny. Ruth turned to watch what she loved to see, the smooth skin of Bunny's face ripple and twinkle as it always did before the giggle came out.

Bunny was nine. Her dark brows went up at the outside just like Peter's. In her blue woolly robe, Bunny hunched on the foot of Ruth's bed, her arms around her ankles. Her dark hair went smoothly back into the fat braids. Ruth's heart felt as if something squeezed it, quickly, and as quickly let it go.

Peter, with a fine-flung gesture, bowed to make-believe applause. Bunny took her cue, let go her ankles, clapped once, lost her balance and toppled over, giggling. "You see!" said Peter, poking the blue bundle on the bed in a ticklish spot. "Going to mow 'em down!"

"Peter," said Ruth in fright and curiosity, "do you know what you're going to say?"

"Oh, sure, I know what I'm going to say, in a way. I don't know how I'm going to put it, if that's what you mean."

"Oh, Peter!" She sucked in breath. She didn't understand how anyone could do such a thing as make a speech. Something made her heart jump at the mere thought of it.

"Don't get me wrong," said Peter. "I'm terrified." She knew he was. She knew he'd make the speech, nevertheless, and do it well. She knew, too, that her own tense partisanship was helpful.

". . . time is it, honey?"

"Quarter after six." Their eyes met, briefly. Hers with a flick of worry. His with that quick dark reassurance.

He picked up his dress shirt. "Which one of you two dames wants to button me up?"

"Me!" squealed Bunny. "Daddy, why does your shirt pretend it buttons in the front when it buttons in the back?"

"Civilization. Tradition in the front. Business in the back. How you doing?"

"O.K.," said Bunny with a puff of effort.

Business, thought Ruth darkly. "Peter," she said, "I hope you know what I think of your sister, Betty!"

"I couldn't print it," he answered promptly.

"Business," said Ruth as darkly as she felt. "Her and her important business appointment! On a Saturday night! I think she's got a heavy date."

Ruth heard again Betty's high and somewhat affected voice on the phone. ". . . Terribly sorry, darling. Of course, if you simply can't get anyone, I'll cut this thing and I *will* come. . . . But I thought perhaps, if you *could* . . . ?"

Important! What kind of business appointment could be so important for Betty Jones, here in New York six months, with her job that paid what? fifty dollars a week?

For years, now, Ruth had resented her sister-in-law's manner that assumed, so ignorantly and unjustly, that Ruth was done for. Oh, Ruth was buried with the rank and file, and the drab stones all said Housewife.

"We'll try, Betty," Ruth had said coldly, and hung up.

But Peter had fixed it. By some hocus-pocus, he had fared forth into the halls and passages of the hotel, and he had fixed it. And Ruth had called Betty back and said, coolly, "Don't bother. . . ."

"But how could she welsh like that," murmured Ruth, "when she knows . . ."

"Hold still, Daddy."

"Excuse it, pet. Look, Ruthie. Sis takes herself awful hard as the career girl. You know that. Besides, I don't suppose she thinks this convention amounts to much. Corn-fed gathering of country editors. Provincial, hm?"

"There you are!" said Ruth indignantly. "There *you* sit, seeing *her* point of view. But can she see ours? It was all arranged weeks ago. What if we couldn't have gotten anybody?"

"She did say she'd come if she must. No use to be bitter."

Ruth blinked, because he was right . . . no use to be bitter. She kicked off her mules and bent to reach for her evening shoes. "Oh, dem golden slippers . . ." whistled Peter, and Ruth saw Bunny's solemn eyes peek around his shoulder.

"Someday," said Peter, with his dark eyes glowing, "do you know, girls, who's going to be putting on her golden slippers to go to the ball?"

"Bunny O. Jones," said Ruth at once.

"And who's going to be sitting with their bedroom slippers on, watching her?"

"You and me," Ruth said. Their eyes met, smiled.

Bunny said, in a practical voice, "Is my sitter coming soon?"

Peter pinched her toes in their furry slippers. "Pretty soon. And you're going to go to sleep in your room with two beds, one for each pigtail. And what do you do in the morning?"

"Telephone room service," said Bunny.

"And say?"

"This is Miss Bunny O. Jones. I want my breakfast, please."

"In room . . . ?"

"Room 809. And if they don't know what I'm talking about, I'll say, 'My Daddy, Mr. Peter O. Jones, ordered it last night.'"

"And when the man knocks on the door?"

"I'll unlock the door and run quick back in my bed."

"That's right. The key's in your door. And then they'll bring in the wagon."

"Daddy, it isn't a real wagon."

"No horses, I'll admit. A mere pushing type of wagon. And

on it's going to be a whole bunch of silver dishes and your orange juice sitting in the biggest mess of cracked ice you ever saw, enough to make about four snowballs. And you'll eat your breakfast, putting on as much sugar and cream as you want."

"And tomorrow's the day," Ruth said, "you're going to the magic eating store."

"I don't bleeve it!" said Bunny, but her face was rippling.

"Oh, you don't, Miss Bunny O. Jones? Well, you'll see!"

They all three had the middle initial O. Ruth's name had been Olsen, and Peter was delighted with the coincidence. People named Jones, claimed he, had to do something.

"Quite a lot like a zoo," Peter was explaining. "A whole bunch of little glass cages and in one there's a hot meat pie, and in another there's a big fat salad, and all you do is put in your nickels."

"Peter," said Ruth suddenly, "do you believe in the elevator boy? Do you believe in his niece? Is she coming?"

"Certainly," said Peter. "Why would he say so?"

"I don't know. . . ." For Ruth, the room was rocking. The bright box it was had become dreamlike. And the city over which it hung was fabulous and all its denizens were phantoms.

"Said she'd be glad to," Peter was saying. "First, I spoke to that colored woman, the one who was so friendly. But she's dated up. So this Eddie overheard us and he offered. Imagine, hon. This Eddie's been running the same elevator for 14 years. You know which one he is, don't you?"

"I guess . . ."

"Lives up in the Bronx. No children, he told me. This girl, now . . . he and his wife seem to have taken her in out of the goodness of their hearts since his brother died." Peter sucked his cheek. "Fourteen years, up and down. And he still runs that elevator as if his heart was in it. Wonder what he gets a week?"

Ruth sighed. Her momentary feeling that it was all myth was blown away. The little man who ran the elevator was real, of

course . . . a human being, with a life, a wife, a budget . . . with
brothers and sisters like everybody else and a niece to oblige.
It was just like home. You needed somebody. You asked around.
It was just like asking the Johnstones who might say all their
sitters were busy but they knew someone who knew somebody.

"The niece comes from the Middle West someplace," Peter
was saying. "Experienced, he says. I suppose a little extra means
something in a setup like that."

Ruth thought, all at once, that it was better to be paying
someone than taking such a one as Betty's time for free. She
smiled and reached out her hand.

"Oh, boy," said her husband, "comes the 12-dollar smell!"

"Twelve dollars and fifty cents, don't forget!" Ruth took the
tiny stopper out, touched her shoulders with the precious stuff.

Peter bent over and sniffed violently. He said in her ear,
"Would a couple of symmetrical tooth marks look good?" She
saw herself laughing, in the glass.

". . . me smell," demanded Bunny.

So Ruth crossed with her pretty petticoat swirling, turned the
plump little paw, touched the back of it with the perfume. "Dee-
licious!" said Bunny, sniffing violently.

Ruth looked down at the white clean part in the dark hair.
All of a sudden, she saw their two connecting rooms, the two
bright boxes suspended above the boiling city. And the rising
noise surrounded them like smoke . . . the honks, clangs, shouts
and murmurs, the sound and fury . . . and her heart was squeezed
again. We couldn't have left her 2000 miles away . . . but we
shouldn't have brought her . . . but we couldn't have left her. . . .

The Hotel Majestic was neither large nor small, neither cheap
nor costly. Not the last word, it wasn't dowdy, either. It was
conservative. Even the elevators, although they ran smoothly, did
so with a modest speed.

Eddie Munro stopped for a light at the eighth floor. A young man got on, turned at once to face the door. They sank downward in silence.

Out of the corners of their eyes, they typed each other, quickly. Eddie saw the easy grace of a tall body, the arrogant carriage of the high head. The sharp cut of the good-looking face, the cool gray eyes, long-lashed and asking for nothing. A type. One of those young men who had come out of the late war with that drive, that cutting quality, as if they had shucked off human uncertainties and were aimed and hurtling toward something in the future about which they seemed very sure.

His name was Jed Towers. It was his last night in New York. He had a dinner date.

If he saw the little man out of the corner of his cool eye, it was just a little man, with his shoulders pulled back from his narrow chest in a frozen strut. With a gray face. With pale hair that never had any color to lose, lying long and lank over the bald part.

The car stopped smoothly at the main floor and Jed walked quickly to the street.

Eddie ran a nervous glance around the quiet lobby. He said to the next boy, "Gotta make a phone call. Watch it, will you?" He scuttled around a bend of wall with his nickel in his hand.

"Marie?"

"Yeah, Eddie?" said his wife's placid voice.

"She leave?"

"She went, yeah, sure."

"How long ago?"

"In plenty of time," his wife said. Everything she said carried the overtone, Don't worry, Eddie.

"Listen, Marie, I think maybe I oughta stay around after I'm off. Folks might be late. Some kind of big shindig, the man said. O.K.?"

"O.K."

"You do think the whole idea's a good idea, Marie? She can earn a little money? You know? Get started?"

"Sure it is, Eddie."

"She — uh — liked the idea, didn't she?"

"Sure she did."

"Well . . . uh . . ." He didn't want to let go of the wire, leading to Marie and her voice saying, Sure.

"Say, Eddie, I think maybe I'll go to the show. Miz Martin said she'd go with me." Eddie squirmed in the booth, blinking rapidly. His wife's voice went on. "That picture we didn't think we'd better take *her* to. You know?"

"Yeah. Sure."

"Don't worry, Eddie," Marie soothed. "I'll be home long before you and Nell, probably."

"Sure. Sure," he said. He heard his wife's tiny sigh whispering on the wire. "Go ahead," he said. "Have a good time."

"It'll be O.K.," she told him. (Don't worry, Eddie.)

He went around the wall to his car. His eyes searched toward the revolving door, across the depth of the lobby. He threw back his shoulders, trying to stand erect, as if he were perfectly sure.

In 807, Ruth slipped the rose-colored frivolity off its hanger and expertly lowered it past her shining hair.

"Something like a princess," said Peter judiciously to the audience "don't you think?"

"Zactly," said the audience solemnly.

Ruth kissed the back of the audience's neck. "And now!"

"Ah *ha!*" Peter took up his ridiculous garment, wiggled into it and patted the flying front sections.

"You said it was *tails!*" said the audience in high sweet scorn.

"You don't think so?" said Peter. He put both hands under the coat at the back and suddenly he was marching up and down with a Groucho Marx kind of crouch in his knees and his tails were flapping.

The audience was convulsed. Bunny wasn't, thought Ruth, a pretty little girl, but how beautiful she was, laughing!

And she herself gasped, "Peter, oh, stop!"

"O. Jones."

"Oh, stop! I'll ruin my mascara. Oh, *my*!"

Somebody knocked gently on the door.

Something squeezed Ruth's heart, quickly, and as quickly let it go, so that it staggered.

## CHAPTER 2

"MR. JONES, here we are, sir." Eddie's bright blinking eye, the thrust of his neck, were as of a mouse at the door.

"Oh, yes, Eddie. Right on time. How-de-do. Come in."

"This here's my niece, Nell Munro. Nell?" Eddie came in, too.

"How-de-do, Nell," Peter said. Ruth moved toward them. All the fizz had gone out of the room.

"Good evening, Nell," she said. "It was nice of you to come on such short notice. Had you very far?"

"Don't take long on the subway," Eddie said. His Adam's apple jumped. He stood with his skinny shoulders thrust well back. "Really don't take long at all."

The girl, Nell, said nothing. She looked to be 19 or 20. She stood demurely with her ankles tight together. Her shoes were shabby black pumps with medium heels. Her head was bent, her lashes lowered. Her hair was the color of a lion's hide, but short, not very curly. She wore no hat, a navy-blue coat of a conservative cut and a little too big for her. Her hands were folded on a black handbag and Ruth was pleased to see that the nails were bare. Then she hooted at herself for so quaint a connecting of character with nail polish, for, after all, her own nails were a glossy rose. Still . . .

"Won't you take your coat off, Nell?"

Eddie said, "Take your coat off, Nell. Go ahead." The girl wore a neat dark silk dress. She held the coat on her arm as if she didn't know what to do with it.

"Just put it here, won't you?" purred Ruth. "And your bag, too? I suppose you've sat with children before, Nell?"

"She did, back in Indiana," said Eddie. "Did it a lot. Not around here, so much. She only came east about six months ago."

"And do you like it here, Nell?"

"She likes it fine," said Eddie. "We've got room in the apartment, plenty of room for her. My wife's real glad to have her."

Is the girl mute? Ruth wondered. Eddie's interposing chatter was nervous, as if it covered something lumpish and obstinate in the girl, who was not helping.

Eddie said, "What I wannida say, I'll *be* here in the hotel. I mean, I'm going to be around, see? So if you folks are going to be late, you don't need to worry."

"We may not be so very late," said Peter smoothly.

"What I mean," Eddie blinked, "I can take Nell home, see?"

Peter looked up, drawled, "That's nice of you." Ruth heard his surprised pleasure. "But I'd have seen her home, of course," said Peter virtuously.

Ruth thought the pupils moved under the lowered lashes in that bent face. She said brightly, "Bunny, dear. Nell, this is Bunny and Bunny, this is Nell."

"Hello," said Bunny.

"Hello," the girl said. Her voice was low and colorless, but at least it worked. She spoke.

"My wife, see," Eddie was saying, "took a notion to go to the show so I might's well wait around." Swallowing made a commotion in his skinny neck. "We was thinking it might be a real nice idea for Nell. There's a lot of guests bring their children. And me being right here, why, it ought to work out good."

An anxious little man, the kind who keeps explaining himself, although nobody cares. The conscientious kind.

"Suppose we show Nell your room, Bun?" Ruth led them. "You see, this door can be left a little bit ajar because Bunny does like to go to sleep in the dark. I thought *you* could sit in here, Nell, in our room, where you can be more comfortable."

Bunny had marched ahead of them into 809. Now she threw one leg possessively over the edge of one of the beds, the one on which her stuffed dog from home was already established.

"Perhaps she ought to turn in quite soon now," Ruth said gently. "She's had a pretty exciting day. Perhaps you'd read her a story? If you don't mind?"

"No, ma'am," said Nell passively.

"That'll be nice, won't it, Bun?" It was like pushing, pushing something heavy. Ruth said with a bright smile, "Suppose you see if Nell would like some candy."

Bunny got the box and offered it. Nell said, "Thanks a lot." And snatched. Ruth felt her heart lighten. That held some understanding. No grown person could care that much for candy. That greedy quickness must have been exaggerated for the child's sake.

"You're welcome." Bunny dipped in herself, companionably.

Ruth felt easier. "Bunny's such a big girl," she went on, "there really won't be anything to *do*." She realized that Eddie's voice and Peter's monosyllables were still going on behind her. "Bunny's bathroom is over there. And this door," she waved at the exit from 809 to the corridor, "is locked. Now, Bunny's to have one more piece of candy and then she's to brush her teeth and have her story and by that time I expect she'll be pretty sleepy." She looked back through the connecting door.

Eddie's high voice said clearly, "Well—uh—probably I'll

look in on Nell, once in a while, if that's all right with you."

"Surely." Peter picked up his wallet. "Well — uh — thanks very much."

"No, sir." Eddie backed away from the dollar bill. "No, I'm glad to do it, sir. It's such a good idea for Nell. You just pay her what she earns. Fifty cents an hour. And that'll be fine. That's the arrangement. Nell's mighty glad to have a chance to earn a little something." He looked rather defiantly past Peter. "You folks go on out and have a good evening, now."

"Thanks very much, Mr. Munro. Good night."

"Good night. Uh — good night. Have a good time now, Mr. and Mrs. Jones." His hand hovered in a kind of admonishing gesture. It fell. At last, he was gone.

"O.K., Ruth?" said Peter with a touch of impatience.

"In a minute. Nell?" Summoned, the girl moved. Ruth could hear Bunny making a great splutter, brushing her teeth. "Peter, do you mind looking up the number where we can be reached? We'll just leave it by the phone in here, Nell, and if there is anything at all, why, you *can* call us."

Nell said, "Yes, ma'am."

Ruth began to turn off lights in 807, leaving only the standing lamp over the big maroon chair and the little lamp between the beds. "That's enough, Nell?" The girl nodded. "If you get drowsy, just lie down in here. I'm sure that will be all right. And," she lowered her voice discreetly, "perhaps you had better use this bathroom. Now, is there anything I've forgotten?"

She stood in all her finery, her brow creased just a little, feeling unsatisfied. The girl had said so little. Yet, what was there for her to say? Something, thought Ruth impatiently, some little thing volunteered . . . *anything* to show she's taking hold! "Can *you* think of anything else?" she prodded.

The girl's head was not so bent, any more. Her face was wide at the eyes with high cheekbones, her eyes large and a trifle aslant. Her chin was small and pointed and her mouth was tiny.

She wasn't bad looking, Ruth thought with surprise. In fact, she might have been stunning, in an odd provocative way. Even her figure was good under that ill-fitting dress, now that she was standing more erect, not so meekly bent. The eyes were blue. There was too much blue in them, as if the seeing center were too small, the band of color wider than it needed to be.

"I guess you've thought of everything," Nell said. The tiny mouth seemed to let itself go into a reluctant, a grudging smile.

For just a flash, Ruth wondered if, in that perfectly flat sentence, there were some mischief lying low.

"Better get going," Peter moved, full of energy. "There's the number, Nell, on this paper. Ask them to page us. Doubt if you'll need it. *We* may call up, so if the phone rings . . ." The whole world, for Ruth, seemed to take up where it had left off.

Bunny was curled around the jamb of the connecting door, toothpaste lingering on her lips. "Pop into bed, baby," Ruth said. "And Nell will read to you a while."

Herself in shadow, she watched them obey . . . Bunny peel out of her robe, climb in and pull the covers up, toss her pigtails behind . . . watched the girl move nearer and seat herself on the edge of the bed, where the light haloed her hair.

Suddenly, Bunny took charge. "Read me about Jenny and the Twins." She pitched her book at the girl.

"O.K.," said Nell, meekly.

Ruth turned away. She bustled, putting things into her evening bag, her wrist watch, her compact, handkerchief, hairpins, lipstick. Her heart was beating a little fast.

Peter was standing silently, with his overcoat on, with her velvet wrap over his arm. She went over and he held it. She looked up at him, wordlessly asked, Is it all right? Wordlessly, he answered, Sure. What can happen?

"Eddie's got his eye on," said Peter in her ear. And she saw, at once, that this was true. Eddie was responsible. Eddie had worked here 14 years. He couldn't risk losing that record. No. And Eddie was conscientious to a fault.

"Take us a while to get across town," said Peter aloud. Together, they went into the other room. The girl was reading. Her voice was low and monotonous. She read like a child.

"All cozy?" said Ruth lightly. "Night, Bunny." Her light kiss skidded on the warm little brow.

Peter said, "So long, honey bun."

"So long, Daddy. Make a good speech."

Oh, bless her heart! thought her mother. Oh, bless her!

"I'll see what I can do, sweetheart," said Peter tenderly.

The girl sat on the edge of the bed with her finger on her place in the storybook. She watched them go. As they crossed room 807, Ruth heard her voice begin again, ploddingly.

Not all of Ruth went through the door. Part remained and tasted the flat, the dim, the silent place from which she had gone. After all the lights and the love and the laughter, how was it for Bunny? Hadn't all the fun too abruptly departed? A part of Ruth lay, in advance of time, in the strange dark. Heard the strange city snarling below. Knew only a stranger's hired meekness was near when something in the night should cry....

Peter put his finger on her velvet shoulder. An elevator was coming. (Not Eddie's, and Ruth was glad. Not again did she wish to hear, "Have a good time, you folks. Have a good time.")

She shook at her thoughts. She knew what Peter wanted. By her will, she pulled herself together. (Bunny was nine. Bunny would sleep.) She drew the tardy part of herself in toward her body until she was all there, standing by the elevators.

It was The Night. At last, it was!

# CHAPTER 3

JED TOWERS picked up his date at her family's apartment on East 36th Street. Her name was Lyn Lesley and she was more than just a date. She had achieved a certain ascendancy on Jed's list. In fact, she was on top. Lyn was slim and dark, with a way of looking out of the corners of her eyes that was neither sly nor flirtatious but simply merry.

He'd known her a year or more, but not until these two weeks, all free time, between jobs, had he seen her so constantly. This had happened easily. Very smooth and easy to slide from "see you tomorrow, question mark" to "see you tomorrow, period" to "what shall we do tomorrow?" But this next morrow, Jed was off to the Coast where he'd be pinned down a while, in the new job. Tonight, their last night, had accumulated without any deliberation on Jed's part the feel of being decisive.

Maybe it wasn't their last night together — but their last night apart. He wasn't stalling. He just didn't know.

They were not in evening clothes. Lyn wore a fuzzy blue coat with big pockets and big buttons and a little blue cap on the back of her head. They decided to walk. They didn't know where they were going, anyway. The mood was tentative and merry . . . no tinge of farewell in it, yet. Lyn hopped and skipped until Jed shortened his stride.

On 39th Street, the block west of Fifth, a beggar accosted them, whining to the girl, "Help an old man, missus?"

"Oh . . . Jed?" She stood still, impelled to compassion, her face turned up confidently.

Jed's fingers bit her arm. "Sorry . . ." He dragged her along. "Just a racket," he said in her ear. The man's muttering faded in their wake.

401

She was really dragging her feet. "How do you know?"

"Know what?" He was surprised. "Oh, Lyn, grow up! That old beetle probably's got more in the bank than we'll ever see."

"You can't know that," she said stubbornly.

He stopped walking, astonished. Vaguely, he realized that his brusque decision might have broken something in her mood, some enchantment maybe. He had no patience with it. He said, "Now, look. Of course I can't know it, but the chances are I'm right. And I don't like being taken for a sucker. Now, skip it, shall we?"

She walked along only somewhat more willingly. He said teasingly, "But you'd have fallen for it, eh? Softie!"

"On the chance he really needed help," she said in a low voice, "I'd have risked a quarter."

"Don't be like that." Jed laughed at her. "Sentimental Sue!" He wheeled her into a restaurant. "This all right?" He was sorry the mood had been broken. It was his instinct to change the setting, and use the difference and food and drink to bring back whatever it was between them.

They took their table and Jed ordered dinner. Lyn had her lower lip in her teeth, kept her eyes down. When their cocktails came and he lifted his glass to her, she smiled. She said, "I'm not sentimental, Jed. It isn't that."

"No?" He wished she'd skip it. He was finished with that trivial moment. "Drink your drink, honey." He smiled at her.

But Lyn said, wanly, "You have an awfully quick way of mistrusting people." Her voice was gentle but he thought there were stormy signs in her eyes and anger stirred in Jed's own.

He said, evenly, gently, "I didn't think you were that childish."

"I can't see," she said, "how it would have hurt. Two bits. Or even a dime."

"Spare a dime," he mocked. "For Lord's sake, Lyn, let's not fight about it."

"No." She pushed her glass to and fro on the cloth and she smiled. "But you do expect the worst of people, don't you, Jed?"

"Certainly," he grinned. "You damn well better, as far as I can see."

She looked across the room. "I don't think I care for cheap cynicism," she said.

"Cheap!" he exploded. Women were the limit! He realized he must have hurt her, somehow. But he also knew he hadn't meant to. "For Lord's sake," he said, "that's about the most expensive piece of education I ever got myself. I'd hate to tell you what I had to pay for it."

"You don't believe . . ." she began, her lips trembling.

"Don't believe!" he scoffed. "Listen — aw, you baby! What I believe or what you believe makes no particular difference to the way things are. This is a pretty stinking lousy world."

"Is it?" said Lyn.

He was annoyed. "If you haven't noticed that, you're unintelligent," he said crisply.

"And what do you do about it?"

"Mind your own business. Take care of yourself."

"If everybody figured the way you do . . ." she began.

"You like the boy-scout type?" he challenged. "The sunshine kids?"

"No."

"The dreamy boys? The old stars in the eyes?"

"Stop it!"

"O.K.," he said. "So I'm not going to water myself down and play pat-a-cake with you."

"I don't want you to," she said. "I'm interested in what you think about things." Her voice was low again.

"But you don't think much of my way of thinking?" he said, more challenging than he had intended to be. "Is that it?"

She turned her hand.

"Well . . ." he shrugged. "I'm sorry, honey, but one thing that stinks high in this lousy world is the lip service to sweetness and light. Look, I didn't expect an inquiry into my philosophy of life. I thought this was a date . . . you know, for fun?"

Her lips parted. He read in her look that they both knew it wasn't just a date . . . for fun. But she didn't speak.

"Show?" he said lightly. If they went to a show, it would deny, somehow, their ability to be together. He felt that, suddenly.

She said, "In such a lousy world, what do you expect?"

"Oh, say, the love of a good woman," he answered lightly. And then he was sorry. He saw her lips tighten. He'd hurt her again, when all he wanted was to get lightly off the subject. "Aw, Lyn, please . . ." He put his hand on hers.

"Please," she said, not smiling. But he thought if he could kiss her, hard, right now, it would be a fine thing.


Bunny listened politely to the story. When Mommy read, the story seemed more interesting. When Daddy read to her, it was interesting, too, although Daddy never did finish a story. He always got off to explaining something, and the explaining turned out to be *another* story. She sat quietly against her pillow, her stuffed dog under her arm, until the voice stopped. Nell looked at her then. "I better go to sleep, now," said Bunny.

"O.K." Nell stood up.

"I can turn off my light," said Bunny kindly.

"O.K., then," Nell said. She put the book down on the other bed. She walked away. She picked up the candy box, looked once over her shoulder and went through the door.

Bunny snapped off the light, watched the pattern of shadows establish itself. She wondered if the window was open. Nell hadn't looked to see. The room felt stuffy and dusty hot. Bunny wasn't quite sure she knew how to work the Venetian blind. She lay still quite a long time, then sneaked her feet out and felt the bristles of the carpet. She fumbled with the thin ropes and after a while there was a soft rattle and the slats changed. Now, she could see. The window *was* open. It was all right, then. Bunny crept back under the blankets. The air smelled dusty, just the same, and the pillow didn't smell like her pillow at home, either. Bunny pushed her nose into it and lay still.

Nell set the communicating door at an angle that almost closed it. Then she stood absolutely still, tipping her head as if to listen. Room 809 was quiet, behind her. Her eyes shifted. The big lamp flooded the spot near the windows where the big chair stood. The small lamp touched the upper ends of the twin beds. Elsewhere there were shadows.

Nell put the candy box down on a bed and walked back with a silent, gliding step to the windows and tripped the blind. The court was too narrow to see very far up or down. Across, there was only one lighted window. The blind, there, was up a third of the way, and she could see the middle section of a woman, seated at the desk. A black-and-white belt marked a thick waist on a black dress. There was nothing else to see.

Nell pivoted, glided in that same step to the middle of room 807 and stood still. She did not stand still long. Although her feet remained in the same flower of the carpet pattern, they began to dance. The heels lifted and fell fractions of an inch, only, as her weight shifted. Her hips rolled softly, and her shoulders and her forearms. Her fingers were the most active part of her body in this dance. They made noiseless snaps and quick restless writhings of their own. Meantime, Nell's eyes, wide-open, darted as she danced, very alive and alert.

In a little while, the feet danced daintily, in the tiniest of steps, off the one flower. Nell swooped over Peter's suitcase. Her hand scooped through its contents. Handkerchiefs and ties flew like sand from a beach castle. There were some letters and a manila

folder flat on the bottom. The girl snatched them out, opened
the folder awkwardly, and all the papers slid out in a limp curve.
She stood with the empty folder in her hands and looked down
at the spilled papers in the suitcase. Then she yanked the letters
from the clip that held them to the folder. They didn't interest
her for long. She dropped all the paper out of her hands, as if it
were merely paper, with no other meaning. With one finger she
flipped the lid of the suitcase shut.

She made three long steps and pivoted with one leg out like
a dancer's, pulling it slowly around. She sat down, with an effect
of landing there by sheer accident, on the bench in front of the
dressing table. She rummaged in Ruth's box of jewelry. There
were three bracelets and Nell clasped them all on her left arm.
There were two brooches and she pinned one above the other on
the left lapel of her dress. There were a string of coral-colored
beads, and Ruth's three-strand pearls, and a silver locket on a
silver chain. All these Nell took up and fastened around her
neck. A pair of tiny turquoise and silver earrings that matched
one of the pins she put at her ears. She looked at herself in the
shadowy glass, solemnly, lumpishly. She smiled. Slowly, she began to take everything off again. As she removed each piece she
did not return it to its place in the box. When the table top was
scattered with most of the things, Nell seemed to lose interest.
She still wore the earrings.

She turned, very slowly, moving her legs as if they were in one
piece. She kicked off her black pumps. Ruth's aquamarine mules
with the maribou cuffs were standing neatly under the dressing
table. Nell put her feet into them. She rose and walked up and
down in them, watching her feet, acquiring more and more skill
and arrogance in the ankles and the arches. At last, she seemed
almost strutting.

Then she sat down on the bench again and picked up Ruth's
perfume. She tipped the bottle on her forefinger and dabbed the

forefinger behind her ears. She held the forefinger under her nostrils and inhaled dreamily, swaying to and fro as if she tantalized her own senses in a dreamy rhythm. The little bottle dropped out of her left hand, cracked on the table top, lay on its side. The liquid began to seep out among the jewelry. (The $12 that had been Peter's, the 50 cents that had been Bunny's, last Mother's Day.)

Nell noticed it, finally. Her face did not change. She picked up Ruth's hairbrush, dipped it, making a smearing motion, in the spilled perfume, and began to brush her tawny hair. She brushed it sharply back from her ears. Now her face took on another look. Now the shape of it, the sharp taper to the chin, the subtle slant of the eye sockets, became older, more sleek.

She drew the hairbrush once around her throat.

She rose and walked between the beds, turned, and let herself fall supine on the one to the left of the telephone. After a little while she lifted her right arm, languidly, letting her hand dangle from the wrist.

Then she sat up, propped her back with pillows and opened the fat phone book. She opened it almost at the center and looked at the pages with unfocused eyes. She lifted her left hand and dropped it on the fine print. Where her left forefinger nail fell she gouged a nick in the paper.

She picked up the phone with her right hand, asked the girl at the switchboard sweetly for the number.

"Yes?" A man's voice came out of the city, somewhere.

"Guess who?" Nell said in a soft high soprano.

"Margaret, where are —"

"Oh-ho, no! Not Margaret!"

"Who is this?" said the voice irritably.

"By the way, who *is* Margaret? Hmmmm?"

"Margaret is my wife," said the voice stiffly. "Who is this?"

"Virginia," crooned Nell. "Don't you remember me?"

"I think you have the wrong number," the voice said, sounding very old and tired, and he hung up.

Nell sucked her cheeks in, turned pages, gave another number.

"Hello?" A woman this time.

"Hello. Oh, hello. Is Mr. Bennet there?"

"No, he's not. I'm sorry." Brightly, "This is *Mrs.* Bennet."

"Oh," said Nell without alarm. Her head tilted, listening.

"Can I take a message?" the woman said, less cordially.

"Oh, dear," simpered Nell. "You see, this is Mr. Bennet's secretary. . . ."

"Mr. Bennet has no secretary that I know of."

"Oh," said Nell. "Oh, dear me! Are you sure?"

"Who is this?" The voice sounded as if the face were red.

"Just a friend. You know?"

"Will you give me your name, please?"

"Why, no," said Nell flatly and then she giggled.

The phone slammed shut at the other end. On Nell's face danced a look of delighted malice. She stretched. She called the girl downstairs again. "Long distance."

Rochelle Parker, at the switchboard, was efficient and indifferent. She dealt with the barrage of calls from 807 for a long time without much comment, even to herself. She got in on part of a wrangle between the long-distance operator and whoever was calling, up there, over the existence of an exchange in Chicago. The person upstairs used language, softly. It was as bad as Rochelle had ever heard over the wires and she'd heard some. And this was worse, sounding so hushed-like.

"Jeepers," said Rochelle to herself. She might say a word to Pat Perrin, the house detective. Probably they were drinking up there. People went on telephone jags sometimes.

She decided it was none of her business. What went over the wire wasn't disturbing the sacred peace of the Hotel Majestic. And the telephone bill would be part of the hangover. "Oh, boy," she thought and grinned. Then 807 suddenly quit calling.

The phone book had fallen off the bed. Nell rolled over on her stomach and looked at it, lying on the carpet.

She sat up, curling her legs under her. She yawned. She listened. Her rambling glance passed the half-open closet door and returned. . . .

## CHAPTER 4

A TALL MAN looks best in tails, they say. Ruth thought that, although Peter O. Jones was not too terribly tall, he looked wonderful. Erect, compact, controlled, he walked beside her.

She saw herself, too, in the mirrored walls of the passage to the ballroom and she began to walk as if she were beautiful. For the frock was becoming, and in the soft light she even liked her nose. Maybe it did turn up, as Peter insisted, against all evidence that it did. At least it had, as he said, the air of being *about* to turn up, any minute.

Her hand with the rosy nails pressed the black cloth of his left sleeve and Peter crossed his right arm over and touched her hand. They were following an usher toward the speakers' table and Ruth could see their path, opening, and the turning faces marked it as if flowers were being thrown under their feet.

Somebody stepped into their way, holding out his hand. "Peter O. Jones?" he said joyfully. "Want you to meet . . ." "Beg pardon, sir, but this is . . ." "How do you do?" "*Mrs.* Jones, ah . . ." They were in a cluster. Yet they were moving slowly, surely, toward the speakers' table. Ruth struggled to remain balanced, to lock names to faces. It was confusing! It was glorious!

Jed and Lyn were still sitting in the restaurant. Coffee, brandy, more coffee and many cigarettes had gone by. They were caught in the need to settle something. Jed shared, now, Lyn's feeling that it was important. They were hanging onto their tempers.

They'd about finished, speaking awkwardly, obliquely for the most part.

"What I know," he said, "the Lord ain't Santa Claus. You got them mixed, honey."

"You don't believe in it at all," she said wearily.

"I don't nag myself about it." He shrugged.

"All I'm trying to say, Jed," she was making an effort to be sweet, "is just this. I'd have *liked* it if you had given that old man a coin. It would have been good for *us*."

"Aw, that's junk, Lyn. Pure junk."

"It isn't junk!"

His voice slipped. "It's ridiculous!"

Her eyes flashed. "I'm glad to know you think I'm ridiculous."

"Maybe it's a good idea to know these things," he agreed coldly. "You called me a cheap cynic, remember?"

"And perhaps you are," she said shortly, "just that."

"It's no chore of mine, Lyn," he fought to sound reasonable, "to contribute to the income of a perfect stranger."

"Suppose *you* needed food . . . or a place to . . ."

"Then, I go beg from organized charities. *I'll* never expect a stranger on the street to shell out for me. Why should he? Why should he believe me?"

"It's not true! People have to believe. . . ."

"Why?"

"Why anything, then?" she blazed. "What are you living for?"

"How do I know? I didn't put me here. Of all the idiotic—"

"I think you'd better take me home. This isn't fun."

"Why should I take you home?" he said, smoldering. "Ask some kind stranger."

She stared. She said, "You're quite right. I do nothing for you.

Or your ego. Do I? I'll be leaving now."

"Lyn..."

"Yes?" she said icily, half up, her coat on her shoulders.

"If you go..."

"I know. We'll never meet again. Is that it?"

"That's it, I'm afraid."

"Jed, I don't want to..."

"Then for Lord's sake," he said irritably, assuming it was all over, "sit down and quit talking like a little jackass."

Her sidewise glance was not merry at all. "Good night."

He settled in the chair, took out a cigarette. "Got your mad money? Here." He threw a five-dollar bill on the tablecloth.

Lyn's lips drew back from her teeth. He could feel, like a strong sudden gust, her impulse to hit him. Then he thought she'd cry. But she walked away.

He sat, staring at the messy table. Of all the stinking lousy dates he ever had in his life! Protectively, he thought of it as just a date. He was outraged. His last night in the East! Last date! And she walked out on him.

For what? He oversimplified. Because he didn't give that mangy old deadbeat a quarter. Of all the ...! He sat there and let anger become a solid lump. After a while, he paid the check and left. Outside, Lyn was nowhere about.

He began to walk, fast, hands dug in his coat pockets. He supposed gloomily it was a good thing he'd found out what kind of stuff passed for thought in her head. So ... cross *her* off the list. Yeah. Couldn't she see he hadn't tried to hurt her? Couldn't she concede he'd learned a few things, had a core of conviction that was, at least, honestly come by? No, she couldn't.

But Towers would have a date tonight, just the same. His little book (with the list) was at the hotel, damn it. He swung north. Hadn't thought he'd need it. But he *had* it. Towers would have a date his last night. Wouldn't be stood up, not he!

Jed slammed through the revolving door. It stuttered, not moving as fast as he. He stood smoldering at the desk, waiting for his key. He went up to the eighth floor, unlocked his door, put on his light, flung off his coat.

He stared around him, then dipped into his bag for that bottle of rye. He could think of nobody on his list who'd do him good. Call any girl, this time of night, and you could hear her little brain buzzing. Oh, will I look unpopular if I admit I'm not busy? So she'd say she had a date. And he'd say, "Break it for me?" Knowing damn well she probably was just about to wash her hair or something. So, she'd "break it." Phony. Everything was pretty phony.

(Not Lyn. She was just too naïve to live.)

He looked at the phone. Call and apologize? But what was there to apologize for? He'd only said things he believed.

The blind across his bank of windows was not drawn. He realized that he stood as one on a lighted stage. It felt, too, as if eyes were upon him. Somebody was watching him.

He moved toward the windows that looked out on a court.

He was looking directly across the narrow dark deep well into another lighted bank of windows. The other room hung there in the night like a lighted stage. The scene had no depth. It was lit by a lamp near the windows. There was a girl or a woman over there. She was dressed in some kind of flowing bluish or greenish thing. She seemed to be sitting *in* the window, probably on the flat top of the long radiator cover. Her neck was arched. She had short yellowish hair. She seemed to be looking down at a point on her right leg just above the knee. A garter or something? Her right foot rested on the radiator top. The nicely shaped leg was bent there, framed and exhibited.

She was not looking out, not looking at him. He was absolutely certain that she had been. He knew he must be silhouetted in the frame of his own windows.

She moved her right palm slowly down the curve of her calf. Her head turned. She looked across at him. He did not move.

Her hand rested on her ankle. Her garment remained as it was, flowing away from the pretty knee. Her head was flung up from the neck. She looked at him.

There was something so perfectly blunt about the two of them, posed as they were, each in his bright box, suspended, aware. . . . It was as if a shouted *Well?* crossed the court between them.

Jed felt himself grin. The anger that hummed in his veins changed pitch, went a fraction higher. What was this? and why not? he thought, pricked and interested.

## CHAPTER 5

THE GIRL took her hand from her ankle, put both hands on the radiator top behind her, bent her body to lean back on the stiff support of both her arms, kept looking out at him. There was something direct about it that fitted with his mood.

Jed was reading the floor plan of the hotel that lay in his head. He felt pretty sure he knew what the number of that room must be. He put his bottle of rye down and raised both hands where the shape of them would be silhouetted for her to see. He signaled with eight fingers, then with both hands bent in an O, and then with seven fingers.

Her head tilted as if to say, What do you mean?

He took up the bottle in his left hand, pointed at it, at her, at himself.

Her chin went high, as if her head fell back in laughter.

He put down the bottle, pantomimed himself at a telephone. She understood because her head turned and she looked behind her toward where the phone in that room must be.

She made the sign of seven.

Jed backed away from the window. He picked up his phone. He said to the girl, "807, please."

Downstairs, as Rochelle made the connection, a thought no clearer than the word "huh?" crossed her mind fleetingly. Pursuing it, she remembered. Oh, yeah, 807 was the whispering foulmouth. What now? Probably, she surmised, 821 was going to complain. She heard a man's voice say, "Well?" It was blunt and a trifle mocking. It wasn't going to complain.

Jed could still see the girl, in the little puddle of light by the beds in there, answering her phone. He waved. "Hi," he said, over the wire. She made a sound like a chuckle. "Hello."

"*Would* you like a drink?"

"I might," she said.

"If I walk around, will you open the door?"

"I might."

"It's a long walk," he said.

He had the impression that she would have teased him, but something happened. He saw her head turn. She said, in a different mood and a different tempo, "Wait a few minutes?"

"This is an impulse," Jed said frankly. "It might not last."

"Five minutes," she said. "There's somebody at the door." Then softly she hung up.

Jed sat on the bed in his room. He saw her at the window, lowering the blind, but she tripped it so that he could still see into the room. He knew when she went into the shadowy part, when she opened the door. The visitor came in far enough so that Jed could identify the hotel livery.

Bellhop, or something. Oh, well . . . He went into his bathroom, looked at himself in the glass. His anger was no longer so solid. It came and went, ebbed and flowed. But the pulse was strong, the beat was urgent. It seemed necessary to do something.

In 807, Eddie was saying, "Little girl went to sleep all right, did she? You all right, Nell?"

"Umhum," Nell murmured. She was in the maroon chair, looking relaxed. Her eyelids fell as if they were heavy.

"What you got on? Nell!" Eddie's voice was thin.

"I'm not hurting anything."

Eddie's flitting eye caught the top of the dressing table and the condition it was in. His gold-flecked teeth bit over his pale lip. He moved closer to the dressing table. After a while he said, in a low voice, "You shouldn't monkey with other people's stuff, Nell. Really, you shouldn't."

"I'm not hurting anything," she repeated and her voice was more truculent than before.

Eddie gnawed his lip. He rescued the perfume bottle and replaced the stopper. Almost furtively, his fingers began to neaten the tumble of jewelry. He began to talk, softly.

"It's kind of an easy job, though, isn't it, Nell? Don't you think so? You like it, don't you, Nell?"

"Oh, sure," she said drowsily.

"Nell, you . . . better take off that negligee . . . and the slippers. Honest. I don't think Mrs. Jones would like that."

"She won't know the difference," said Nell shortly.

"Well," said Eddie, "will you take them off, like a good girl?"

"Umhum," she murmured. "Sure I will, Uncle Eddie." She lifted her eyes and smiled at him.

He was enormously encouraged and pleased. "That's right," he cried. "That's good. You want to get more jobs like this. Don't you see, Nell? It'll be a real nice kind of little work for you. And you can do what you want with the money, after. You can buy some fancy slippers like those for *yourself*, Nell."

She turned her cheek to the chair.

Eddie wished he knew how it was Marie talked to her, what it was she did. Because Nell was good when Marie was around, real quiet and good.

"Tell you what I'll do," he said heartily. "When I get off duty,

I'll bring you up a Coke. O.K.? It won't seem so long. You'll be
surprised how the time will go by."

"Sleepy," she murmured.

"Well," he said, bracing his shoulders, "nap a little bit. That's
a good idea." He looked at the perfume bottle, now nearly empty.
He said in a nervous rush, "And you ought to apologize for spill-
ing the perfume . . . right away when she comes back."

Nell's lids went up slowly until her eyes were very wide. "It
was an accident," she said an octave higher than before. Her
whole body had tightened.

"I know. I know," said Eddie quickly. He stepped near her
and put a gentle hand on her shoulder. She twisted away from
it. "Of course it was an accident. I believe you, Nell. But it's a
good idea to say so, before she notices. It'll be all right. You
couldn't help it. Now, you just — just take it easy a little bit. I'll
be back." He looked nervously behind him. The open elevator,
standing too long on the eighth floor, was present in his con-
sciousness. "I gotta go. But you're all right, aren't you?" He swallowed. "Please, Nell," he said in a thin pleading voice, "don't get
into no more mischief with their things."

"I'm not doing anything," she said sullenly.

But, when he sighed and paused as if he would plead some
more, she said quickly, "I'm sorry, Uncle Eddie. I'll put everything back. You know I get . . . restless." Her hands moved to
the earrings. "I'll take them off."

Immediately, he was pleased. "Sure, I know you get restless.
I know you don't mean anything. I want you to . . . kinda get
used to this idea. We could work up a kind of a little business,
here. If you'd just . . . If you like it."

"I do like it," she said, sounding thoughtful and serious.

The little man's face reddened with his delight. "Good girl!
That's swell! I'll bring the Cokes." And so he withdrew, pointed
little face going last, like a mouse drawing back into its hole.

Nell waited for the door to close. She got slowly to her feet. Then they began to move on the carpet in that tiny dance. She listened. She went to the blind and it rattled up under her hands.

Jed was standing in the middle of his room, his weight even on both feet, looking rather belligerently across at her.

She flung up both hands in a beckoning gesture, until her arms were in a dancer's high curve, and she whirled backward from the window. Jed stood still. And the girl stood still, posed with her arms high, looking over her shoulder.

In a second, Jed put the bottle in his pocket, and his finger on his light switch. His light went out.

Nell pawed, disturbing the order Eddie had created, and she snatched at Ruth's spare coral lipstick.

## CHAPTER 6

Jed's impulse had been flickering like a candle in a draft. He put the bottle in his pocket for the necessary little drink that you take while you look the situation over, heard the elevator gate closing. So he waited for the faint hum of its departure before he went around the corner. His mood was cautious when he tapped on the door marked 807.

She was not very tall, not very old, not bad-looking, either. Her face, tilted to look at him, was a triangle and the eyes were set harlequinwise. Jed's nostrils moved. She reeked ... the whole room reeked ... of perfume. She opened the door wider, quickly. He took a step and the door closed behind him as if she had fanned him into this perfumed place. His glance went rapidly around. He looked, and knew it, as if he were ready to take the step back again, and out.

"What's in the bottle?" she asked.

He took it out of his pocket and showed her the label. He said, mechanically, "Too nice a night to drink alone."

Her blue eyes examined his. For a minute, he thought there wasn't going to be any act . . . and he was fascinated by that same sense of blunt encounter that he had felt before.

This wasn't a type he knew.

He set the bottle on the desk and walked past it, going warily to the big maroon chair. "Nice of you to let me come over," he said, perfunctorily. His eye caught certain signs and he was not pleased. He thought he had better get out of here as quickly as was graceful. It was obvious that this room was half a man's.

She walked over a bed on her knees and then was standing between the two of them with complete dignity. It was odd, almost as if she didn't notice how she had got there. She put her hands on the phone. "We must have some ice," she said grandly.

"Fine."

"Ginger ale?"

The name on that envelope caught in the hasp of the suitcase was Jones. "Whatever you like, Mrs. Jones," Jed said.

She was startled. Then her reddish lashes swept down. Into the phone she said, grandly, "Please send ice and ginger ale to Mrs. Jones in 807."

Jed guessed she was being some movie star or other. But they'd cut a line out of the picture. She forgot to ask for room service. The operator obliged. Looking over Jed's head, posed like a model, the girl repeated her order with exactly the same inflections. It was mimicry all right.

But when she hung up, her whole face changed. "I'm not Mrs. Jones," she told him with sly delight. "Mrs. Jones went out."

Jed looked mildly interrogative.

"This isn't my room," she chuckled.

He thought to himself that this was no worse a dodge than

any. "That's funny. The room over there isn't *my* room, either. Coincidence?" He leaned back, grinning.

"Mr. and Mrs. Jones went out," she said, frowning.

"The fellow whose room I was in went out, too," said Jed, still grinning. "He's got a date."

She sat down on the bed and stuffed a pillow behind her. "I'm going to South America tomorrow," she remarked lightly.

"Oh? What part?" She didn't answer. "I'm off to Europe, myself," he lied cheerfully.

"Mr. Jones is my brother," said the girl. "I hate him. I hate all my relatives. They won't let me do anything. They don't want me to have dates." She looked both dreamy and sullen. Jed began to believe some of this. Something was real about it.

"Shall we make it a date?" he suggested. "And go dancing?"

Her head jerked. He saw her quick desire to go and her recollection of some reason why not . . . "I haven't any evening clothes," she said, and he gawped at such an excuse. If excuse it was. "Mrs. Jones had a beautiful evening dress."

"Your . . . sister-in-law?"

"And a velvet wrap the color of this." She touched the negligee. "You can't buy that for 50 cents an hour."

A rap on the door cut into Jed's puzzling. Boy with the ice. Jed got up and turned his back, looking out through the blind as if there was something to see. There was nothing to see but some old biddy writing letters over there.

"Sign, miss?" the boy was mumbling.

Jed turned around. "Better let me get it, honey." He fumbled for money. "What time did your brother go out?" he asked her.

She said nothing.

"Do *you* know?" Jed watched the boy's worldly young eyes. "Notice a couple in evening clothes?"

"Yeah, they left quite a long while ago."

"How long will they be?" Jed asked the girl.

She shrugged. "Some shindig..."

"Yeah? Well..." Jed watched the boy whose eyes were first satisfied, then veiled. The boy took his tip and departed.

The boy, whose name was Jimmy Reese, went down the corridor jauntily, his lips pursed to whistle. Eddie's elevator picked him up. They eyed each other with a kind of professional contempt. Jimmy's whistle went right on.

The guy in 807 belonged in 821. This Jimmy knew. Who that girl was, Jimmy did not know. So she was Jones's sister. For all he knew. He didn't know she had anything to do with Eddie.

Eddie didn't know that Jimmy had just been to 807. He'd listened at the eighth floor. He'd eyed the boy. All seemed quiet.

Jed, fixing drinks, thought it over. He had established something. Mr. and Mrs. Jones *had* gone out. Who was this, then?

"You got a name?" he asked gently.

"Nell." She told him so absent-mindedly he believed it.

Nevertheless, he lied, saying, "I'm John." He handed her a glass, went over and fixed the blind. Then he sat down on the bed next to her. "Where you from, Nell?"

"California."

"What part?"

"All of it."

"You can't do that. California's too big. San Francisco?"

"Sometimes."

"Tulsa?" he said.

"There, too," she answered serenely.

"Where is Tulsa?" he asked, in sudden suspicion.

"In California." She looked surprised.

"Nell," he said amiably, "you're a liar."

"Oh, well," she said, suddenly soft as a kitten, leaning against his arm, "you're lying to me, too."

"I haven't said anything."

"You're lying, just the same."

He took her chin in his left hand, turned her face.

"Well?" he said, aloud. He bent his mouth to kiss her.

The taste of her lips was very close when a ripple went down his spine. He turned Nell's quietly waiting face with his hand, pressing it to his shoulder. His neck worked stiffly, slowly. He looked behind.

There was a little girl with dark pigtails, barefooted, in pink pajamas. She was watching them silently.

A wild animal could have startled him no more.

## CHAPTER 7

THE SHOCK seemed to lift him into the air. He croaked, controlling his voice better than his reflexes, "Seems to be an audience." He had pushed Nell to her balance. He was suddenly sitting on the other bed, facing the child.

Jed, going about his business, brushed by the children in the world without making any contact. They didn't interest him. They were out of his orbit. It seemed a long time ago, if not in another planet, that he himself had been a child. Jed didn't know any children, as friends. He would have mentioned "a bunch of kids" as he would comment on a "flock of chickens" or a "hill of ants." He didn't individualize them. He simply had no truck with them.

This little girl, with her dark eyes in an angular face, wasn't a pretty little girl. Too thin. Too solemn.

Nell was in a crouch, leaning on her arms. "Get back in there," she said viciously.

"I want—"

Nell went across the bed on her knees. "Go on. Get back in

there and go to sleep." Her fingers clawed the little shoulders.

Nobody spoke to Bunny O. Jones in such a fashion. Nobody handled her so cruelly. She began to cry.

"And shut up!" said Nell.

"Yours?" said Jed coolly.

"She belongs to the Joneses," said Nell angrily.

"Oh . . . your niece?"

Nell laughed.

"You've got my mommy's things on," wailed Bunny.

"Shut —"

"Just a minute." Jed rose. He came toward them. He was very tall next to Bunny O. Jones. He had no instinct to bend down. "What's your name?" He felt awkward, speaking to this mite, and was impelled to speak loudly as one does to a foreigner or someone who may not readily understand the language.

"I'm Bunny O. Jones." She twisted in Nell's harsh hands.

"Let go of her! Bunny *Jones,* eh? This isn't your aunt, is it?"

"She's my sitter," sobbed Bunny.

"Oh, for Lord's sake," Jed put his glass down angrily. Now he knew what he had got into.

"I don't like you," sobbed Bunny.

"I don't like you either, you damn little snoop," Nell said.

One did *not* speak to these strange little creatures in such terms. Jed felt this much out for himself. It came slowly to him with a sense of how big he was, how big and how powerful even Nell was, and how helpless was the child.

He said, "Nobody's going to hurt you, Bunny. Don't cry."

But she kept on crying. Perhaps she didn't believe him. He couldn't blame her for that. She was shrinking away from Nell. And Nell contrived to loom closer and closer, so that the child was menaced and pursued and sought to escape, although the chase was neither swift nor far, but done in tiny pulses of the foot on the carpet.

"Why don't you ask her what she wanted?" Jed said.

"She wanted to snoop," said Nell.

But it was clear to Jed that the little girl had done nothing in malice. He put his arm like a bar across Nell's path. "No," he insisted. "There was something. What was it, hm? Bunny? What did you want?"

"It's too hot," wept Bunny. "I want my radiator off."

"You might have asked," Jed said scornfully to Nell. "I'll take care of it."

He strode through the communicating door. The other room was stuffy. He found a valve. He thought, Towers, fold your tent. He noticed the exit to the corridor from here, from 809, and the key in the lock.

But the crying child, the girl again pursuing her in that gliding stepless way, were in the room with him.

"It's O.K. now," Jed said. "Better get back to bed."

"*She'll* get back to bed."

Bunny broke and ran. She rolled into the bedclothes. She burrowed as if to hide. She was still crying.

Jed stalked into 807, making directly for the bottle. What a stinking evening! First one thing and then another! *Now* he understood that crack about 50 cents an hour . . . this late! He was furious for having been stupid. He was embarrassed and humiliated. He was even half angry with the little girl for having walked in and stared at Towers making a jackass of himself. A baby sitter!

He wanted this Nell to know he was angry. So he freshened from the bottle the drink in the glass.

As Nell, on his heels, entered 807 and closed the door firmly behind her, he snarled, "Were you going to pay me my two bits an hour? Or wasn't this a 50-50 proposition?"

"What?" she spoke as if she'd been preoccupied, as if she hadn't quite heard. Her face was serene. She touched her hair. It was as if, now that the door was closed, it might as well never have opened.

But Bunny was crying bitterly beyond the wall.

Jed said, furiously, "Why didn't you tell me there was a kid in there?"

"I didn't know she was going to come in here," Nell said.

Jed looked at her. For the first time, something nudged him, something said the word inside his head. But he didn't believe it. The word is easy to say. It falls off the tongue. But it is not so easy to believe, soberly, in all reality.

She walked to where he stood, fitted herself into the hollow of his shoulder and turned up her face. She was back where she'd been when so rudely interrupted. She was waiting for them to take up where they had left off. Jed stood still, angry enough to throw her brutally away from him, but bitter enough to stand still in unresponsive contempt.

The little kid was crying, in there, a tearing, breaking — a terrible sound.

Nell's tawny head rested against him. He grabbed her shoulder. "Don't you hear that?" He shook her.

"Hmmmm?" She was smiling. She enjoyed being shaken. So he let her go. Her eyes opened. "I heard you. I know what you said. You're mad at me. I don't see why you're mad at me, John. Johnee! I haven't done anything."

"Well," Jed said. He put the stopper in the bottle of liquor and kept it in his hand. He was ready to go.

"Don't go," Nell said rather shrilly. "I haven't done anything. It's all right now, isn't it? She's gone."

"Gone!" The sound of the child, crying in the next room, was preying on Jed's nerve ends. As bad, he thought, as if a cat had been yowling under his window and he trying to sleep. It was too irregular even to be a background noise. It pierced. It carried you with it into its anguish. "Can't you hear that!"

"That? She'll go to sleep."

"She will?"

Nell shrugged. Using one hand, she lapped the long silk robe so that it didn't drag. "Can't I have another drink?"

The sounds the kid was making were not, Jed discovered, quite like a cat crying. He didn't know anything about kids. But you didn't need to know anything. Just listening told you. *This* sound of *this* crying had to stop.

"Does it bother you?" the girl said rather casually.

"It bothers the hell out of me," Jed said roughly. "She's scared. Why did you have to jump at her like a wildcat? This the way you always treat your customers?" He poured whisky into her glass, hardly aware he was doing so.

She looked sullen. "I didn't mean to scare her."

"But you knew she was in there. You're supposed to be taking care of her, aren't you? Listen . . ."

He was listening, himself, all the time. The sound was intolerable. "You better get her to stop that."

"When she gets tired . . ."

"You want the whole hotel up here?" he snapped.

"No." She looked alarmed.

"Then do something, I'm telling you."

"If I go in there, you'll sneak out," Nell said flatly. The thought was crossing Jed's mind as she spoke. He put the whisky down beside the phone. He took his hand off the bottle as if it were hot.

"I don't have to sneak out, you know," he said cuttingly. "I can walk out, just about any time."

"If she stops crying, will you stay?"

Jed was thinking how that little throat must ache. He growled, "Get her quiet. Get her happy. Go on."

"If I do?"

"If you do," he said rather desperately, "well . . . maybe we can have a quiet little drink before I go."

The girl turned, put down her glass, went to the door and opened it quietly. She vanished in the darkness.

"Mr. Towers' room doesn't answer," Lyn said. "But you did see him come in a little while ago?"

"Yes, I did."

"Well . . ." she turned uncertainly.

"A message?" the desk clerk suggested politely. She was a cute girl, trim and cuddly in the bright blue coat with the big brass buttons. And she seemed distressed.

"Yes, I could leave a note."

He used a pencil to point the way to a writing desk in the lobby, aiming it between a pillar and a palm.

"Yes, I see. Thank you." Lyn sat down at the desk. She shifted the chair slightly so that she could keep an eye on a spot anyone entering the Hotel Majestic from the street must pass.

She thought he must have gone out again, perhaps through the bar. She hoped he wasn't, even now, upsetting her family. This was something she had to work out for herself.

Anyhow, she didn't think Jed would go to her apartment. It would be capitulation. He wasn't that type. He was pretty proud.

Was she the type, then, to hang around? All right, she thought stubbornly, I *won't* be the huffy female type who, right or wrong, sits and waits for the male to come with his hat in his hand, like the dopey heroines of old romances.

Ah, nobody was a type! This was Jed and Lyn, and this had to be worked out on the basis that they were unique and alive, and it had to be worked out *now*. Tomorrow, the plane . . .

Wherever he was, he'd come back here. He hadn't checked out. It was all so childish. . . . She could at least say that much.

"Dear Jed," she wrote. "It was all so childish. . . ."

How could such bitter words have been spoken between them? Because she'd been riding a high romantic crest of expectation

428                       *MISCHIEF*

and been dragged rudely off it? Maybe, for him, there'd never
been such a crest. No, no. She *had* known that Jed was fond of
her. She'd had *reason* to expect him to say so or say more.

She tore up the sheet and wrote again, "Dear Jed: I've been
trying to find you because . . ." A tear fell and the ink blurred
and she thought, Oh, no . . . not this! Wouldn't he be amused!

Would he? Lyn sat a long time with her hands quiet on the
desk. She worked it out. It was true. She was in love with Jed
Towers . . . in love enough to lash out at him.

It was true. She had thought he might ask her to marry him
tonight. They'd been together, together . . . until that old man
touched this off.

And it was true. She'd have said "yes." Gladly, yes.

And they had quarreled.

But it was *not* true that she thought him a cheap cynic. He was
. . . wary. Yes, he was. And he talked cynically. Part of it was
simple reporting — what he saw around him. Part of it was de-
fensive . . . or something like that. But it was talk.

So Lyn worked it out, painfully. It was also true, whoever began it, she had been the one to walk away and cut off communication, and she didn't (she'd always *said*) believe in that.

She took up the pen. "Dear Jed: I can't let you go — " But
you can't keep him, Lyn. He isn't that type. Maybe he was only
something charming and exciting flashing through your life.
"Misunderstanding," she wrote desperately. It was too late. She
ought to go home.

What can I say? she wondered. What can I do? How can I go
home?

Get out of here, Towers. Get out, quick. And forget it.
Skip it. Jed paid his inner talk to himself no heed. He sat
down on a bed. Under the verbalized thought ran uneasy pictures. What if the child were to cry a long time, and he, in his

own room, could hear? How was he in a position to protest, to do anything about it? *He'd* been stupid. Nell, the baby sitter, had already made a complete jackass out of Towers. He looked into his glass and contemplated this state of affairs.

When Nell came back carrying the child, he knew her reason. She didn't trust him not to sneak away. He was not entirely displeased. He wanted to watch her quiet the child.

"If you're scared, that's silly. Nothing to be scared about," Nell said impatiently. "Now don't start to cry any more. Shall I read another story?"

"No," said Bunny. She wasn't quite crying at the moment, but she was shaken by an aftermath of shuddering. It was a reaction not subject to her control.

Nell set her down on her bare feet. Three strangely assorted people looked rather helplessly at each other.

"You know, *you* nearly scared the life out of me," Jed said in a friendly tone. "And Nell, too. That's why Nell was cross."

"She was . . . too . . . cross," said Bunny.

"That she was," he agreed grimly.

Nell looked as if she would flare up defensively, but she did not. "You O.K. now?" Her voice was edgy.

Bunny wasn't sure enough to say. Her eyes turned from one to the other.

"I'm a friend of Nell's, stopped by to see her a minute," Jed said, feeling his face flush. Why he should be trying to explain himself to this half-pint creature he didn't quite know. "You ought to be asleep, I guess. How old are you?"

"Nine."

Nine. What was it to be nine? Jed couldn't remember. The drinks were beginning to blur his concern a little.

"I'm too hot," said Bunny. "I'm all sticky."

"Come over here, then." Nell went to the windows. "We'll let some cool air blow on you. Then you'll be cooler. Then you can go back to sleep." She nodded wisely. She pulled up the blind, pushed up the sash.

Jed jumped quickly out of the line of vision through those windows. His back felt for the headboard. He poured another drink. The ice was all the way over there. So, no ice. Because he wouldn't cross in front of the windows. Place like a goldfish bowl. He knew. And that was where you made your mistake, Towers.

"See the lady, Bunny?"

Sob and shudder answered.

"I see a man, down there. He's playing cards."

Jed's warm drink was nauseating.

"I think," Nell went on, "there's a kitten under the table."

"What"— sob — "table?"

"Down there. The card table."

"I don't see . . ."

"Maybe it isn't a kitten. But it looks like a kitten."

"Is it gray?"

"Maybe."

Miss Eva Ballew wrote, on the Hotel Majestic stationery, in her flowing script: ". . . seems to be a child crying in this hotel and I am so distracted, I hope you can understand what I am writing, since I seem to have two predicates and no subject in my previous sentence! My dear, this trip has really . . ."

Her pen paused. The child had stopped crying. Thank goodness, she thought. But now the night seemed hollow. She ducked her head enough to glance briefly out, under her blind.

The pen resumed: ". . . been a treat for all us teachers to have visited so many historical sites here in the East. . . ." It was not a sentence.

She put down her pen suddenly and ducked again to look out, across the dark well of the inner court.

"I don't see any kitten," Bunny said, "at all."

"Well, you're not looking," Nell said softly. "But you won't cry any more, will you?"

Jed glanced across at the bowl of ice. He rose. Why did she have to put the damn blind up? Dare he cross over? *Was* there anybody taking all this in?

When he turned his head over his shoulder, the question dropped out of his mind. He stood quite still, puzzling about what was wrong. It seemed to him, definitely, that something was wrong. Bunny was kneeling on that radiator top. And Nell sat there beside her. Nell's hand was flat on the little rump in the pink sprigged muslin —

*Her hand was flat!*

And there was some wild throbbing in this room.

Miss Eva Ballew, peering out, exclaimed. Nobody heard her, for she was alone. "No!" she said. Then, whimpering, "Oh, no!"

The back of Jed's neck prickled. He began to move, silently.

"Way down under the table?" Bunny asked.

"Way down . . ." crooned Nell. "Way, way down. Are you going to be quiet, I wonder?"

Bunny screamed.

Jed, with his fingers tight around the little brown ankle, caught her forward pitch with one arm and said, on a rush of breath, "Excuse me. Shouldn't lean out like that, for Lord's sakes. I *had* to grab."

Nell's face turned, tipped back and up. She looked drowsy and unstartled. "What?" she murmured. "What's the matter?"

Jed had the child. "Better come away," he said to her. He squeezed her as gently as he could manage. "I'm sorry, honey, if I scared you. Trouble is, you scared *me* again. Sure did. Awful long ways down — kind of tough landing."

Bunny, having screamed once in her surprise, did not begin

to cry. Her face was pale. Her big dark eyes seemed to turn and keep some wisdom of her own.

Jed said, "You're shivering. Aren't you sleepy now?"

Bunny nodded. She wiggled out of his arm, looked at him gravely. "I can go to bed myself," said Bunny O. Jones.

Miss Ballew straightened her cramped body. Her heart still lurched with that old devil of hers, that hair-trigger onset of the physical sickness of fear. She felt her throbbing throat. But what was going *on,* over there? Her pale lips tightened. She'd heard the man say, "Put that blind down!"

So, it was to be secret, and it was male, and it was, perhaps, evil? She focused on her letter. "And even in this wicked city," her pen wrote, at last, too shakily.

"Put that blind down!"

Nell was still sitting by the window, still looking dreamy. She stretched to obey and Jed thought there was something snake-like in the smooth uncoiling of her arching back.

He stood at the door of 809, through which Bunny had marched herself. 809 was quiet . . . dim and quiet in there. So he closed the door, gently.

Bunny's rigid neck muscles let go a little. The head began to dent the pillow. The eyes were wide open. The hand reached for the little stuffed dog and tucked it under the stiff chin. The throat moved, against the fluffy toy, in a great and difficult swallow.

Jed swung around. You're nuts, Towers, he said to himself, angrily, using the words in his mind to knock out the pictures. You must be nuts. Where'd you get such a nutty idea? No-body shoves kids out of eighth-story windows so they won't cry any more! Made his hair curl, the mere idea, even now.

He began to fish ice out of the bowl.

It crossed his mind that there is something wild about total immersion in the present tense. What if the restraint of the future didn't exist? What if you never said to yourself, "I'd better not. I'll be in trouble if I do"? You'd be wild, all right. Capricious, unpredictable ... absolutely wild.

He looked at the girl. She was leaning beside him, watching the ice chunk into her glass, with a look of placid pleasure. She glanced up. "You've had more than me," she stated.

"That's right," Jed said. He felt perfectly sober. But he wasn't going to have any more liquor, not for a while.

He gave her the drink. He sat down, nursing his warm glass.

He couldn't get rid of the shimmer on his nerves of narrowly missed horror. Nuts, Towers. Forget it. She was careless. She just wasn't thinking what she was doing.

"I guess I wasn't thinking," Nell said, with a delicate shrug.

"Are you a mind reader?" He sagged back on his elbow. "That's a couple of times you've said what I had in my mouth."

She didn't answer.

"But you sure should have put a good hitch on the seat of her pants or something. Don't you know that's dangerous?" If the future didn't operate in your thinking, you wouldn't even know that word, he thought. Danger wouldn't have a meaning.

If there *was* such a thing as telepathy, why, it would work both ways. If she could catch an idea out of his mind, then he might catch one of hers. Couldn't he? *Hadn't he?* Listen, Towers, don't be any nuttier than you have to be! Mind reading, yet! Fold your tent ... fade away.

He remembered something. He said, "So you couldn't go dancing on account of the kid?" (So you did feel responsible?)

"Uncle Eddie's on the elevator. He'd have caught me, going out," she said placidly.

"Your Uncle? Uncle Eddie runs an elevator? In this hotel? Oh." Jed turned this information over. "Maybe he got you the job, eh?"

"Yeah," she said with weary scorn, "my wonderful job."

"You don't like it?"

"What's there to like?" she said. And he saw the answer come into her head. He saw it! He *read* it! "There's you, though," Nell was thinking.

He considered, and on the whole he thought he felt relieved. The future tense had operated. Hadn't it? If she thought ahead of her, to Eddie on the elevator?

His mind skipped to his own future. Tomorrow morning on the airplane. By tomorrow night, a continent away, looking back on a weird evening, which was about over, he judged. Time to go.

His anger was gone. *He* was operating in the future tense, saying to somebody, "And *what* a sitter! What a dame she turned out to be! Nutty as a fruitcake!" he would say.

"Well," he spoke, "Nell, I'll tell you. It might have been fun. We'll never know. So here's to the evening. Bottoms up and then good-bye. See you in South America, sometime?"

He grinned. Her eyes were too blue, not in the quality of the blue, but in the quantity. Strange eyes . . .

"You're not going," she said. It wasn't even a protest. She just said this, as if it were so.


## CHAPTER 8


THE UNWRITTEN LAW that links green peas to roast chicken had not been flouted tonight. Peter pointed with his fork and winked. He wasn't really eating.

Ruth could eat no more than he. They picked and pretended.

But nobody, she thought, was there for the sake of nourishment. The food marched by, perfectly conventional, so that nothing about it should interrupt the real business of the banquet. Be seen, buzz, bow . . . Oh, it *was* fun!

But now they were nearly past the ice cream. They were at the coffee . . . the end of the line. Peter's conversation with his neighbors had been slowly lessening.

Ruth's nerves tightened right along with his. She let a little ice cream melt in her dry mouth. Peter was taking tiny sips of water, oftener now.

Every once in a while, the buzzing and the bending-to-chat got a little unreal for Ruth — whenever Bunny came into her mind. It was a little distressing that her vision of Bunny in her bed was shaky and unreal, too. Bunny, she told herself, was sound asleep. Oh, Bunny was real! Warm and beloved, Bunny was there. But those hotel rooms, those formulas, did not wrap her around with the safe sense of being home.

It was a great city, vast and unknown, and the West Side seemed divorced from the East Side, where they were . . . seemed far.

"I'd like to call back to the hotel pretty soon," she murmured to Peter. "Where are the phones?"

"Saw them as we came through," Peter said. "Around the corner, past those mirrors . . ." He dabbled in his ice cream.

"Have I time, do you think?" breathed Ruth. They, at the speakers' table, were as far as it was possible to be, away from the telephones. Parade, in my pink, thought Ruth. Conspicuous. Peter could not go, *now*.

The toastmaster shifted in his chair. He sipped his coffee. Ruth felt all Peter's muscles wince. For the toastmaster glanced their way and made a tiny nod.

Imperceptibly, Peter responded. The toastmaster shoved with his hips and his chair began to move backward.

Not now! No time, now! Ruth would call, afterward. It would be good to call, later, with this tension gone. And all clear. Oh, yes, it would be much better.

There was no doubt that Bunny was sound asleep, anyway. Ruth must now lift her chin and turn her head and listen sweetly to the Speaker of the Evening. (Oh, what was he going to say? Oh, *Peter!*)

Bunny was nine and surely had fallen asleep by this time.

The toastmaster rose like Fate. Ruth released her glass and patted her cold hands together in tune with the crowd. "I am particularly glad," the man said, "to have this opportunity . . ."

Ruth smiled faintly and let her fingers play with her water glass. She must display the perfect confidence she felt, that under her pounding heart lay so truly sure. . . .

Jed fended her off and it was balm to do so. It was sweet revenge on the whole female race who had loused up his evening. He laughed at her. He had her by the elbows, at arm's length. "It's not that automatic, toots," he said. "I know. There's a school of thought that says it is. But make a note, why don't you? There is such a thing as being choosy."

Her rage made him laugh and he let himself go back against the headboard. "The time, the place and the girl," he mocked. "*I'll* choose them all, and this ain't *any* of them, sweetheart."

She looked ready to screech. But then her face closed down, took on that sleepy look. She leaned heavily on his grasp.

"So I'll say so long, Nell," he snapped. "Understand?"

The wild thing about her which, he knew now, had attracted him in the first place, and then made him uneasy, was getting entangled with her will. She wasn't sleepy. Oh, no! Now, he knew that the dreamy look was, on her, a dangerous sign. Maybe a part of her did go to sleep. Maybe it was the part that took into account the future.

He sat up, thrusting her with stiff forearms. He was a little bit sorry for having indulged himself in that laughter. He said, quietly, "I'm really sorry, but I've got to go. Some other time, Nell."

She didn't seem to hear. Then, she did seem to hear, not his voice, but something less loud and less near.

He heard it, too. There came a discreet tapping on the door of room 807.

Oh-oh! Exit Towers! Jed muttered under his breath, "I'll get out the other way, through the kid's room."

"No." She spoke no louder than he, not a whisper, only a movement of the lips that was nearly mute. "You won't." The words were clear and stubborn on her small mouth.

". . . find me," he said in the same fashion, "you'll lose your job."

The tapping was gently repeated. It would persist, insist. It was patient.

Nell's face lit in malice and delight. "No, no. I'll say . . . you pushed in here. Say you're . . . after me."

Jed's eyes flickered. She would, too. She damn well would! For the sheer wild mischief of it! And, if she did, the benefit of the doubt rests with the female.

"You wait," she said. "I know who it is."

Their almost soundless conversation was taking place in a depth of silence that was uncanny. The room pressed silence around them. The city bayed at the feet of the building, but here, high, they spoke without voices in a soundless place. Although someone kept tapping in gentle hope upon the door.

"Who?" Jed was rigid in alarm.

"It's Uncle Eddie. I can get rid of him."

"I can get out," Jed gestured. His eyes were somber.

"No." She knew her wild will held him.

"What, then?" He ground his teeth.

"In there. Be quiet." She pointed to the bathroom.

He rose, slowly, letting her go. He could knock her aside. He could get swiftly into the kid's room.

And she could yell. And she was opening her mouth.

Jed stalled, by picking up the bottle and hiding it in his pocket. Quickly, she put his glass into his hand. And then she had him by the elbow. She was pushing, guiding.

The tapping faltered. "Nell?" someone said anxiously.

Nell said, "Who's there?" Her very voice seemed to stretch and yawn. But her eye was watching Jed and her face rippled. She would just as leave cause trouble . . . just as leave as not!

"It's Uncle Ed. You all right?"

Nell's brows spoke to Jed. Twitted him with it. *Well?* they asked. *Am I?*

He growled, voice muted in the bottom of his throat. "O.K. Make it snappy." He went into the bathroom and pushed the door back behind him, not quite tight.

"Gee, I'm sorry, Uncle Eddie. I guess I must have been asleep," he heard her saying.

Towers stood in the bathroom and cursed Towers in his mind. Of all the damned lousy situations. You picked up dames, sure. Every once in a while. On a train. Maybe in a bar. Sometimes a thing like that turned out not bad. If it was sour, you blew. You got out, fast.

How come Towers was hiding behind a door?

He sat on the edge of the tub, to wait, reciting curses, rehearsing in his mind his swift passage out and away.

Lyn turned away from the phones. No answer.

I will smoke another cigarette, one more. I will wait until ten more people come in from the street, ten more. I can write a better letter. I know I can. I can try.

# CHAPTER 9

EDDIE LOOKED at his niece in negligee and his eyes were disappointed. He said, "I brought the Cokes." Disappointment made his voice bleak. He had the bottles in his hands and he went toward the desk and stood there looking down at the tray, the bowl of melting ice, and Nell's glass. "What's this?" An inch and a half of rye and ginger ale remained in the glass.

Nell said, "You were a long time, Uncle Eddie. I got thirsty. Let me wash that out." She took the glass out of his meek hand. "Mrs. Jones said I could order ginger ale," she said.

"That was nice of her," said Eddie.

Nell pushed in the bathroom door. She went to the wash basin and rinsed the glass.

Not even in the mirror did her eye meet Jed's. There was not a gesture, not a wink, not a sign that she even knew he was there. Jed felt his blood rage. A little grin, a tiny glance, a hint that they conspired to fool this Eddie, would have eased the thing, somehow. But, oh, no! She'd forced him into this ignominy and now she let him stew in it.

Eddie said, "Little girl sleeping? I see you closed her door."

Nell left the bathroom, pulling its door behind her. She would have closed that, but Jed held the inner door.

"Could you hear if she cried or anything?" Eddie was saying.

"The light bothered her," Nell lied calmly.

"Now she's sleeping, though, it won't bother her." Eddie, gentle on the knob, released the catch. "I think Mrs. Jones would rather it was a little bit open, Nell."

"O.K.," she said indifferently. She waited for the Coke.

"And it's getting later. It would be better if you took Mrs. Jones's clothes off, Nell. Honest, I thought . . ."

"Gee, I meant to." Nell's fine teeth bit her lip. "I was so kinda comfortable . . . I just didn't hurry. . . ."

At once, Eddie brightened. "Sure you meant to, Nell. I know that. Uh —" he fiddled with an opener. "Why don't you do it now, though?"

"All right, Uncle Eddie." She slipped her feet out of the mules and into her own black pumps. Then she took the earrings off, slowly. She put them into the jewel box. Her fingers began to pick up other things, tidying them, putting them away.

Eddie brightened with his lightening heart. "Good girl!"

She turned her bent head, smiled at him. She rose and her hands worked at the sash of Ruth's gown. Nell said, sounding modest and shy, "I'll just step into the closet."

Her Uncle Eddie took a long relieved pull on his Coke bottle.

She came out of the closet in her own rumpled dark dress. It had been a heap on the closet floor for some time. But now Nell made elaborate motions of finicky care as she hung the negligee on a hanger and arranged its folds. "There," she said, "is that O.K., Uncle Eddie?"

He beamed on her. "That's fine, Nell." He sighed. "Mightn't be long before they get back, you know. But you're all set."

"We'd better drink our Cokes," she said mildly. "It might look better if I was alone in here. Do you think?"

"You're right," he said. "Yes, you're right. I told them I was going to drop in, but it *would* be better if they find everything quiet and you on the job, eh? Well, here you are. You know I want to do everything for you, don't you, Nell?" he blurted.

"I know, Uncle Eddie." She was all meekness.

He took a swig. "Well, it's because I believe in you, Nell. And Aunt Marie does, too." His blink was contradicting the courage in his voice. "I think you'd rather be here with us than back in Indiana."

"Oh, I would," she murmured.

"If the insurance company would have paid on the house and furniture — but as it is, there's nothing left. You know that. So you'd be on some kind of charity till you got a job, and I wouldn't like that for Denny's girl."

"No," she said.

"You know I haven't got much money," he went on. "You can see why it's a good thing if you can . . . kinda get over this trouble pretty soon."

"I'm O.K.," she said without force.

"You're *better*. That's sure."

She was looking at him with that blind blue abstraction she sometimes had. "But they ought to pay," she said. "Why can't we make them pay?"

"I don't know how we can," said Eddie uneasily. "You see, they claim, because the fire was *set* . . ."

"It was an accident." Her voice went higher. And he cleared his throat nervously. "*Wasn't* it?"

"That's what they said in the court, yes. It was an accident."

Suddenly her face was calm, her glance cold. "So why don't they pay?"

"Well, the insurance company, they figure — I tell you, Nell. Might take a lawyer and quite a lot of money and you wouldn't be sure you could win, you see? I think the best thing is, forget about that and try and get started. . . . There wasn't so much insurance. How's the Coke?"

"It's good," she said meekly. "Is yours?"

"Fine." He took another swig. It might have been wine, for he seemed to mellow. "You just needed somebody to stand back of you," he said. "Me and Marie knew that, Nell, at the time. And we do stand back of you. We really do. I can understand just why it is you get kinda restless streaks."

"You've been good, Uncle Eddie." Her lips barely moved. But he looked very happy. "It's just that I can see how it is," he said eagerly. "After such a terrible experience, a lot of little things seem pretty *little*. Don't matter much, eh?" Every fiber of his worried little being was yearning to make contact, to understand and be understood.

The girl didn't look up, but she nodded.

He swallowed and leaned closer. He said softly, "You want to remember, Nell, your father and mother don't blame you. You mustn't ever think that they would. They know you wouldn't ever have done anything bad, Nell . . . not to them. You see, wherever they are, *they* must know that even better than we do. And . . ."

"I don't want to think about them," she said in a perfect monotone. "I don't want to think about them."

"No, no," said Eddie quickly. "Nobody wants to make you think . . . about that. But I been trying to tell you one thing, Nell. The doctor said it would be good if you'd know . . . and here we're so quiet and all, maybe I can say it. Me and your Aunt Marie, we stand back of you. We don't doubt, for one minute, you set the fire walking in your sleep that night. . . ."

He watched her face. Her lashes flickered. "That's what the court said," she remarked lightly.

"But—but—don't cry," he whispered to the tearless blue of her eyes.

"I'm not going to cry, Uncle Eddie." She turned her empty glass in her fingers. She put it down.

Eddie blinked the tears out of his own eyes. He swallowed the sick flutter of his heart. That Julia his brother married, something about her he never had liked. But surely she'd never been mean to Nell. Denny wouldn't have stood for it. Denny wouldn't be mean to anybody. There could be *no reason*. She was still shocked, poor Nell. She *couldn't* cry. She'd cry, someday. *Sure,* she'd cry.

"Tasted pretty good, didn't it?" he said cheerily.

Jed controlled his rage almost immediately. He'd got into this jam by getting senselessly angry and it was about time, he told himself, that Towers used the brains he was born with. He settled coldly to wait this out.

"And so, I thought," Eddie was saying, "the best idea is for you to start out easy. Take a little job once in a while. The thing is, Nell," he was expounding his creed, "you do something for somebody else and you do a good job. So they're glad to pay you for it. Then you're earning. You're being useful. You'll get into the idea. You'll get over being so restless."

"You told me all this," she said. Her ankle was swinging.

Eddie saw it and silenced himself.

"Going?" she murmured. Her eyes closed.

"I'll take the Coke bottles. I don't think the Joneses are going to be so long, now. Couple of hours, maybe. Tired?"

She didn't answer. Eddie rose and the bottles clinked together as he gathered them. She was breathing slowly. "I'll be in the building," he murmured. His eye checked over the room. Everything was in pretty good order. Looked all right. He took up the glass from which Nell had sipped her Coke.

Absorbed in his own thoughts, his anxieties, his endeavors, his gains and his losses, Eddie went mechanically toward the bathroom to wash out the glasses.

## CHAPTER 10

EVEN BEFORE he met, in the mirror, the little man's shocked and unbelieving eyes, an appraisal of this new situation flooded clearly through Jed's thoughts. The jig was up, all right. O.K. But this could be handled.

The mind has an odd ability to play back, like a tape recorder, things heard and yet not quite attended to at the time. Jed knew,

immediately, that Eddie could be handled. And that it was a way
out for Towers, too.

He knew from what he had overheard that Eddie was by no
means sure of his little niece, Nell. Eddie had stuck his neck
out, getting her this job. Eddie knew she was unreliable, to
put it mildly, although he tried, he struggled, to make himself
believe everything was going to be all right. Oh, yes. Eddie
had taken an awful chance here and Eddie was liable.

All Jed needed to do was use Eddie's self-interest. Very simple.
Jed would apologize. Had a couple of drinks, very sorry, sir,
he'd say. I'll be leaving now. No harm done.

Jed would make it easy for the other fellow. He'd ask silence
as a favor to himself. Eddie could escape by magnanimity the
consequences of his own folly. Eddie would be glad to say "good-
bye" and only good-bye.

So long, Nell, Jed would say, quietly. And he'd be out of it.

So Jed rose, smiling, knowing he had the power of charm and
attractive friendliness when he chose to use it. In the time it
took him to rise and open his mouth, the little man had jerked
with a mouse squeak and backed toward the door, keeping a
frightened face toward Jed's tall figure in the tile-lined gloom.
Jed, not to alarm him, stood quietly where he was.

But Nell, like a cat, was lithe lightning across room 807.
She had the standing ash tray, the heavy thing, in her wild
hands. She swung it up. Jed's lunge and Jed's upraised arm
missed the downswing. The thing cracked on Eddie's skull. The
detachable portion of heavy glass clanged and boomed and
echoed on the tile. And Jed said something hoarse and furious
and snatched the thing out of her hands cruelly, and Nell
jabbered some shrill syllables.

All at once, the noise was frightful.

Only Eddie made no noise. He sank down, very quietly.
There was an instant when everything was suspended. Then

the phone began to ring, in 807, and at the same time Bunny's voice screamed terror, in 809.

"Now!" said Jed thickly. "Now, you . . ." He squatted beside the crumpled little body.

Nell turned and walked over to the telephone, which in some freak of time had rung four times already.

"Hello?" Her voice was fuzzy and foggy.

Jed touched Eddie's temple and then his throat.

"Oh, yes, Mrs. Jones," Nell said. "I guess I must have been dozing."

There was a pulse under Jed's fingers and he stopped holding his breath.

"She's fast asleep," Nell said, blithely. (And Bunny kept screaming.) "Oh, no, no trouble at all. Everything's just fine."

Jed, crouching, found himself listening to that voice. It was pretty cool. Just the faintest undertone of excitement. It could pass for enthusiasm. He could feel the child's cries pierce him, and he shuddered.

"Yes, she did. Went right to sleep after her story, Mrs. Jones. I hope you are having a nice time."

Phone to ear, Nell pivoted to see what Jed was doing and one stare was as blank as another.

The kid was frantic in there! Frantic!

"Please don't feel you need to hurry, Mrs. Jones," purred Nell, "because I don't mind — What?"

Her eyes widened as her voice acted surprise. "Noise? Oh, I guess you can hear the sirens down in the street." Her hand clamped on the mouthpiece. She said, through careful fingers, "They're just going by. There isn't any fire near here." She laughed. "Oh, no. You just have a real good time," she advised gaily. She hung up the phone.

"It's a wonder he's not dead," Jed growled. "You little fool!"

"Isn't he?" said Nell absent-mindedly.

She walked into 809.

Jed's hand, going about the business with no conscious command from his numb brain, felt carefully of Eddie's head. Couldn't tell what the damage was, but there was, at least, no bleeding. Gently, he straightened the body. He lifted it, shifting it all the way over the threshold within the bathroom and, reaching for the thick bath mat, he slid it gently between the hard tile floor and the head. He took a towel and wet it. He washed the forehead gently, the eyes and the cheeks.

Eddie's breathing seemed all right . . . a little difficult, not very. Knocked out, of course, but perhaps . . .

He lifted his own head suddenly.

Bunny was not screaming. The empty air pulsed in the sudden absence of that terrible sound.

Jed sat motionless on his heels. A trickle of sweat cut a cold thread of sensation down his neck.

Ruth stepped with slow grace out of the phone booth. "Have a real good time." Not the *mot juste* for such a night as this! This Night of Triumph! A time to keep in the mind for reference, forever. Even now, so soon afterward, it was an hour to live over again, and feel the heart stop, when Peter got up from his chair, and lurch, when he began, so nervously. And pound proudly, because she soon knew that all these politely listening people were warming to the man, who began a little bit shyly.

And then, Peter getting interested himself in what he was saying. First, the words coming out grammatically, properly placed, in full sentences. Then, the thought transcending and driving the grammar into vivid astonishing phrases that rang just right. And, finally, Peter in the full power of his gift, taking from his mind and heart the things he knew and believed.

He was still excited (oh, bless Peter!) and he was reaping his reward. Now that his speech was over, now that they were

pushing the tables out of the middle of the floor, and music was playing, and people stood in little groups, and he in the middle of the largest group of all.

A victory! But the rehashing, the wonderful fun of this, might go on for hours.

Ruth turned her bright nails into her palms. Bunny was fast asleep. Everything was fine. The girl had said so.

But Ruth stood, trembling, in the hall of mirrors, and she knew in her bones that everything was *not* fine.

"Don't be silly!" she gasped to her own image. "Don't be such a *mother!* Don't spoil it now!"

Peter's head craned toward her out of the group, and she gave him a gay little signal of the hand that meant "all's well."

But that hadn't sounded like the same girl. The girl on the phone was neither dull nor passive. *She wasn't stupid enough!* No, she'd been too decisive. Too . . . too darned *gay!*

She shook herself and walked forward.

"What's wrong, oh, what's wrong where Bunny is?" her bones kept asking.

Peter was in full flight, amplifying something he hadn't touched on quite enough in the speech. Men, standing around him, were nodding, and breaking in to quote themselves. "As I said at lunch the other day . . ." "I was saying to Joe . . ." It seemed as if only last week or the other day they'd been telling somebody, in some fumbling fashion, that which Peter has just told them so well. (Ah, sweet praise!)

"O.K., hon?" Peter was tuned in on the wave length of Ruth's bones. Often and often he'd heard what they were muttering. But now, when she answered, smiling, "All quiet," Peter didn't hear her bones proclaim, "But I don't believe it."

"Good." He squeezed her, swung her. "Ruth, this is Mr. Evans, and Mr. Childs, and Mr. Cunningham."

"How-de-do . . . how-de-do. . ."

"Husband of yours has a head on his shoulders and a tongue in his head, Mrs. O. — uh — Mrs. Jones. Fine talk. Fine."

"I thought so, too," said Ruth in sweet accord.

"Isabel, come here. Turn around, want you to meet. . ." The women murmured.

"And how old is your little girl, Mrs. O. — uh — Mrs. Jones?" Isabel was cooing.

"Bunny is nine."

"Ah, I remember Sue when she was nine," said the woman sentimentally. "A sweet age. A darling year."

Ruth smiled, bright-eyed. She had no voice for an answer.

## CHAPTER 11

M RS. Parthenia Williams said, "I can't help it."

"Aw, Ma," her son said, keeping his voice down in the evening hush of the place where they stood. "Listen to me —"

"I can't help it, Joseph, hear?"

For old Mr. and Mrs. O'Hara in the front suite, the Hotel Majestic had somehow, in the inertia of the years, acquired the attributes of home. Now, Mrs. O'Hara wasn't very well, but she wasn't ill enough to warrant a nurse. So Mrs. Parthenia Williams came by day, and sometimes, when Mr. O'Hara had to be away, she remained late into the evening. Whenever she did so, her son, Joseph, came to see her home.

As they stood in the hush of the eighth-floor corridor, Joseph said, "You better keep out of it, Ma. You know that. Don't you?" He was a thin nervous Negro with an aquiline face.

"I know what I know," his mother said.

Mrs. Williams' chocolate-colored face was designed for smiling, in the very architecture of her full cheeks, the curl of her generous mouth, the light of her wide-set eyes. Nothing repressed her. Nothing could stop her from saying "good morning," in the elevators in her beautiful soft voice. She seemed to acquire through her pores scraps of knowledge about all these strangers, so that she would say, in the corridor, "Did you enjoy the boat trip, ma'am? Oh, that's good!" with the temerity of an unquenchable kindness. Mrs. O'Hara, who was 62 and so often annoyingly dizzy, felt at rest on Parthenia's bosom.

Joseph knew his mother's ways and adored her, but some of her ways . . . He tried to protest this time. "Some things you can't — Ma!"

"Something's scaring that baby in there nearly to death," Parthenia said. "She's just a bitty girl. She's in 809 and her folks next door. And I can't help it, Joseph, so don't you talk to me."

Her big feet carried her buxom body down the corridor. "If her folks ain't there, somebody ought to be comforting her. It's not good for her to be so scared."

"Ma, listen . . ."

"All right, Joseph. Her papa was asking about a sitter and I *know* they were planning to go out. I got to ask. I can't help it."

Jed got to his feet. His eyes rolled toward the frosted bathroom window. He unlocked it and pushed it up.

The deep court seemed quiet. He thrust his head through to look down into the checkered hollow. He couldn't, of course, see all the way to the bottom. He couldn't see Bunny's window, either, for it came on a line with this one.

He could see that old biddy across the way and she was walking. She walked to a chair and held to the back of it with both hands and let go with a push and walked away. And back again.

The fear that hadn't been verbalized, even in his mind, seeped away, and he wondered why he was looking out of the window. He wondered if the dame over there was upset because she had been hearing things. He wondered and in the act of wondering he *knew* that someone must have heard the commotion.

Get out of here, Towers, he warned himself, while you got the chance, you damn fool! Before all hell breaks loose. This guy's not going to die. Look out for Towers!

Jed realized that he had a perfect chance, right now. While the wildcat was in 809, Towers could fade out of 807.

What he heard himself growling aloud, as he stepped over Eddie's body, was, "What in hell is she *doing* in there?"

The knock made him jump. Too late? He groaned. He eyed the distance from where he stood to 809. That would have to be the way out now that someone, and he didn't doubt it was trouble, knocked on 807. How would he get by whoever it was, once in the corridor? He would get by and he'd better.

Then, he saw Nell standing in the way. She looked at him and moved her left hand. It said, "Be still." Jed shook his head and tightened his muscles for the dash. But Nell was swiftly across 807 . . . so swiftly that Jed caught himself and ducked backward again, only just as she opened the door to trouble.

"Yes?" Jed could see her and he cursed, silently, the fantastically cool lift of her chin.

He expected a man's voice, an official voice, cold and final. But the voice was deep music, and not a man's. "I heard the little child crying so bad," it said. "Is there anything I can do?"

"Why, no," said Nell in chill surprise.

"You taking care of the little girl for Miz Jones, ma'am?"

"Yes."

"That's good. You know, I spoke to the little girl and her mama . . . she might know me. I wonder could I comfort her?"

"She's all right now," Nell moved the door. But Parthenia's big foot was within the sill.

"I had so much experience with children. I get along with children pretty well. She was scared, poor child? I hear that."

"Just a nightmare," said Nell indifferently.

"Come on, Ma," Joseph said. "You asked. Now, come *on*."

"Hurts me to hear a baby cry so bad," Parthenia said. "Just hurts my heart like a pain."

"It's none of your business that I can see," said Nell coldly.

"Maybe not," said Parthenia. But her big foot stayed where it was. A big foot, worn with carrying a big body, bunioned and raked over at the heel . . . a big strong stubborn foot. "Maybe not," the lovely voice said sadly, "but I got to try to stop my pain. Can't help trying, ma'am, whatever child is crying."

"She's not crying now," said Nell irritably. "And it's too bad you've got a pain. Please let me close this door, will you?"

"Ma—"

"You got a charm for the nightmare?" Parthenia asked.

"If you don't get out of here, I'll call somebody."

"Ma . . . Excuse us, miss . . . Ma, come *away*."

"I can't feel happy about it," said Parthenia softly mournful. "That's the truth. Could I be sure she ain't scared any more?" her soft voice begged. "Little children, being scared sometimes in the night, you got to be sure. Because it hurts their growing if they're not comforted."

"She's comforted," spat Nell. Then she changed. "But thank you for asking," she said in a sweet whine that had a threat to it, somehow. "I guess you mean well. But I really can't ask you in."

Joseph plucked his mother from the doorway roughly.

"Good night, then," Parthenia said forlornly and, as Nell closed them out, "If I was white I wouldn't—"

"Shush!" said her son. "You ought to know better, Ma. We can't fool around that white girl. Believe me, not *that* one!"

"I wasn't fooling. Something's bad wrong, Joseph. Baby's mother's not there. I can't feel happy about it."

"Listen, Ma, you can't stick your nose in that white girl's affairs, if you're right a million times over." He rang for the elevator, jittering.

"No child," said Parthenia gravely, as they waited, "no child gets off the nightmare as quick as that. No child, Joseph."

"You can't do anything, Ma. Forget it, can't you?"

The elevator stopped. The door slid. Parthenia's enormous foot hesitated. But she stepped in at last, and Joseph sighed.

He heard her mutter, "No, I wouldn't go. I'd make a fuss. I wouldn't go."

## CHAPTER 12

". . . niggers!" said Nell.

All of a sudden, all Jed's cool purpose to depart was burned up in the flame of his raging need to tell her off.

"You damn wildcat! What's the idea of swatting him down like that? What in hell did you think you were doing?"

He shook her. The dark dress was too short. Also, it was cut to fit a more matronly body. So she looked younger and less sophisticated, but also older and dowdier. Her head went back on her neck, as a snake's head poises to strike, and her tiny mouth over the sharp tiny chin looked venomous.

"Answer me!"

She was angry. "What's the matter with you?" she cried. "You didn't want to be seen. Well? He was walking right in there."

"So you'd just as leave murder the man, eh? Just for walking? So you don't care whether he lives or dies?"

"He's not going to die," she said scornfully. "I didn't hit him so hard."

"You hit him as hard as you could. Just luck you didn't . . ."

"Did you want to be seen?" she hissed.

"So you did *me* a favor? Don't do me no more." He flung her to one side of him, holding both her wrists in one hand. It crossed his mind that time was sifting by. It began to look as if no one had sounded any alarm. Nothing was happening. He yanked her along as he went to peer through the window blinds.

The dame across the court was just standing there. He could see her hands on the back of that chair.

He swung Nell back into the center of the room. She stumbled, unresisting, although she looked a little sullen. She said, "I thought you didn't want him to see you."

"So, you shut his eyes. That's logical. That's great!" Jed took his hands off her as if she would soil them. "But I'm still going. I'm going faster and farther, if that's possible. And don't think you can frame me with any lying yarn," he stormed. "I'll be gone," he snapped fingers, "like smoke! You don't know who I am, and you'll never see me again in this world, Nelly girl."

She said nothing. But she moved a little bit, working around, he thought, to put herself between him and the door. He laughed. "Single track, your mind. One-idea-Nell. One at a time is all you can handle? Listen, you never had a chance to keep me here since I found out you were a baby sitter. Never."

"Why not?" she said.

"Say I'm allergic," said Jed shortly, "and skip it. I've got nothing against kids." His hand chopped the air nervously. "That's got nothing to do with it. They let me alone, I let them alone. Nothing to me." He didn't like this line. He shifted, quickly. "Start thinking about yourself and think fast, Nell. How *you're* going to get out of the jam you got yourself into, I couldn't say."

"I'll get out of it," she murmured carelessly.

He didn't hear. He was listening for something else. "It's quiet in there," he muttered.

"She's all right," said Nell.

"What did you tell her?"

"I told her nothing to be scared of. Somebody just fell down." Suddenly Nell laughed, showing her teeth. "Somebody *did*."

"How true," said Jed thoughtfully. He stepped around one of the beds and looked into the bathroom. "Eddie's going to be missed, you know. Naturally, you didn't think of that."

"He won't be missed," she said indifferently. "He's off duty." She sat down and put her ankles together and looked at her feet. Her toes made a miniature sashay.

Eddie was about the same, still out, breathing better.

Nell fell back on her elbows, smiling up. "Take me dancing?" she said coquettishly. "Johnee?"

"Dancing!" he exploded.

"Uncle Eddie's not on the elevator now." She seemed to think she was explaining something!

He wanted to say, I'd just as soon take a cobra dancing. But he said, "And? Who sits with the baby, in the meantime?"

"It's a dumb job," she said. "I don't like it."

His lips parted, closed, parted. He sat down, facing her. It seemed necessary to try to cut through a wall of fog, to clear things up. "You're in a mess," he said, rather patiently. "Don't you know that?"

"What mess?" She was sulky.

"You bop this guy, this Uncle Eddie. O.K. Now, what's going to happen? Look ahead a little bit. The Joneses come home from the party. There's a body in the bathroom. What will you say?"

"It's only Uncle Eddie," she murmured.

Jed took his head in his hands. He meant to make a semi-humorous exaggeration of the gesture, but it fooled him. He was holding his head for real.

"Now, listen carefully," he said. "What's *going* to happen? Future tense. Consequences. You ever heard of them?"

She used a word that rocked him with the unexpectedness of its vulgarity. "——, Uncle Eddie isn't going to say it was *me* who hit him."

He had to admit that he himself had reasoned along this line.

For a moment, he was stopped. "O.K.," he resumed patiently. "So Eddie won't tell on you. Then what *is* the story? Did he knock himself out? What did knock him out? Who?"

"I can say you did it," she answered placidly.

"*After I'm gone,* you'll say it!" He was furious.

"Unless we're out dancing."

He stood up. This time he spit it out of his mouth. "I'd just as soon take a cobra dancing as you."

"You asked me when you first —"

"*Then,*" he snapped. "That was before I knew what I was getting into." He looked down coldly. "I think you're insane."

It's easy to say. The word falls off the tongue. This was the first time Jed had ever said it in perfect sincerity.

She lifted her head on the neck, slowly. It was the neck that lifted, as if it uncoiled. She said a few ugly words. Then she was screeching and clawing at him and biting his self-defending hands with savage teeth and her shrill refrain was, "No, I'm not! No, I'm not! Take it back! You take it back!"

He handled her, but it wasn't easy. He got her in a locking hold and he shut her mouth with his hand. "Cut it out! You'll scare the kid. You'll have cops in here."

She was still screeching, as well as she could, "Take it back!"

"O.K. O.K. I take it back. Cut it out!"

She cut it out. She seemed satisfied. It was necessary to her that the word not be used. The word "insane." But it was a matter of words. The words "I take it back" were just as potent. Which, thought Jed grimly, is insane.

He felt chilled. He did not want this to be true. She was a crazy kid, a wild kid, in the slang sense. She was limp in his hold. Then he knew she was not so limp but too happy to be held so tightly.

He loosed her, warily. He said, vaguely, "Why should we fight? Makes too much noise." He listened. There was no sound from the child's room and he let out his breath. "Good thing *she* didn't begin to howl again. I can't take any more of that."

Nell said, "I know." A flicker of contempt crossed her face. "I understand about the future," she muttered.

"I talk too much, sometimes." He was trying to be careful. "What I need . . . Finish the bottle with me?" He took it out of his pocket. "Good thing this didn't get smashed in the excitement." He tipped the bottle.

She took it from him with both hands. The notion of drinking out of the bottle seemed to tickle her.

He said, "Say, where did the Joneses go?"

"Why?" Her voice was as careless as his.

"I was wondering how late. . . . Was it theater? Or a party someplace?" He feigned relaxing.

She still had the bottle in both hands. Carrying it, she walked between the beds and sat down near the head of one of them. "I don't know," she said vaguely.

"A party in somebody's apartment?"

"Your turn." She gave him the bottle. Her face was full of mischief. She said, "I understand about the future, Johnee. Everybody does."

"I guess so," Jed said.

She took a slip of paper off the table between the beds where the phone was. She began to pleat it in her fingers. "You think I'm stupid?" she asked, looking sidewise.

"Everybody's stupid, sometimes. Looks kinda stupid of the Joneses not to say where they'd go. What if the kid got sick?"

"Oh?" Nell said brightly. "You mean they should have thought ahead? About the future?"

"Did I say something about the future, ever?" He grinned.

Nell tore the paper idly into fancy bits. When Jed passed over the bottle she let the bits fall on the carpet. Too late, Jed saw them fall. He received, in a telepathic flash, the news. What had been on the paper. Why she had torn it. How she had foxed him. And the news of her sly laughter.

He was chagrined. He kept himself from showing it, he hoped, and from anger. They may know at the desk downstairs, he comforted himself, where the kid's folks went. He said, and perhaps this was the result of the damped-down anger, "Say, what was this about a fire?"

"Fire?" Nell smoothed the bedspread. She cocked her head. She seemed willing to talk about fire if that's what he wanted to talk about. It didn't mean anything to her.

"I got a little bit of what your Uncle Eddie was saying."

"Oh, that."

"Was it your house burned? Your parents? I thought he said so." She didn't answer. "Upset you, Nell?"

"That's what they say," she said demurely.

"Who?"

"Oh, doctors. Uncle Eddie. Aunt Marie." She frowned.

"Where was the fire?"

"Home."

"Some small town, was it?"

"It wasn't big." She curled up her legs.

Small, all right, Jed thought to himself, if they let this one loose. But he said to himself quickly, No, no, there must have been some testing. His thoughts went on. Probably, Eddie showed up ready and willing and anxious to take her far, far away. Nell wouldn't be any of the town's business, far, far away.

"So it was an accident," he said, making a statement. "Well, I'll tell you something. The future's one thing you got to look out for. The past is another. Because the past adds up. You know that?"

She frowned.

"This accident. Your father and mother both died in it?"

"It was an accident." He heard the jump of her voice to a

higher pitch. He knew it was a threat. It warned, Look out! It reminded him of that screeching tantrum.

"Well, I'll tell you," he drawled, nevertheless, "and it's a funny thing. You take one accident, why, that's too bad. Everybody's sorry. Poor Nell." She was curled up as tense as a coiled spring. He tried to fix her gaze, but it was all blueness. He kept on drawling, "But you take *two* accidents, that's different. That's not the same. It's really funny, how, after a second accident, right away, the first accident doesn't look so much *like* an accident any more."

Her face went blank, either because he'd hit her with an idea, or she didn't know what he was talking about.

"Good thing to keep in mind," he said lazily. "You better not have any more accidents."

She didn't move. He thought, *I got it over*.

He gathered himself to get up now, and go quietly.

Miss Eva Ballew believed in many things. One of them was duty. She walked toward the telephone. One of them was justice. She walked back to the chair.

But however strong her beliefs and her conscience, Miss Ballew was a physical coward and knew it. She couldn't seem to make up her mind what she ought to do. Sometimes, if you take time to decide, the need to do anything passes of itself. . . . Miss Ballew reproached herself with bitter shame and she walked toward the phone . . . . But . . .

She walked to the chair. She banged her fist on the chair back and the pain helped her. Very well. She would do her duty and deny her cowardice.

She went to the dresser and got her purse, not to be naked without it, once away from her room. She left the room and marched around the hollow square of the eighth floor.

Nell hadn't moved. Jed, all the way up, standing, said, "So

long." He felt a pulse of compassion for her, who was lost and had no inner compass to find the way again. "Be seeing you."

Once more, and briskly, somebody's knuckles knocked on 807's door.

Nell was up, lynx-eyed.

"Oh no," said Jed softly. "Oh no, my lady, not again!"

He faded. Towers faded, the way he had to go, through the door to the kid's room, to 809 . . . and closed it behind him.

## CHAPTER 13

Miss Ballew rapped again. Because she was afraid, she did her best to be angry. She knew someone was in there. Did they think they could lie low?

The door opened so swiftly it surprised her. A girl in a dark dress, not a very big girl, not very old, looked at her with blue, blue eyes and said, with an effect of stormy anger, although her voice was low, "What do you want?"

"My name is Eva Ballew. My room is across the court on this floor." Miss Ballew's words were as neat and orderly as herself. She tended to begin at the beginning.

"Yes." The girl seemed to listen but not to hear, almost as if she were listening for something else. And it seemed to Miss Ballew that her anger was aimed elsewhere, also.

"Before I call the manager," said Miss Ballew more boldly, "I think it only fair to ask whether you can explain."

"Explain what?"

"What is going on in these rooms," said Miss Ballew, loudly and firmly.

"I don't know what you mean." The girl was looking at the caller but not seeing her, almost, thought Miss Ballew, as if she were *also* watching for someone else.

"There is a child," said Miss Ballew coldly. "Is she your child?"

"I'm taking care of her."

"I see." Miss Ballew's mouth was grim. "Yes, so I imagined. Is there or was there a man in here?"

"A man?"

Miss Ballew longed to cry, Pay attention, please! "I saw the man," she announced, sharply, "so that is an unnecessary question and you need not answer it." She could see into room 807 and no one else was visible, at least. She did not feel physically afraid of rather a small girl. And if the man had gone . . . Miss Ballew was encouraged. She said, "Who was the man?"

"Listen, you can't—"

"The child," cut in Miss Ballew coolly, "has been crying in a most distressing manner, twice. And I have witnessed certain rather strange scenes over here. I must ask for an explanation."

"But why should you?" Nell stepped closer, with the door behind her now. Her glance slipped down the corridor to the right, briefly.

"Because," snapped Miss Ballew, "it seemed to me, for one thing, that the little girl very nearly fell out the window."

"Well, she didn't," said Nell carelessly. "While you were at your snooping you must have noticed that."

Miss Ballew bridled but stood her ground. "Snooping or not, I wish to see the child."

"See her?" For the first time, Miss Ballew felt that her words were heeded. "You've got a crust!"

"Nevertheless, if I do *not* see her, I intend to call the authorities." So much for rudeness, Miss Ballew's eyebrows remarked. "Why did she scream?" Miss Ballew narrowed her eyes.

"When?"

"The second time. Come now, stop evading, young woman."

"What?"

"I think you'd better let me in."

"*You* listen," Nell said. "I'm here to take care of her. You're a stranger. How do I know . . ."

"You don't," agreed Miss Ballew, "but unless I see her for myself, the manager or the detective here *must*."

"What business is it of yours? I don't underst—"

"Are you afraid to let me see her?"

"I'm not afraid," said Nell shrilly. "But I can't do it. I'm not supposed to. You talk about duty—"

"Now, see here. I am a schoolteacher. I'm sure I look like one. You ought to be able to tell that I'm a responsible person."

"You're trying to cause trouble."

"On the contrary. I could have called downstairs directly. I felt, however, that it was not fair to cause trouble, as you say, if there is no reason. If the child is perfectly all right and asleep, then there is no occasion for any trouble at all. Is that clear?"

"What would her mother say if I let in any old person?"

"What would her mother say about your entertaining a man?" In the same tone, Miss Ballew would have said "about your smoking opium."

"He's gone." The girl's eyes flickered toward the right again. "And she *is* perfectly all right. She *is* sleeping."

"I beg your pardon if I seem to insist in the face of your direct statements, but after what I saw—"

"Saw?"

"Perhaps you don't know that the Venetian blind was so adjusted that I *could* see."

"See where?" Nell's head went back on the neck.

"Into the child's room."

"It's dark in there," Nell said stupidly. Perhaps a little drowsily.

"Not quite. There was a very little light, perhaps through the connecting door."

"Light?"

"And the child did stop her screaming rather abruptly," said Miss Ballew.

Nell's eyes slipped sidewise. "What did you see?" she asked.

Ruth was only half listening to the women's voices. She would have preferred to be in the group of men where the talk, she was sure, must have more meat in it. These women, from far-flung spots, had no basis for gossip and, since they weren't even sure who each other's husbands were (except Ruth's, of course), they didn't even have the fun of ranking each other.

Except Ruth. She could have been preening herself. But her heart wasn't in it. Some sense of danger fluttered her heart.

Peter strode out of his group to dance with her. "Smatter, hon? Worried? About Bun?"

"I'm sure I'm silly."

"Did something on that phone call bother you?"

"I don't know." She slid her hand higher on his sleeve. "Probably it's just because I'm a hick and this great big town scares me. Listen, Peter, even if I don't always act it, I am a grown woman. Let me take a cab over to the hotel and see, and I'll come straight back and dance till dawn."

"We could leave now," he said.

"But . . . the fun!"

He grinned, admitting the fun. "Man from Chicago I'd like to have a few words —"

"Then do. Please. If you go, I'll feel terrible. *You* can't go."

"My night to howl," he grinned. "Got cab fare?" He would let her go. Peter wouldn't *make* her spoil it.

"Not a penny," she confessed.

He danced her into the mirrored exit, squeezed her, let her go, and gave her a five-dollar bill. "Don't trust any handsome strangers with all this moolah on you, baby."

"I won't." Ruth thought, I don't trust that stranger, that girl. It's what's wrong with me.

Ruth smiled at him. She left the scene. She felt, at once, much better to have escaped, to be going.

A doorman found her the cab. The city thought nothing of a young woman in evening clothes taking a cab alone in the night. The city minded its business.

## CHAPTER 14

J ED STOOD in the dark. He heard Miss Ballew introduce herself and knew at once *this* was the old biddy from across the way. Through the slats of Bunny's blind he could see her room.

He wondered if he were going to be able to get around the two of them out there without an uproar.

He rehearsed his exit in his mind.

And he meant exit. Total exit. There were worse things in the world than sitting the night out at the airport.

The stairs went down, he knew, just beyond the elevators. Well, he could move fast on his long legs. In his mind, he placed all the stuff in his room. He could be in and out of that room, he thought, in a matter of 60 seconds, and exit bag and baggage.

Then let her screech her lies.

He had little doubt she'd cook up some lies, all right. If necessary. Or even just if it seemed like fun at the moment.

Unless his warning words had knocked a totally unfamiliar idea of caution into her head. Of course, he'd been thinking of the kid. He'd been trying to get into Nell's head the danger, the undesirability, of harming the kid.

So that Towers could fade, of course.

Damn it, Towers had to get out of this! A fine mess! Assault, maybe, on account of Eddie in there, and the benefit of the doubt on Nell's side. And Eddie, tempted, if not almost obliged, to say something hit him but he doesn't know what. Eddie could even kid himself that it was true.

So there's Towers, in a jam. Nuts! He had to get out of here. Never *was* any business of his, the kid and the sitter. If the parents didn't know any better ... Probably didn't give a damn what happened to the kid, he thought angrily. Off on a shindig, all dressed up. Probably drunk as skunks by now and painting the town. Why should Towers care?

Why should he be so angry about it?

He still stood, just inside room 809, still listening. He didn't know what he was waiting for. That old biddy had her teeth in it now. Listen to her. "I wish to see the child." Sounded like a pretty stubborn old dame. Well, let her do it. She was the type to do it. The kid was none of his business.

He might drop a word at the desk on his way out, though. He could have heard a commotion over here from his own room. The old biddy had, from hers. Just as well tip the hotel. Then Nell *couldn't* stall her.

His eyes had adjusted to the dark in here. He could see the far bed was undisturbed. On the other, the kid must be asleep.

Funny thing she didn't wake up during his late wrestling match with the wildcat. It hadn't been a silent one.

That bed was awfully flat.

His hair moved with his scalp.

He crept a few steps in room 809. Of course, she was an awfully little girl, wouldn't make much of a hump on a bed. He didn't know. He'd hardly ever *seen* a sleeping child. He didn't know if they made a hump or not.

There wasn't any little girl on the bed.

He looked at the windows and Towers was sick and sickness was going through him like cream swirling down through a cup of coffee and something thumped on the floor.

He knelt in the dark crevice between the beds. He felt, blindly. Something threshed. He wanted light but he didn't dare. His fingers found a thin chilly little . . . what? Shoulder? Yes, for he touched a soft braid. He felt for the face, the warm lips and the breath, but touched, instead, fabric.

Damn her to hell, she'd bound and gagged the little thing! "Bunny?" he whispered. "Aw, Bunny, poor kid. Listen, I wouldn't hurt you for a million dollars." His fingers verified. Yes, her ankles were tied together. Wrists, too. And that cruel — stocking, he guessed it was, in and over the mouth!

"You fall off the bed, honey? Aw, I'm sorry. Mustn't make a noise, though."

Oh, Lord, how would the child *not!* if he ungagged her. It was not possible for her not to cry! He knew this. She must cry out, must make sound as soon as she was able.

But she mustn't! Or Towers would never get away.

Now, what could he do? Thoughts flashed like frightened goldfish in the bowl of his brain.

Grab her, just as she was? Take her with him? Yeah, and run past the two women at the other door with the kid slung over his shoulder. A kidnaper, yet! Fantastic!

He sat on his heels. His hand tried to comfort the little girl, smoothing her hair. He thought, "So you're in a jam, Towers?"

But then his mind went all fluid again and he thought, Damn it, no! He thought, I've got to fix it for the kid and get out, too!

*Look out for yourself, Towers! Nobody else will.* It came back to him, in his own words. A guide, a touchstone.

All right! Use your head! Nothing was going to happen to the kid beyond what already had. The woman out there would keep Nell busy. And he, Jed, would tip off the hotel. So, for five minutes' difference, five minutes more. . .

He leaned over and whispered, "I'm afraid you'd cry if I undo your mouth, honey. I wouldn't blame you. I'm just afraid you can't help it. We can't make any noise, just yet. Listen, I'm going. Going to get somebody. Get your daddy." His hand felt the leap of the little heart. "I am a friend," he said, absurdly, out of some pale memory in a boy's book.

He got up and went softly to the door of 809.

## CHAPTER 15

I saw," said Miss Ballew in her precise fashion, "the child, as I suppose, sitting up in the bed and a figure approach and appear to struggle with her. The cries then stopped, most abruptly. So you see, I require," said she hastily, "some explanation. I cannot believe," she added vehemently to cover the shake that was developing in her voice, "that any grown person would use force on a child. What, actually, were you doing?"

Nell looked sleepy.

"If it wasn't you, who was it?" said Miss Ballew angrily.

"You said you *saw* — " There was hint of impudence in the girl's face, something saucy that must be crushed at once.

Miss Ballew said coldly, "I certainly did see *someone* doing *something,* which has very much alarmed me. I would advise you, young woman, to take me to that child at once." (But she was afraid again. She was dizzy with her fear.)

A door, to her left and the girl's right, opened and closed very fast. A man was in the corridor and had passed rapidly behind Miss Ballew almost before she could turn her head. He rushed on, he vanished around the corner. Miss Ballew staggered in the wind of his passage. It had been so swift, so startling, so furtive, and there had been a white roll of his eye.

"Who was that!" Her knees felt mushy.

The girl looked as if she could hop with rage, as if she would begin to bounce, like popcorn.

"Explain, at once!" cried Miss Ballew and reached out to shake this stupid creature.

The girl collapsed at her touch. "Oh, oh," she said "Oh —" and bent her arm against the doorframe and buried her face in her arm. "Oh, I was so scared! Oh, miss, whatever's your name. Oh, thank you! You've saved me!"

"What!"

"That . . . man!" said Nell, muffled.

"Why, he must have come out of the next — Yes, I see he did! Out of the child's room!"

"Yes. Yes," cried Nell. "Now do you see? He was in there all the time. He said if I didn't get rid of you . . . Oh!"

"Oh, dear," said Miss Ballew faintly.

"He said he would —" Nell's body pressed on the wood as if in anguish.

Miss Ballew rocked on her feet and reached for the wall.

"He just forced himself in here. He was so wild," Nell cried, "and strong!" Her face peeped now, from the sheltering arm. "I didn't know what to do!"

Silence beat in the corridor while Miss Ballew fought with her wish to fall down. One heard, one read, and all one's life one feared, but not often did one encounter. . . . But the ruthless predatory male was, of course, axiomatic.

"There wasn't anything I could do." The girl's whine broke the spell. "I couldn't — I'm not very strong."

"But he is getting away!" moaned Miss Ballew. For she heard, in the mists of her horrors, the yawn of the door to the fire stairs and the hish-hush of its closing. This, she felt, was outrageous. Outrageous! That such things . . . in a respectable hotel . . . and go unpunished! The anger was starch to her spine. She tightened her mouth, gathered her strength and bustled past the girl into the room. She threw her stout sturdy form on the bed and reached for the telephone.

Downstairs, Rochelle Parker shifted the Life Saver expertly into the pouch of her cheek. "Yes?"

"This is Miss Ballew," said the agitated voice. "I'm in room —what?" she cried to the girl. "What is this number?"

"Number 807," said the girl quite promptly and calmly.

"Room 807. A man has just fled from here."

"*What* did he do, madam?"

"Fled. He ran away." Miss Ballew was often forced to translate her remarks. "He was up to no good." She tried to be basic. "Get him!" cried Eva Ballew.

"Just a moment, *please*," said Rochelle. She pressed the button that would discreetly summon Pat Perrin to a phone. Almost at once, she plugged him in.

"Yeah?"

"807's on, Pat."

"Yeah, what is it?"

"There was a man in here," said Miss Ballew. It was as if she said "African lion." "He is trying to get away, right now."

"What did he look like?"

"What did he look like?" cried the teacher to the motionless girl.

The girl's lips opened and her tongue slipped to moisten them. "He . . . had red hair."

"Red hair!" Miss Ballew's voice both informed Perrin and doubted the information, for this had not been her own impression.

"Very dark red," said Nell, "brown eyes, freckles."

"Dark red, brown eyes, freckles and tall. I saw that. And I think a gray suit."

"Brownish," Nell said, "and a blue shirt."

"Brownish? Well, some light color. And a blue shirt."

"I'll see if we can pick him up," said Pat Perrin, sounding competent and unruffled. He hung up at once.

Miss Ballew rolled a bit and sat up. She propped herself on the headboard. She was trembling. "This really—" she gasped. "I don't know when I've been—How did he—? Who—?"

The girl, who had closed the door, came slowly around the bed and sat down on the other one. Her eyes were a trifle aslant and an odd blue. She clasped her hands in her lap. Unpainted nails. Dark, decent dress. Modest ankles, shabby shoes.

Miss Ballew read all these signs as she was bound to do. "You poor thing," she said. "I don't know your name."

"Nell." Not Sonya. Not Toni. Plain Nell.

"I am Eva Ballew," said that lady warmly. "I suppose you were under such strain. I thought your manner was odd. How ever did he get in here?"

"Oh, he knocked and, of course, I went to see who it was." Nell twisted her hands. "And then he just pushed me."

"Didn't you scream?" It was Miss Ballew's conviction that a woman always screamed.

"But he said . . . said he was a friend of the people's," said Nell. "I didn't know."

"No, of course, you couldn't know. Tsk-tsk. Do you think he had been drinking?"

"Oh, he was!" cried Nell. "Look!" She seemed very young and lithe as she reached for the whisky bottle. The cheap dress twisted tight to her body. Miss Ballew felt a shiver, rather a delicious one, along her nerves. She gazed, horrified, at the bottle's emptiness.

"Now, now," she soothed. "It's all over now." And then, fearfully, "Isn't it? There wasn't? Nothing?"

Nell shook her head vigorously. Her tawny hair tossed.

Miss Ballew's heart raced. She felt unwell.

"Anyhow," said Nell moodily, "he only tried to kiss me once. He just kept on drinking and drinking."

"You should have screamed," Miss Ballew said trancelike.

# MISCHIEF

"But I was so scared, I didn't dare. And I thought maybe, when Bunny cried, someone might notice." The girl's eyes rolled.

Miss Ballew felt herself flushing guiltily.

"And she didn't really 'almost fall,'" said Nell with sudden passionate indignation, "at all! He thought I was trying to, you know, get somebody's attention out the window like that, so he dragged her away."

"Oh, dear . . ." Miss Ballew thought how wise one is never to believe too hastily in what one thinks one sees. "And when she began to scream so, later? Why was that, my dear?"

Nell looked wildly around her, and her shoulders heaved. "She got scared and began to cry," she sobbed. "She just got scared. That's why she began to cry. But he was so mad. It made him wild. He said she had to stop that noise."

"Then, it was *he* in her room?"

"You saw . . ." the girl challenged.

"Yes, I saw. But it was too dark. I couldn't clearly see. Oh, my dear, if he has harmed—"

"Oh, he didn't *hurt* her." Nell said and suddenly she sat up again. "He just made her stop crying." A little smile—pitiful, it might have been—worked on her face. "And there wasn't anything I could do because he locked me in the closet. . . ."

"Incredible." The teacher's lips were stiff.

Nell looked solemnly at her. The room fell . . . as if all its emotion-laden air swirled, falling . . . to silence. "You know," she said, "I think he was insane."

In the dim bathroom of 807, on the cold floor, Eddie stirred. His right arm moved as one moves in sleep. He turned a little to his left side. Then he lay still.

# CHAPTER 16

THE HOTEL detective, Pat Perrin, put up the phone and crossed the lobby, moving quietly. He opened the door to the base of the tall rectangular tube where the fire stairs ran. He discounted, from long practice, 90 percent of what he had just heard. But for the sake of the other ten percent, he stood and listened. Any sound, he knew, would come booming down to him.

And so it did. Someone was on those bare stairs. He waited, quietly. He wore a gun.

Jed realized the echoing clatter of his descent in this confined space. Nimbly, he brought himself up against a door, tugged the door in upon himself and stepped out to the sixth-floor corridor.

As he crossed the carpet toward the elevators a man — just a man — joined him. The man pressed the down button and, superhumanly, Jed did not. He set his suitcase down, denying the need of his nervous hand to hang onto it. His jaw cracked and he deliberately let tension out of it. Without fidgeting, he watched the dial, as the other man was doing, as all elevator awaiters seem compelled to do. The hand was coming down.

Disinterested, strangers, they stepped on in silent sequence as the elevator obeyed the call. And in silent sequence they stepped out, below. Jed walked to the desk.

He said, crisply, "Checking out. Towers, 821."

"Certainly, Mr. Towers."

"Mind making it quick?" Friendly and crisp but not too urgent. "Just got hold of a cancellation. I can get out of here tonight if I make it down to the station." Jed looked at the clock in the woodwork back of the man's head.

"Yes, sir." The clerk did not seem to put on speed but Jed

was aware that he did, in fact, waste no motion. He recognized
the skill in it. He made himself stand still.

Pat Perrin knew when no feet rattled on the stairs. He caught
a boy and posted him, here near where the stairs came down,
at a door to a narrow passage that was the back way out. He
caught another to watch the entrance to the bar, for one could
exit to the street through that dim corner room. He himself had
a brief word with an elevator boy. Then his skilled eyes ran
down every man in his sight. "Tall. Light suit." He weaved
among the chairs. He moved along the carpet.

"You figure," Jed was asking pleasantly, "about 25 minutes
to Penn Station?"

"That's close, sir. Might do it. Here we are." The clerk turned
the reckoning around. He took an envelope from a box and
presented this, too. Jed saw his name before him in a script he
knew. A note from Lyn. Lyn Lesley. He stuffed it into his coat
pocket. (No time for her now.) He took money out.

Perrin's eye checked Jed's tall figure in the gray suit. *Dark*
hair, *no* freckles, *white* shirt. He walked on by.

Jed put his wallet back, picked up his bag, surveyed the way
ahead, the not-very-long distance to that revolving door and
out. He was the same as out already. But Jed put his palm noiselessly on the blotter and the clerk looked up.

"You'd better," said Jed, speaking slowly and soberly and
emphatically to be understood and heeded in this, the first and
only time he would say it, "send someone to room 807, right
away. A kid's in trouble. 807 and 809. A little girl. If you know
where Mr. and Mrs. Jones went, call them. It's their kid."

He turned swiftly and went in the shortest line to the revolving door and through it without a check.

Then he stood in the air, in the open night, and he was out
of it, and it was their kid, wasn't it?

Pat Perrin knew someone on those stairs had got off the stairs. So much was true. Whether he rode down or not was a question. Now, Perrin peered through to the street, saw tall, dark and handsome, in the white shirt, harmlessly pausing to light a cigarette. He pushed through and crooked a finger to the doorman, said a word or two. He raked Jed's back with his glance, conscientiously, turned, looped on his own tracks and went back through the lobby because the other exit would be the one a fugitive would like. He saw Milner at the desk lift a startled hand as if to beckon. He signaled with his own, Busy (no time for him now), and he walked on by.

Jed shook out his match. All right. So he'd established that Towers had nerves of iron. And what now? Cab? Bus? Subway? To the airport? His thoughts were jumpy.

A cab swerved in to the curb and braked in his very face. He thought it was querying him. Then he saw that it had a fare to discharge here. He stepped aside. As the dome light went on, he could see her. Young woman, blonde, attractive, in party clothes.

He stood with his bag at his feet and blew smoke out. Here was a cab, emptying before him, becoming available, and in it he would be gone, like smoke. He half turned his head. He looked (because he was in some way forced to look) up behind him at the checkered façade, the tall bulk, the flat and secretive face of the Hotel Majestic.

The girl from the cab, with her change in her bare hand, got out. Her golden slippers stepped quickly on the gray sidewalk. She went by Jed. Her gaze crossed over his face blankly, and he, blankly, watched her by, for they were strangers.

Jed saw the door spin. The cab door remained open. It hinted, tempted, invited. Finally it said to him, "Well?"

He moved nearer and put out a hand, ducked his head. . . . Something hit him. It seemed to him that he was struck in the face by something that was no more substantial than the air itself. Only a faint scent . . . breathing into his face from the cab's closed place. A perfume, it was, that stopped him because he knew that scent and it made his stomach turn over. Why, he reeked of it himself! Of course. It came from himself.

He barked, "Sorry," and slammed the door. Go ahead. The cab's gears snarled at him.

Jed trod his cigarette out. He felt rooted to the sidewalk and his feet kicked at the invisible chain. All right. He would not shut himself up with that sickening odor. He'd air himself free of it. Walk. But get gone, stupid! He held hard for anger, this kind of anger. His hand came up to brush before his face.

Milner, the man at the desk, leaned over, full of summons, but Pat Perrin was out of range of a soft hail and a loud hail would never do. Milner's still-startled eyes blinked. Towers, 821. Eighth floor, sure enough. Fellow might know what he was talking about. Something wrong in 807? Peter O. Jones, 807 and 809. Mr. Milner didn't know where the Joneses were. He was annoyed as well as startled. But of course he would check. It would never do not to check up on such a warning.

He took up a phone and pivoted, looking anxiously for some reason at the hands of the clock. "Give me 807, Rochelle."

"Sure thing." Rochelle alerted. She thought, "Oh, boy, something's up!" She thought, "I smelled a rat up there hours ago." She was rather pleased. There were long stretches on this job that were pretty dull. She hoped this was going to be interesting. She said softly, "What goes on, Mr. Milner?"

Since Mr. Milner did not know, he was haughty. "If you'll ring them, please?"

"O.K., O.K." He heard Rochelle ring them. He stood, holding the phone, staring at the clock as if he could by the willful power of the human eye stay the hand, as Ruth O. Jones went rustling by behind him.

No need to stop for her key, she reflected, since, of course, Nell was there to open the door. Besides, it would take time. Her feel of time wasting was because she'd been wishing too long to come. Only that. Why, the lobby was just the same.

Ruthie and the jitters. How Betty would laugh! Betty the louse, who'd begged off. Although why on earth I assume *she's* so darned reliable. Betty who doesn't even know yet what a woman's in the world for . . . It was the blood tie, of course. It was the mere fact that Peter's sister could not be a stranger.

There was a man in a brown suit talking in rather an official manner to the elevator boy. He kept on talking. "I beg your pardon," Ruth asked. "Is this car going up?"

"In a minute, ma'am."

"Thank you." She stepped by. They kept muttering together. The boy said, "Never rode with me."

Ruth's foot in the golden slipper twitched. Oh, don't be silly! Surely a minute doesn't matter! (Except on the inner clock of her apprehensive bones.)


## CHAPTER 17


NELL LET the water run. Then she filled the glass. She stood, holding the glass, and twisted the faucet once or twice, on and off. Her face was sullen and a little bored, as she looked down at the little man on the bathroom floor, lying as if he were asleep, twisted a bit to one side, as if to be comfortable.

The skin around his eyes twitched, as if the bright light affected him. She frowned, and then her whole body seemed to shrug, to lift off the problem and let it go. The hell with it.

She snapped off the light, opened the door that she had so speedily put between her and room 807 and pulled it shut. "Miss Ballew?" She was all sweet service.

The schoolteacher, with her eyes closed, was silently reciting poetry. It was a trick to play on the release of the fearful substances to the blood, on the whole panicked interior chemistry, the pound of the goaded heart.

"Oh, thank you, my dear. Really, this is so feeble of me." Her teeth chattered. "But I lead rather a quiet existence. I rarely . . ." The phone rang. The glass was still in Nell's hand. "I'll get it," chattered Miss Ballew and jerked around.

Nell sat down quietly. Her toes turned in, then out, almost imperceptibly. Her fingertips danced on the cool damp glass.

"Yes?" quavered the teacher.

"This is the desk. I've had word of some trouble. Perhaps you can tell me?"

"Trouble!" burst Miss Ballew. "Yes, *certainly,* there has been trouble. I spoke to *someone,* long ago! Didn't you *stop* him?"

"I beg your pardon," said the astonished voice.

"Did you or did you not stop that man! I told you — I described him."

"Who is this, please?"

"This is Miss Eva Ballew. I have 823 but I am now in 807. Now, I reported this trouble minutes ago — "

"Yes. Yes, I see, Miss Ballew," he broke in. "The house detective must have taken — "

"*Must* have! Are you guessing? Who are *you,* pray?"

"I'm at the desk, ma'am."

"And do you mean to tell me that you do not know! See here. Is anything at all being done?"

"The house detective evidently — "

"Evidently! Are you men or mice down there? Where is *he?*"

"He is evid — He is looking — That is, I see now."

"You are too late and too slow," she spoke on top of him, "and it has been too long. You have irresponsibly allowed that ruffian to escape."

Milner's spine curled. "But is the child all right?" he demanded.

"The child? Why, yes, I believe —"

Milner, man, not mouse, was delighted to say, disagreeably, *"Do you mean to tell me that you do not know!"* and snap, "Someone responsible will be up there at once," and slam down the phone. But all the same, he was relieved. Pat Perrin knew about it.

Miss Ballew hung up and her eyes were pained. So often this physical weakness had betrayed her. She knew so well what one ought to do, but the weak flesh was a drag.

"What was it?" Nell said.

"They . . . someone will be up. They seem confused." And I, thought Miss Ballew, am a pitiful, despicable, cowering wretch. And she tried to shift her legs.

"He got away?"

"Evidently." It was no use. Her legs were mush, still. "My dear," she said sadly, "hadn't you better see to the child?"

"Oh, yes," said Nell quickly. But she rose without haste, in fact, rather slowly and tentatively. "Don't you want the drink of water?" She didn't seem to know what to do with it.

Miss Ballew received the glass. She was not a fool. Now, as she knew her guilt, and realized that someone ought long ago to have gone in to the poor frightened child, the terrified little girl, she began to wonder why Nell had not gone. Nell, whose responsibility she was, had fetched water for a stranger instead. It didn't ring right. No, it rang wrong. Echoes of their first exchange began to come to her. Nell's rudeness and the odd manner. She could no longer so glibly excuse it. And she seemed, besides, to see in her mind's eye that the man in the corridor had no freckles on that averted cheek and no blue in his clothing.

She looked at Nell. She murmured. "It's incredible, really."

The girl seemed to be waiting politely for her to go on and perhaps she didn't understand. "It's hard to believe," translated Miss Ballew. "I've never heard such a wild story. There seems to be no sense . . . not even a mad method to this man's actions. Are you sure?"

"What?"

"Are you sure you didn't encourage him?"

"I haven't done anything," Nell said, looking surprised. "I don't know what you mean."

This was an echo, too, and it rang false. "Come now, of course you know what I mean." Miss Ballew looked annoyed but she checked herself. "Never mind. This is no time for debate See to the child, my dear, and bring her in here, do. Poor, poor baby. When the detective arrives," her voice faltered from its habitual tone of instruction, "I daresay he . . ."

"He what?" Nell frowned faintly.

"I mean to say," said Miss Ballew dryly, being fair, "perhaps he's seen more of this sort of thing . . . perhaps more of it goes on than is dreamed of in my philosophy. And, of course," she added thoughtfully, "the child . . . How old is the child?"

"How old?"

"She is old enough to talk?"

"Of course," said Nell wonderingly. "She's nine, I think."

"Then that is fortunate," said Miss Ballew, "for, of course, she will be able to corroborate your story."

Nell was just standing there, looking stupid.

What a handicap to have so limited a vocabulary, thought the teacher. "Corroborate means to confirm," she explained, "to tell the same story, or enough to prove it, do you see?"

"And fortunate," said Nell, "means lucky." She was smiling. Why, she was dancing! She stood on the same spot, there at the foot of the bed, but for a moment Miss Ballew had the distinct impression that she was dancing. Even her face had a twinkling, sparkling look. Impish, as if she'd thought of something, had an idea or knew a mischievous secret. "I know more words than you think I do," said Nell. "And I understand the future." She flung up her hands . . . yes, it was a dance! (Miss Ballew looked on, bewildered.) And then the dark skirt flopped and fell out of the moving arc and reversed. . . .

And the girl was leaning on her two stiff arms, her knuckles white on the footboard, her eyes very wide, very blue. "I . . . I wonder . . ." The eyeballs turned in slow fear and the slow fear welled in Miss Ballew.

"She's awfully quiet," Nell said, softly, softly. "*Isn't* she?"

Miss Ballew clawed her own throat.

"Don't you think . . . it's funny?"

"F-fun—" Miss Ballew wafted her arm across the air.

Nell's teeth enfolded her lower lip. Now she looked very grave and thoughtful. She walked on soft toes to that inner door. Her hand was slow on the knob and nerves in the teacher's temple turned excruciatingly with it.

The latch fell out. The door yawned. No sound from 809.

"Bunny?" Nell called, softly, softly. There was no answer.

"Bunny!" The girl's back shook as if with a long shiver. Only quiet answered her. Her eyes rolled as she looked over her shoulder. "I'm afraid . . ." she whimpered.

Miss Ballew was afraid, too. She could *not* move. Her own ears knew that frightening silence was really there. "But you said—But you told me he didn't . . . hurt . . ."

"He was in there *afterward*. After you knocked. Do you think—"

"Don't think! Don't even say!"

But Nell's words fell like Fate. "Maybe he remembered . . . she's old enough to talk. . . ."

"Our Father which art in heaven," mumbled Miss Ballew. "Beseech thee . . . from evil . . ."

"It would," said Nell, glassy-eyed, "be so easy. She's just . . . a little thing. . . ."

"Go see!" screamed Miss Eva Ballew, up on her elbow but paralyzed for all that. "For the love of heaven, girl! Go *in* there and *see!*"

## CHAPTER 18

LYN TOUCHED his arm. He veered away from her touch as if he expected a blow to follow. (Yah! Iron nerves, Towers?)

"Lyn! Oh for — I thought . . ."

"Didn't they give you my note?"

She was there, and not an apparition, standing beside him and, in the light of the city night, her face was sweetly, soberly, wondering why he was as startled as this to see her. Ah, she was sweet and sane!

"Gosh, you look . . ." He grabbed her woolly blue arm. "What are you doing here at this hour? You been rattling around this town *alone!* It's too damn late, Lyn."

"I'm not afraid. . . ."

"The street's no place . . ."

"I *haven't* been . . ."

"You ought to know better!"

"Oh, don't be so . . ."

"Little fool . . ."

"Oh, Jed!" she wailed. They teetered back from the brink of the same quarrel. The same damn thing. Jed even stepped backward on the sidewalk.

"I guess this is where we came in," he murmured.

"Where I walked out," she laughed uncertainly. Her eyes were not merry. But they were sweet and sane.

He put his hand in his pocket. "Jed, didn't you read it?"

"No, I . . . Not yet." He fumbled for the envelope. He felt troubled . . . troubled. Not ready to meet her. He held her note passively in his hand.

"I've been waiting and waiting," she said breathlessly. "In the lobby, Jed. It was safe enough. I was just about to give up and go home. I went into the drugstore . . . saw you . . . I've been calling your room."

He made no reply, no excuse, no explanation.

"I waited the longest time," she said.

"Why, dear?" he asked gently.

Lyn's face looked as if she were touched to tears but she did not weep and she did not turn her face away. "Because I'm sorry, Jed. That's about all there is to say about it. I'm sure you were more in the right than I was willing to admit."

"Never mind." He slipped his arm around her. "Never mind." He thought, If this isn't like her! This kind of weird, overdone fairness, this proud dragging down of her pride.

"I couldn't bear you to go all that way," she said quietly, keeping her own balance, although he embraced her, "and us mad. That's . . . all."

"Was I mad at you?" he said, scarcely believing it.

"Where were you going?"

"Oh, I . . . was more or less lighting out," he said vaguely. He felt very sad, very sad. He had a sensation in the breast as if the heart would break.

"Could we have one drink somewhere? Will you make it up, Jed, and get the nasty taste out of our mouths, before you go?"

He looked down at her. "You beat all," he said gravely.

"I called you things I don't believe," Lyn said in a low voice. "Is it a date?"

Something bigger than he was took him and shook him like a rat. He covered the shudder up by grabbing for his suitcase. "It's a date, Lyn." He let his mouth curve, his voice be as ten-

der as it wished to be, and she smiled like the rainbow. Jed
looked away, off over her head. Why did he feel so troubled
and sad? Here was she, stubborn little love, trying to get back
where they'd been. The night was young and nothing was lost.
Proceed, Towers. From where you were.

"Please, Jed, let me have my note?" she begged softly. "You
don't need . . ."

He looked down. He said, "No." He put it back in his pocket.
Oh-ho no! he thought. This we look into, in some dark bar.
"Just a minute, honey," he went on. "Something I want to check
a minute. In here."

She smiled. It was all right with her. Anything he said, of
course. He thought, What a reckless attitude *that* is! But he
touched her and with tenderness pushed her into a slot in the
door and pushed the door, following.

What the hell was he going back in for? Curiosity? One
thing, he'd surely keep it from Lyn, what he was up to. It was
nothing anyhow. Take a minute. No need to invent a lie, for
her . . . innocent, reckless little love! No, he'd just take a quick
look around, that's all. He thought he could tell, pretty quickly,
if they'd got up there to the little kid, all right. Surely reper-
cussions would sift down to the lobby, which he would be able
to feel. And rest his mind about it.

That would really close it off. Lyn would never ask. There'd
be nothing to mention, nothing even to think about, once he
knew nothing was . . . dangling.

Towers could then proceed.

In itself, the hotel now knew something was up. The news
ran on its nervous system, in the minds of its own people. The
guests were unaware and might never become aware of this as
guests had been unaware of many things on many other occasions. But the hotel knew now.

Rochelle sat at her board. She knew. She prepared to be the

spider in the middle of the web. All things would eventually come to her.

Milner knew, and was nervous behind his front, although his front remained as wooden and polished as the walnut around him. He'd had a quick word with the Assistant Manager and that one agreed that Milner himself must go up there. He would emerge from his inner place and take over at the desk.

The bartender knew, in his dim barricade in the far corner of the farthest corner. The porter, emptying ash trays, had a faint knowledgeable air. The bellboys knew. "Some guy got away," they dared say to each other softly, but they veiled their watching eyes.

Perrin was almost resigned to the idea that the man had got away. If he had not but still lurked somewhere, where was it? No redhead and so forth in the corridors, in any of the public rooms. If he was registered and had a room and lurked *there,* it might take a little doing.

Perrin strode up to the desk and caught Milner. "Who we got that's tall, redheaded, freckle-faced, light suit, blue shirt?"

"Nobody," said Milner. "Say . . ."

They wiped trouble from all their faces. The Assistant Manager said, "Yes, Mr. Hodges." A guest took his key, made a firm statement about the weather, went away.

"On the trouble in 807?" the manager said.

"Yeah, dame described this man . . ."

"Just what did he do?"

"Intruded," said Perrin dryly.

Milner said, "It was a man who tipped me. Is the kid all right?"

"Who?"

"Little girl. Jones."

"I'd better get up there," Perrin said thoughtfully. "Nobody told me about a kid."

"That's not good, having a kid in it. I was just going . . ."

The manager said, "Uh—keep it quiet."

Two of them swung off separately. Milner negotiated his way around the walnut embankments. Perrin met him again, near the elevators.

The elevators knew, although they whispered up and down without telling.

"Couldn't have hurt the kid," Perrin remarked. "All she said, he intruded."

"All she said to me, did we stop him," agreed Milner. "Ran out, did he?"

"Yeah, he's not up there now."

"Nerves?" said Milner hopefully. Perrin shrugged. Whatever it was, they assumed it was all over but, of course, the hysterics.

An elevator whispered down. "Say, that's Towers now." Milner peered. "Fellow who tipped me. Thought he—oh . . ."

"Oh, what?"

"He's got the girl. She found him." Milner relaxed.

"Eight," said Perrin quietly and stepped on. The boy moved only an eyelash. But he knew.

"Up? Up?" caroled Mrs. McMurdock. "Come, Bobo. Come, darling. Time for beddy-bye." The little dog ran into the elevator and sniffed moistly at Perrin's socks. Milner and he exchanged looks. The car started upward.

"He loooves to ride," said Mrs. McMurdock. "Doesn't he, Bobo? Doesn't he, boy? Loves to ride! Just loooves to ride!"

She did not know.

# CHAPTER 19

RUTH, as she rode gently upward, stuffed her change into her little evening bag without looking down at her hands. She kept watching the blank metal door beyond which the floors were sliding by. She was the only passenger. The car made no stop but hers. It sailed toward a soft landing and went into the little shuffle for the precise level of the eighth floor.

She stepped out. Behind her, the car stayed where it was a second longer than was normal while the boy listened to the quality of the silence up here. It seemed to be mere silence. Disappointed, he looked at his lights, yanked the lever and sailed upward. For Ruth, the corridor was just the same, just the same. She hurried to her left. She turned the corner.

The door of 807 looked just the same . . . as bland and blank as all the others. Prepare to shift. Inside, the girl would be dozing, and Bunny fast asleep, and the debris of her parents' dressing would be strewn about just as they had left it. All's well. Naturally. Of course it is. Ruth tapped gently.

At once, a much agitated female voice cried, "Oh, yes! Come in! Oh, come in!"

Ruth's mood leaped like lightning. Her hand leaped to the knob. She burst into the room and met the frightened eyes of a stoutish middle-aged woman she'd never seen in her life before, who was half sitting, half lying, in a strained position on Ruth's own bed. The woman's black dress was awry over her stout leg and her mouse-colored hair was awry, too. "Who are you!" cried this stranger in a voice that was also awry.

But Ruth put first things first.

Her gold bag fell out of her hand. Without a word, she flew, hands up, across 807 to 809. She batted the partially opened

door and it swung wider. 809 was unlit. Ruth aimed herself
like an arrow at the light switch. She flashed around.

She saw Bunny's two bare feet twitching on the bed and the
girl's dark back bent. Ruth cried out, "What's the matter?"
She got one glimpse of Bunny's bound mouth, and then saw the
girl's face blinking at her over the shoulder, the drowsy evil in
the sullen careless glance, and she knew what the wicked hands
were about to do.

Making no cry, Ruth simply flew at her. Her hands bit on the
shoulders, and with all her might she heaved backward, to get
the evil away. Still she did not scream. Instead, she called out
in almost a cheerful voice, "It's all right, Bunny. It's Mommy."

The shoulders rolled, writhed and slipped away from her.
The girl's body turned with vicious speed. Ruth felt herself
knocked backward and the small of her back was wrenched as it
slammed against the other bed and she felt her neck crack with
the backward weight of her head. She flipped herself quickly
over and slipped downward to her knees, hearing silk rip. She
fastened both hands on an ankle. She crawled backward, yank-
ing and pulling, out from the narrow place between the beds.
*Get it away from Bunny.* This was first. And Nell came, hop-
ping, tottering, kicking . . . and her hands clawed for Ruth's
face, hunting Ruth's eyes.

Ruth had not always been a gracious young matron, a pretty
wife, a gentle mother. In her day, she'd climbed many a tough
tree and hung by knobby knees off ladders with pigtails dragging. And she'd played basketball on a tough team, even in so-
called free style, which meant she had pulled hair and bitten
and gouged with the rest. She'd had her bruises and given them.
The world of direct physical conflict, violent and painful, had
not always been beyond her ken.

"So!" she hissed with her teeth closed. There was lightning
on her eyeballs as she got her hands in that yellowish hair and

yanked and the girl screeched and fell forward, twisting, and
Ruth rolled on the hard floor to get from under her.

She felt the teeth in her forearm and pain as claws ripped
at her cheek. Ruth's long rosy nails went into the other's flesh
where she could, and with the sharp spurs of her heels she
slashed at the other's shins. Her own head thudded on the carpet and hands like wires sank in her throat.

She wouldn't have screamed, anyhow.

She pulled up her knee. Silk ripped, velvet tore. She put her
sharp golden heel in the wildcat's stomach and straightened
her leg and Nell went sprawling. Ruth walked on her knees and
dove on her, got the hair, whammed the head to the floor.

But the head bounced. The body in the dark dress was taut
and strong. It wasn't going to be that easy.

Ruth heard herself growl in her gullet, now it was free. Fast
as the fighting went, she yet summoned with a cold brain old
strengths, old tricks, and when they were not enough she began to invent. . . . She had realized that she fought, here, something wild and vicious, that wanted to hurt, that didn't care
how. Probably mad, and strong by that perfect ruthlessness.

But Ruth, too, was fortified. She was wilder than the tom-
boy she used to be. She was more vicious than the girl athlete.
She was Bunny's mother and she was easily able to be absolutely
ruthless in that holy cause.

She said to herself, O.K. *All right.* And she was not afraid.

It never crossed her mind to scream. It seemed her sole and
simple duty and even her pleasure to fight with all her body's
strength and her mind's cunning. (Outside of any rules, if that
was the way it was, and O.K., too.) It did not cross her mind
to wonder who would win, either. She sank her own strong
teeth in the enemy's wrist, while she tried with her mind to
think just how she was going to conquer . . . even as she was
tossed and the merciless elbow was crushing her breast.

Miss Ballew managed to get to her feet but her weight would not balance over them. She knew now she would be forever haunted by remorse and shame if she did not force herself to help in this emergency. But she was not well. Her heart hurt. There was a sharp pain in her side. Her mind knew that her body was lying, and her heart pitied the body's treasonable victory, as her lips prayed cravenly for someone else to come.

## CHAPTER 20

THE MOMENT he was inside the lobby, Jed knew that the hotel, in itself, was aroused. The alarm was spread. He saw it in the stiff pose of a different head behind the desk. He knew, too, that there had been, and yet was, a search going on.

It came to him that he was taking a certain risk in the mere act of stepping back within these walls. Sure, they were looking. Once more his mind played back its recorded impressions, a glimpse of the fellow in the brown suit weaving among the chairs, and his beckoning hand and the doorman's response. The man in the brown suit had been looking for someone all right. For whom, if not for Jed?

All the way across the lobby, he could see that very suit, the same man, over there right now, waiting for an elevator. The clerk to whom Jed had given warning was beside him, and all the way across the lobby, Jed knew when they spoke his name.

What was this?

They were *looking* for him and they for some reason were not looking for *him*. He saw himself split in two, the object of their search, and merely Towers who had just checked out of 821. They hadn't put it together yet. They would, sooner or later. And easily. For instance, right over there lounged the boy-who-had-brought-up-the-ice. Who was, all by himself, the missing link.

When would his hunting eye catch sight of Jed and recognize?

Jed guided Lyn so that she stood with her back to the elevators and he, bent as if to listen to her, could watch them. Those two men were authority. Were they *only now* going up to see what was wrong on the eighth floor? If so, they were darned late! Wires must have got crossed. It had been a long time.

(A long, long time for a helpless, frightened little girl to wait in the dark for her daddy or his equivalent.)

He ground his teeth. What was going on? Lyn stood obediently, her head thrown back to look up into his face.

He said, rapidly, "Do you mind? I just want to see. . . . Talk to me. Make some remarks, hm?"

"You're being mighty mysterious," Lyn said lightly. It was so plain she trusted he had good reason. "Mine not to wonder why. Me and the six hundred. Lyn, number 601."

He felt his jaw crack. "Keep talking."

The elevator took on its passengers . . . two men, one woman and a scampering little dog.

"Nothing is quite so numbing as to be told to say something. Hm . . . I like raspberry pie very much but the seeds do get in my teeth. I'm very fond of cucumber sandwiches in the summertime. Am I doing all right?"

"You're fine."

Jed was farsighted. He could see from here the indicator moving on the dial. He could not read the numbers but then he knew already where the eight came. He said bitterly, "Why in God's name didn't I lock the damn door!"

"If I ask questions," said Lyn placidly, "I won't be making remarks, will I? Cross out 'will I.'"

"The door *between*," he growled. What he was telling he didn't know.

"Oh, between. Well, that's nice. That's quite illuminating."

"If I had any brains . . ."

"Oh, you have, Jed. I think you have. Good-looking as you are, you must have a brain. Lessee, what's my favorite flower. At a time like this, I ought to know so I could tell you. But I like too many kinds, too much. But you take roses."

Although he kept his eye on that dial, he knew Lyn's face was full of peace. She had no right! His glance flicked down. She had her hands in the big pockets of her coat and her eyes were sweet and sane and full of peace because she believed. . . . She was a little fool to believe in anybody!

"You look about nine years old," said Jed with a whipsnap of anger. And he sent his eyes again to the dial.

"Oh, I don't think so. I think I probably look about 19 and just as if I've got a terrible crush on you. And you look like thunder, Jed. If I knew what the matter was I'd try to help. But you know that, of course. Mine only to keep talking, eh? Why, then, I'll go ahead. Babble. Babble. Do you care for the chamber music? No, that's a question. Well, I always say it depends. Everything depends. . . ."

The hand on the dial had stopped . . . must be at about four. It seemed to be stuck there. Was it out of order?

"Come, boy. Come, boy. Ah, naughty Bobo! (Loves to ride!) But this is home, boy. Now, Bobo must be a good boy. Biscuit? Bobo want his biscuit? If Bobo wants his biscuit . . . Oh, what a naughty, bad doggy! Bobo! Beddy-bye, now. Come, Bobo."

Bobo retreated to the inner corner of the elevator.

Mrs. McMurdock giggled in her throat. "So ki-yute! Isn't that—Little monkey! Bobo, boy, Mama will leave you. Biscuit?"

The hotel's people stood silent. Mrs. McMurdock was a guest. Bobo was a guest. A guest need not know all there is to know. They wore small chilly smiles, not too impatient, not too amused.

In the lobby, Jimmy said, "Hey, kids, sumpin's funny! See that fellow over there, one with the girl? Say, what was the room again?"

"Room 807."

"Yeah," drawled Jimmy. "Yeah . . ."

Jed's eyes flickered in his stony face.

". . . partial to rum," Lyn said, "with pink stuff in it. Is it all right now? Can we go?"

In Jed's head exploded the loud NO for an answer.

Her face changed. One second, sweet and pretty, and pleased with the nonsense she was able to spin. The next it had lost all that pretty animation, light and color. Jed did it. By the look he bent on her, he wiped the pretty peace off her face.

He said, quietly, "I'm a rat, Lyn. A complete rat. Go home."

"But, Jed, I've been wait—"

"Don't wait any more. Never wait for me."

He stepped around his suitcase. His face was flinty. He went across the lobby to the fire stairs in a walk so smooth and fast that he seemed to float.

He knew that bellhop straightened with a start.

The hell with that!

He shouldn't have run out on that little kid! What kind of rat did such a thing? A rat like Towers. A complete, no-good . . . Who would ever know? *Towers* would know. Rat forever, amen.

But he went up. Went up with all the great strength of his long powerful legs, three steps at once, then two, but pulling on the rail, around and around, climbing the building more like a monkey than a man going upstairs.

Passed the buck. Towers! Let the old lady take care of it. Towers! He thought, I don't know what I'm doing . . . know what I did . . . Never even thought to lock that door. Could have made sure to keep her out of there. He and he *alone* (not Eddie—Eddie was out on the bathroom floor) knew what kind of sitter that Nell turned out to be. Knew the poor kid was waiting.

Revulsion was making him sick. O.K. Cut it out, Towers. What's done is done. Take it from here.

Eighth floor?

He must be in pretty good condition.

There was the elevator. And there they stood, talking. Questions and answers, with the elevator boy. The hell with them. They didn't know there was a risk. Jed rushed past.

Aw, probably Bunny was all right. Probably. Pray so, and if so, here's Towers heading right back into the middle of this jam, for nothing. Doing no good. But maybe not for nothing. He didn't know. All he knew was, he was going to bust in there and if the old biddy hadn't found her yet, Towers was going to untie the little kid and the hell with everything else . . . and five seconds more, one second, one pulse beat more was too long.

Room 807's door was wide open. The old biddy, crouched on the edge of the bed, took one look at Jed's wild figure and heaved in her breath and let out a scream to wake the dead!

But Jed was in 809 before it died.

Nell, hair hanging over her eyes, had one knee on either side of the slim body of a woman, supine on the floor. Their hands were braced, hand against wrist, arms against aching arms. The woman had blood on her mouth and her cheek was scratched and her breathing was shallow and difficult. But her eyes were intelligent and they yet watched for her chance.

Jed took Nell by the short hair of her head. He ripped her away. She came up in his grasp, screeching, and hung from his hand, limp in surprise like a sawdust doll.

In the corridor, Milner and Perrin saw the racing figure and in their startled ears rang the woman's scream. Perrin got his gun in his hand as they began to run.

The door of 807 was wide.

"The man," croaked Miss Ballew, voice thick and hoarse. "That's the man! The man . . . the same one!"

Perrin looked toward 809.

He saw a tall man with a face of utter fury drag, by the hair, a blond girl through that door. Saw him drag her around the wooden frame as if he didn't care if he broke her bones.

"Drop that girl! Let her go!"

Jed's head went back and the eyes glittered down the long straight nose. "The hell I will! You don't—"

Perrin fired.

## CHAPTER 21

R UTH O. JONES lifted her shoulders from the carpet, and pulled her twisted rags and tatters aside to free her legs. She wiped the blood off her mouth with her arm. She combed her fingers through her hair. Some of it, torn out at the roots, came away in her broken nails. She walked on her knees — there was no need to rise higher — over to Bunny's bed.

She paid not the slightest attention to the gunshot as it blasted off behind her.

She said, in her firm contralto, "O.K., honey bun? What happened to *you?*" Her cut mouth kissed the temple lightly. Her fingers were strong and sure on those wicked knots.

Jed kept standing, somehow, because he had to keep an eye steady on Nell. She fell on the floor when he had to drop her as if she had been a sack of meal. As soon as he was sure she lay as limp as she seemed to lie, he looked at his right hand. He took it away from his left side and looked at the bright blood.

He looked at the men, standing tense and threatening in his path, and he tried to smile. The elevator boy was behind them. Then he saw his girl, Lyn, behind *him* . . . looking as if she peered through trees in a glade, between the men's bodies, in at the strange tableau.

Ah, the little fool! "Go home," he said.

Then he heard it. In the other room Bunny began to cry.

Over Jed's face passed a look of peace and thanksgiving. He turned, reeling, because he was wounded and no kidding, stumbled, and made for the big maroon chair.

"Oh, Jed!"

"But that's Towers. . . ."

"It's the same man. . . ."

Now, he was three. Or maybe only one, again. Or nothing. No matter. There was a difference in the way a kid cried. Funny . . . could you write down the difference in musical terms, he wondered. Pitch or timing or what? One kind of crying that gnawed on your nerves and pierced your head. This kind didn't do that. No, it didn't do that at all. It was a thing not unmusical to hear. . . .

Perrin, kneeling over Nell, barked, "What did you do to this girl?"

Jed didn't feel like bothering to say.

Miss Ballew let out another yelp of pure shock. Eyes starting from her head, she reacted to her sight of the little man in the hotel's livery who was standing in the bathroom door, holding his head, looking out mouselike at them all.

"Munro!" thundered Milner. "What—"

Eddie blinked. Silence rustled down, that they might hear his feeble voice. "I guess . . . Nell musta got into more mischief. Did she? My niece? Nell?"

"Who?"

Jed pulled himself from the mists. "Nell, the baby sitter. On the floor." He braced himself, watchfully. "Nutty as a fruit-cake," he said.

But Nell only rolled, drowsily. Her arm fell aside in sleepy grace, revealing her face. Her eyes were closed. The blue gone, her small face was left perfectly serene. There was a long scratch from eye corner to jaw. It looked as if it had been painted there, as if she felt no pain. She seemed to be asleep.

"That's Nell. Yes, she . . ." Eddie tottered to look. "That's the way she did—before," he said in awe. "After the fire, they say she slept . . . just like that." He swallowed and looked around at all their set faces. "How can she sleep?" he whimpered.

"Somebody," said Jed wearily, "go see. I suppose it's Mrs. Jones. This one pretty near killed her."

Perrin got off his haunches and lurched through the door. Milner's horrified eye sent fury in sudden understanding where, from his point of view, it belonged. "Munro!"

"I . . . didn't think . . ." said Eddie. "I kinda kept hoping she'd be all right. But I guess . . ."

"Next time, don't guess," said Jed. "Lyn, go home."

"Not now." She moved toward him, drawn. "I won't, Jed. I've got to know. . . ."

He closed his eyes.


When a fresh scream rose up, out there in the other room in another world, Ruth's fingertips did not leave off stroking into shape the little mouth that the wicked gag had left so queer and crooked. "That's right. Just you cry. Golly, Bun, did you see me fighting! Wait till we tell Daddy . . . missed the whole thing . . ." Ruth held the little head warmly against her battered body. There was comfort soaking through from skin to skin. "Cry it all out, sweetheart. Cry."

"Mrs. Jones?" a man said to her. His hair seemed to her to be trying to stand on end.

"Go away. Hush. Please call my husband. . . ."

She stroked and murmured on. Not until she heard Peter's voice did her wounds and gashes remember pain.

"We're just fine," Ruth said quickly. "Jeepers, have we had an adventure!"

Peter's face was dead white when he saw his wife and child.

"She was the crossest sitter I ever saw," Bunny said indignantly. Her arms went around her daddy's dark head where he had hidden his face against her. "She tied my mouth all up, Daddy, so I couldn't cry. She certainly didn't want me to cry awful bad."

Peter roused and looked at those stockings.

"Bound and gagged," Ruth said quietly. Her face said more.

"G-gosh, she must have had terrible ears." Peter's voice trembled. "I expect she's got sick ears, Bunny."

His hands curled and uncurled. Ruth's eyes said, I know. But it's over. Be careful.

For Bunny didn't realize what had almost happened to her and it was better if she didn't. You mustn't scare a little girl who's nine so that all her life she carries the scar. You must try to heal what scar there is. Ruth knew, and deeply trembled to know it, that someday she would leave Bunny again. And with a sitter, of course. She must. (Although not for a good while with a stranger. Maybe never again with a total stranger.) Still, they would go gaily as might be and they would not permit themselves to be cowed, to be daunted. They dared not.

Poor Peter, shaken and suffering right now, and fighting so hard not to betray it. Peter knew all this as well as she. They were tuned to each other. "Bunny's fine and I feel fine, too," she told him. "Really. A few scratches. Did they take her away?"

"They're coming. They'll take her to a hospital," added Peter, for Bunny's sake, "because she's sick, really. She doesn't know how to get along with people who are well."

Bunny's shuddering sobs were becoming like the soft far murmur of the last thunder of a departing storm. "Daddy."

"What, Bun?"

Ruth felt the head turn on her breast. "Did you have fun?"

Peter couldn't answer. But Ruth could. "Oh, Bunny, it was

lots of fun. And Daddy made a good speech. I wish you'd been big enough to go." She rushed on. "Daddy stood up and all the people, everybody was dressed up. . . ."

Peter looked upon the condition of his wife's clothing. "Those . . . scratches, hon," he said in a minute, sounding as if half his throat was closed. "There's a doctor out there."

So the doctor came in and looked them both over.

"You know," said Ruth when he had gone, licking the antiseptic in her mouth, "I pretty near had her licked! I think!" She laughed. "I must look terrible but I feel fine."

And she did. Ah, poor Peter with the retrospective horror and the wrath locked in and buttoned down. But Ruth had got rid of it by tooth and claw. And she remembered now, with relish, certain digs and blows. She felt quite peaceful. Fulfilled, she thought, the tigress in me. "Hand me in some of my things, Peter. I'm going to bed in here with Bun."

"O.K., girls."

"Maybe we'll order hot chocolate! Shall we? Lets!"

"In the middle of the night!" squealed Bunny and the smooth skin of her face rippled in the warning of delight to come.

Peter O. Jones, with a smile covering (from all but his wife) the tears bleeding out of his heart, went back to 807.

## CHAPTER 22

EDDIE was gone, damned for a reckless fool, for all his anxious, ignorant hope. (Don't worry, Eddie, Marie would say.)

Milner was gone, to harmonize with the walnut, downstairs. (Keep it out of the papers, if we possibly can.)

Perrin was gone. ("Sorry, Towers. You can see how it was?" "Sure. That's O.K.") He went with Nell.

And Nell was gone. Still seeming asleep, looking innocent

and fair. Only Jed spoke to her. Jed said (and it seemed necessary — once, this he had planned to say), "So long, Nell."

She was asleep so she didn't reply. Yet there was a lazy lift of
the lashes. (They won't do anything to me.)

Nearly everyone was gone. Miss Ballew remained, sick in
her soul, with the doctor's suggested sedative in her hand. Jed
was in the big chair again, bloody shirt loose over the vast
bandage. Lyn was still there.

The doctor warned once more that Jed must take a few days'
rest before trying to travel with that wound. Then he was gone.

"You'll stay over, Jed, won't you?" Lyn's mouth was stiff.

"A couple of days, at least. I'll see." Jed's side was stinging
like the devil now. Telegrams, he thought, but time for that
later. "Lyn, will you please . . . Your family's probably . . . Why
don't you go home?"

"I will, soon." She didn't look at him. She looked at her
trembling hands.

Peter took Ruth's things to her, came back, sat down, put his
head in his hands.

Lyn said, "You're terribly upset, of course. Shouldn't we go,
Jed? If I can help you to your own room . . ."

"Or I," said Miss Ballew drearily.

"Don't go. Ruth wants to say good night."

"Your little, uh, Bunny's all right?" asked Jed.

"Soon be. Kids bounce back. Thank God. Drink with me?"

Jed didn't feel sure. He felt this room rejected him. But he
had *fallen* in this chair.

"I ought to go home," said Lyn whitely. "I don't mean to
hang around . . . be in the way."

"I ought to go," said Miss Ballew. (To be a worthless old
coward and on top of that be fooled and fail in the mind, too!)
"I was of very little use."

"Take it easy," Peter said. "Better try and take it easy."

Jed shifted his stiff side, reached slowly for the pocket of his coat, for the envelope. He managed to open it with one hand. It said, "Dear Jed:" And that was all. No more.

Well. He looked back into dim reaches of time. It would have been enough. It would have been plenty. He crushed it up and put it back in his pocket. He didn't look at Lyn.

Peter passed drinks. "Nonsense, Miss Ballew. You need this. There." He sat down. His brown eyes locked with Jed's gray. "As I understand it, you left Bunny tied up? But you told them at the desk on your way out?" Peter's voice was light, tentative.

"I figured it wasn't my business," said Jed levelly. "I didn't want to get into a mess. I figured to get away."

Well, he hadn't got away. He'd got shot. And Towers was a rat. So, then, he was. The little girl was O.K. now. Mother, too. Nothing, thank God, they couldn't get over. So . . . if Towers was left in his rathood, that was not too important to them, any more.

Gray eyes locked on brown. "That's the kind of rat I am, I guess," Jed said quietly. "Later, I got a little nervous . . . a little too much later."

Miss Ballew's lips trembled. "I was so stupid," she said. "I was worse than no use. My *fault* . . ."

Jed's eyes met hers. They said, Don't blame yourself too much. They said, I understand. They said, Us sinners . . . .

"Seems to me," Jed drawled, "if you're hunting for blame . . . if I hadn't come over here in the first place . . ."

"If I hadn't walked out," Lyn said bleakly.

"No. Lyn . . ."

"You think *I'm* not doing any if-ing?" Peter asked. "If I'd even looked at the girl with half my brain on it. Me and my big important speech! I left it to Ruthie. Of course, she got it. In her bones, the way she sometimes does."

Peter got up to pace. "Ruth says she had her licked. But I don't know . . ."

"I don't know either, sir. I couldn't say." Eyes locked again. "Now, don't kid me, sir," Jed said gently. "They weren't two steps behind me. They'd have been on time."

And then he smiled. Because it only mattered to Towers now, and Towers could take it. "Tell you, it isn't often a man says to himself, You ought to be shot, and right away someone obliges." He moved and made the wound hurt. It was not so bad. It was like a session with the hairbrush, or a trip to the woodshed.

But then Lyn said, as if she broke, "I'm afraid." Why, she was all to pieces. She wasn't *Lyn*. She looked white and old and sick and she was shaking to pieces. "I'm scared to go home. That's the truth," she wailed. "I'm scared of the night. I'd g-go but I'm afraid. Such t-terrible things . . . I don't know anything. I'm scared of what a f-fool I've been." She wept.

Jed winced. "And you ought to be," he said grimly. But it wasn't *Lyn*. It was sick and ugly.

Ruth said, "Ssssh . . ." She stepped out of Bunny's room, leaving the door wide. She wore a man's woolen robe because she was cold now, with shock. But her battered face was serene.

Peter held Ruth's hand to his cheek. "Asleep?" he whispered and she nodded.

"Ruthie, would you be scared if I took this young lady home?"

"Why, no," Ruth said, smiling.

"Uh, you see, Towers can't do it. He ought to be in bed."

Jed said, appalled, "Yes, and I'm going there. But you can't leave Mrs. Jones, sir." She's had enough! he thought.

Ruth smiled at them all. "Don't be afraid," she said, gently.

"Here we sit, with our hair turning white," murmured Peter, his eyes shining. " 'Don't be afraid,' she says."

"Well, you *dasn't!*" Ruth smiled. "Or what would become of us all?"

She kissed Peter's brow, made her good nights. She didn't say thanks. Perhaps she forgot, or she knew ... She withdrew, went back to her sleeping baby, and the door closed behind her.

They sat, sipped quietly. Lyn's face was pink, her eyes were ashamed, her back was straighter. Jed thought, I know her. I know what she's made of. And, he realized, *she* knew more about Towers, the real Towers, than anyone else on earth. Something grew, here ... never could have grown had they gone, say, to a show. Something known, for better, for worse. He touched her hand. She turned hers and her icy fingers clung.

"Put an ending on my letter sometime, honey?"

"How, Jed?"

"The regular ending," he said, soberly. Yours truly. That was the way to end a letter. Lyn smiled like the rainbow.

Peter said, "Yep. We oughta be scared, all right. Ignorant optimism won't do it. But we've got *not* to be scared, just the same."

"Courage," sighed Miss Ballew. She rose to say good night.

"We are strangers," Peter said darkly. "Whom do we know? One — if you're lucky. Not many more. Looks like we've got to learn how we can trust each other. How we can tell ... How we can dare ... Everything rests on trust between strangers. Everything else is a house of cards."

Peter sat down, gazed at the two of them, moving his lips. "Damn it," he cried, "I wish I'd said that!"

"Said what, Mr. Jones?"

"What I just said!" Peter was cross.

Lyn's eyes met Jed's and dared be a little merry. "But ... Mr. Jones, you just *did*. Didn't you?"

"In my speech!" cried Peter. "*Now*, I have to think of a better ending." He glared at them.

*Charlotte Armstrong*

BORN IN 1905, Charlotte Armstrong grew up in the iron-mining country of northern Michigan, where her father was a mining engineer and inventor. After two years at the University of Michigan, she moved east to Barnard College in New York and was graduated in 1925.

A variety of office jobs in New York followed until she married a young advertising man named Jack Lewi. While caring for a house and raising three children, Miss Armstrong also managed a little theater with a troupe of 20 high school students and wrote two plays which were produced on Broadway.

In 1942 she published her first mystery novel, *Lay On, Mac-Duff*. Two others followed in this vein, with increasing critical appreciation, and with the third, *The Unsuspected*, Miss Armstrong really hit her stride. Serialized in *The Saturday Evening Post*, *The Unsuspected* was sold to Hollywood before it appeared in book form and was a success in both media.

*Mischief*, which critics say surpasses even *The Unsuspected* in tension, has been bought by Twentieth Century-Fox for a moving picture, and the noted director Alfred Hitchcock plans to produce it in play form.